Antiquities from the Collection of Christos G. Bastis

VERLAG PHILIPP VON ZABERN
MAINZ ON RHINE

3a King Amenhotep I

Antiquities from the Collection of Christos G. Bastis

New York · 1987

Preface — Christos G. Bastis

Introduction — Dietrich von Bothmer

Catalog — Bernard V. Bothmer
Pat Getz-Preziosi
Diana Buitron-Oliver
Andrew Oliver, Jr.

Editor — Emma Swan Hall

Coordinator — Alexandra Antoniou

Photography — Justin Kerr
David A. Loggie
Sarah Wells

The Brooklyn Museum

The Metropolitan Museum of Art

Photography of front cover: David A. Loggie, New York

CIP-Kurztitelaufnahme der Deutschen Bibliothek
Antiquities from the Collection of Christos G. Bastis : New York 1987 / [pref. Christos G. Bastis. Introd. Dietrich von Bothmer. Catalog Bernard V. Bothmer ... Ed. Emma Swan Hall]. – Mainz : von Zabern, 1987.
Ausstellungskatalog
ISBN 3-8053-0951-1
NE: Bothmer, Bernard V. [Bearb.]; Hall, Emma Swan [Hrsg.]

Library of Congress Catalog Card Number: 87-50794

XII, 340 pages with 58 color- and 366 black-and-white photographs
Printed on fade resistant and archival quality (PH 7 neutral)

ISBN 3-8053-0951-1

Type: Hurler GmbH, Notzingen
Lithography: Repro-Müller, Eppertshausen
Paper: Papierfabrik Scheufelen, Lenningen
Printed in Germany/Imprimé en Allemagne
Design: Franz Rutzen
Manufactured by Verlag Philipp von Zabern, Mainz on the Rhine

Contents

Preface

The catalog was first suggested to me by Bernard Bothmer in the early nineteen seventies, but as I was still collecting rather actively, nothing definite was arranged until four years ago. It was agreed that Bernard Bothmer would write the Egyptian entries, Pat Preziosi record the Cycladic items, Diana Buitron-Oliver and Andrew Oliver work on the Classical material, and Emma Hall would be the editor. Alexandra Antoniou attended to the task of coordinating the whole preparation which included keeping up to date with the constant and necessary revisions, supplying countless details when needed, and making the whole project work. Her energy and interest are gratefully appreciated. To all I extend our heartfelt thanks and wish to record here that without their help and understanding this catalog could not have been produced.

A debt of a different sort I owe to my friend Dietrich von Bothmer who introduced me to scholarship and its problems. He has helped in the formation of the collection by his eagerness to discuss many of the objects purchased as well as his willingness to cooperate with Diana Buitron-Oliver and Andrew Oliver in the cataloguing of the Classical section. It was my good fortune to have known both Dietrich von Bothmer and Bernard Bothmer and to have been exposed to their expert knowledge and, above all, their friendship for so many years.

For the realization of this catalog I should also like to extend our special thanks to both the Metropolitan Museum of Art and The Brooklyn Museum for their cooperation in providing photographs and allowing us to photograph in their galleries. In particular I appreciate that objects I had donated to the museums have become part of this catalog. For their constant support and assistance we express our gratitude and indebtedness.

We are very happy that Franz Rutzen of Philipp von Zabern took a special interest in producing and publishing this catalog and that this undertaking has now been brought to completion with the traditionally high standards of the publisher.

Christos and Jo Bastis

Introduction

The desire to collect, one of the oldest human instincts, takes many forms and can be exercised on many levels. Under the most ideal conditions it becomes a life-time occupation that brings its own rewards not easily measured by established standards: by necessity collecting is a very personal if not private activity governed by factors not always nor ever totally controlled by the individual. Nor can collecting be practised with the same degree of regularity as, for example, gardening whose rhythm is prescribed by the seasons, the quality of the soil, and the vagaries of the climate.

Collecting works of art is surely one of the noblest passions. Long the prerogative of the church and the state, their princes or potentates, it has in the last couple of centuries become an endeavour shared by an ever increasing number of participants who have through their efforts not only broadened the field but also demonstrated that art can be enjoyed by all. As a group, even if not organised, collectors thus constitute a community that especially in this country has led to the creation of great museums, assured their continued existence, and in many ways bridged the gap between the academic curators and the public at large.

Within the vast domain of art that spans the millennia and represents so many different cultures, antiquities demand a special predilection not readily understood or developed by everybody. Christos G. Bastis, whose collection is here published for the first time, was attracted as a young boy by the great artistic achievements of Greece, his native country, and even after he left Volos in 1922 to work and live in America, the memories of Greek art accompanied him across the ocean and throughout his early years in a foreign land. When after less than a year in the Middle West he settled in New York he soon discovered that these memories could be refreshed by visiting the Metropolitan Museum of Art. In the meantime, by hard work and determination he laid the foundations of a successful business that allowed him to start a collection. By June 1948 when I first was introduced to Mr. Bastis, the collection was already quite representative. From this period, too, dates his support of the Metropolitan Museum and its Department of Greek and Roman Art. Beginning with the loan of his Chalcidian oinochoe (No. 149), a vase that had been lost sight of since its publication in Rumpf's monograph, he unfailingly obliged us with loans of his objects whenever we called on him. His gifts of objects to the Museum started in 1964, but even earlier, in 1954, he realised the need of the Department for supplemental funds to make certain purchases possible. It is with deep gratitude that I wish to acknowledge here, in his catalog, the generosity of a friend who has never let us down. He was elected a Benefactor on March 14, 1967, and appointed a member of the Trustee Visiting Committee to the Greek and Roman Department on February 4, 1969.

The nucleus of the collection also contained several Egyptian objects acquired in the 1940's in New York, for Mr. Bastis, never parochial in outlook, developed a genuine appreciation of Egyptian art, an interest that was strengthened over the years by his close association with my brother, Curator and later Chairman in The Brooklyn Museum until 1982. For many years a Trustee of The Brooklyn Museum, Mr. Bastis lent most of his Egyptian objects to Brooklyn, and it was, in fact, Bernard Bothmer who first thought of publishing the Bastis Collection of Antiquities in a catalog.

Each collection, unless inherited, reflects in some manner the preferences and special interests of the owner, but to understand the composition of such an assembly fully one also has to take into account the circumstances under which objects are acquired. The growth of a collection is often accompanied by an increased knowledge of the field: the amateur becomes an expert, his discrimination is heightened and, if he has been successful in his profession, he can afford to consider objects that had not been in his reach before. It has been my privilege to watch Mr. Bastis and his acquisitions for almost forty years and to see his enthusiasm grow as his expertise deepened. What has not changed in these decades, however, has been his love for the works of art, a love that with the publication of the catalog can now be shared by a larger public.

Dietrich von Bothmer

PART I

Egyptian Antiquities

by

Bernard V. Bothmer

ACKNOWLEDGEMENTS

In the study and attribution of some of the Egyptian antiquities in the Bastis Collection the following have been most helpful:

Cyril Aldred	Mark Lehner
Ricardo A. Caminos	Erik Lieber
Jean-Louis de Cenival	Luc Limme
J.J. Clère	Joan B. Mertens
Jean-Pierre Corteggiani	Elizabeth Milliker
Herman De Meulenaere	Bojana Mojsov
Milton Girod	James F. Romano
Gerhard Haeny	Edna R. Russmann
Barbara Hale	Hermann Schlögl
Emma Swan Hall	R.R.R. Smith
T.G.H. James	Victoria Solia
Sally B. Johnson	Claude Sourdive
László Kákosy	Zbigniew E. Szafrański
Norma-Jean Katan	Helen Vassilika
Jean Leclant	Edward K. Werner

My warmest thanks, however, go to the man who with a keen eye brought together this fine collection of Egyptian antiquities and has given me the opportunity to discourse on them: Christos Bastis.

1 a

1 b

1

FRAGMENTARY HEAD

Middle Kingdom
Dynasty XII
Reign of Amenemhat III
1842–1794 B.C.

Black Basalt

The use of hard stone, instead of limestone or sandstone, is one of the characteristics of private statuary in the Middle Kingdom that distinguishes this period from an earlier era. On the other hand, the scale continues a tradition established in Dynasty VI, namely, that sculptures representing non-royal persons are half lifesize or even smaller.

Such is the case of a fragmentary male head which, with a restraint typical of Dynasty XII, represents a priest or high official wearing a striated wide wig and a beard vertically grooved with small hatch marks. The face is full and round and, at first glance, appears idealizing. On closer inspection, however, it shows a firmness and determination, enhanced by the worry lines descending from the nostrils and the slightly outthrust lips – more signs of a mature man than of a youth.

The eyebrows are straight and in faintly raised relief, but the eyes are naturally formed, the eyeballs quite convex in spite of their small size. Conversely, the large ear is highly stylized. The nose is short and fleshy, and the nostrils were scored with a pointed tool; the philtrum is marked. The upper lip is thinner than the lower; both descend toward the corners, lending the mouth a vaguely disdainful expression. This is not the mark of a given individual, however, as it follows the style set by one of the great kings of the Middle Kingdom, Amenemhat III (1842–1794 B.C.), during whose reign, or shortly after, the sculpture to which this head belonged was made. The beard lends it distinction.

The fragment was broken off across the beard, just below the chin; thus the latter is well preserved, and the nose intact. The left side of the head, just behind the left eye, and the back are missing. The entire surface is worn and somewhat pitted. The very fine-grained stone, though black, has a brownish sheen.

MEASUREMENTS: Height 6.0 cm.; of face 3.3 cm. Width 5.6 cm. Distance between outer canthi 3.0 cm. Depth 4.1 cm.

PROVENANCE: Not known.

BIBLIOGRAPHY: None.

COMMENT: The type of sculpture from which this head was severed is not easily determined. If it wore a tripartite wig (Vandier 1958, p. 252), it perhaps came from a seated figure, but since the head is bearded, it is more likely to have come from a standing statue. The wig was presumably none too wide and, flaring slightly, ended on the shoulders or just below.

Sculptures of bearded men in hard stone are rare in the Middle Kingdom, and the beards, almost without exception, have horizontal striations. The exceptions are the Bastis head and a statue in London (BM 1237: PM IV 1934, p. 65; Vandier 1958, pp. 228, 261, pl. LXXV:5–6) where the face and coiffure are comparable. It is probably no accident that a sphinx of Sesostris III in New York (MMA 17.9.2; Vandier 1958, p. 606) appears to be the only royal example with this kind of beard, because the British Museum statue can be attributed on stylistic grounds to the latter part of Dynasty XII. And the same goes for the Bastis head whose facial type very much resembles that of Amenemhat III and his followers. In other words, the novelty of decorating the beard with vertical lines is first employed by royalty and soon becomes a feature applied also to the private statuary of a few outstanding individuals.

The determination of the material as "basalt" is based on the terminology used by Egyptologists, and it is useful to reread what Lucas has to say (Lucas 1962, pp. 61–62, 65, 407, 410). The generic term, dolorite, is often used when the material is less homogeneous and more grainy than that of the Bastis fragment. The brownish overtones of this kind of material when it is of Egyptian and not Western Asiatic or European origin are worth mentioning.

2

WISDOM OF AGE

Late Middle Kingdom
Dynasty XIII
About 1780–1700 B.C.

Gray Diabase or Granite

Most Egyptian statuary is idealizing, and although the style changes considerably from the early Old Kingdom (2670 B.C.) to the end of the Ptolemaic Period (30 B.C.), the aim of the ancient sculptor remained for the most part the same: to represent the human being as a youthful, vigorous individual who was going to enjoy life after death in the presence of his gods as well as or better than he had in real life. Many prerequisites were needed to achieve this, spiritual and material, but one basic aim remained the same throughout the ages: to have a likeness made in material as durable as possible that showed the deceased in excellent physical condition with a youthful, unlined face and features full of confidence and anticipation. Yet, there seems to have been no prohibition against realistic representations of mature, even sorrowful and aged, human beings, and time and again, in the long history of Egyptian art, we find striking exceptions to the basic rule.

The head of a wise old man in the Bastis Collection is one of these exceptions. It is of such an arresting, startling quality as almost to defy description. Although the outer features are stark and precisely drawn, an introspective, brooding element in the deeply lined face conveys not so much the feeling of aging and sorrow as of maturity in the best sense, of a lifetime's experience, of wisdom and profound knowledge. It is immensely human, and in this it is moving and beautiful.

The head is that of an older man, wearing the kind of bag wig which is found late in the Middle Kingdom, mainly in Dynasty XIII. It is used again in the Late Period, from the end of Dynasty XXV until well into the Ptolemaic Period. The wig covers part of the forehead. The eyebrows are full, but not truly plastic. They overshadow the deep eye sockets from which the naturally modeled eyes protrude. The eyes are very impressive, with thick, heavy lids that give them a brooding expression. A short plastic paint stripe extends from the outer corner of the left eye. On the right eye the upper lid slightly overlaps the lower one. The eyeballs are actually small, but the large,

2a

2d

deep eye socket and heavy eyelids render the eyes lastingly impressive.

The ears are summarily modeled; the left one more so than the right. There are no tabs in front of the ears. The bone structure of forehead and cheeks is very noticeable, the latter especially since the cheeks are sunken. From the nostrils two furrows descend below the cheeks. There was once a philtrum. Next to the eyes, the mouth is the most impressive element. It is not straight, but has a wavy medial line; it is slightly protruding, and the upper lip is very thin, while the lower lip is full and visibly, almost defiantly, projects. Yet, the overall appearance of the face is not grim, but pensive, moody, mature and wise. The back pillar, uninscribed, reaches up beyond the lower edge of the wig.

A fairly close parallel to the head, still attached to its body, is in the Cairo Museum (CG 42041), in gray sandstone. It represents a seated man, dressed in a cloak folded over from right to left, leaving the right shoulder bare. The right hand lies on the right thigh, the left is held to the right chest. The wig is the same as that of the Bastis head, and face, eyes and mouth resemble it closely, but cannot be compared because they lack the force and intellectual depth, the impressive features of the hard stone head.

The Bastis head's ears, eyebrows, and chin are chipped; there is some damage to the left eye. The nose is almost entirely lost.

MEASUREMENTS: Height 16.4 cm.; of face 8.8 cm. Width 17.5 cm. Depth 16.6 cm. Width of break 16 cm. Depth of break 15.7 cm. Width of back pillar 8.5 cm.

PROVENANCE: Not known; perhaps Elephantine.

BIBLIOGRAPHY: None.

COMMENT: For the complex problems of idealization versus realism in Egyptian sculpture, see *Expedition* (Philadelphia) 24,2 (Winter 1982), pp. 27–39. It is not yet possible to pin down precisely the period at which the bag wig makes its appearance in Middle Kingdom statuary. It must have been around the time of King Amenemhat III (1842–1794 B.C.), if one accepts the niche sculpture from Hawara, in Cairo (JE 43289; Evers I 1929, p. 111 fig. 27; Vandier 1958, p. 596 no. M. E. IV), as dating from his reign. Eaton-Krauss (1977, p. 33, no. 2) and others have shown conclusively that the god with this headdress in the Hawara niche sculpture is really wearing the headcloth called *khat*, known from reliefs of Amenemhat III (Evers II 1929, pp. 16–17 par. 95, and p. 70 par. 467). There the headcloth, however, does not rest on the shoulders like the bag wig, and thus the latter is more likely to have been derived from the well-known wide wig of the Middle Kingdom, either striped or plain, that bulges forward around the ears, sideways over the shoulders and, although it rests on the shoulders, is taken in, with a kind of entasis, at the lateral ends.

The closest Middle Kingdom parallel to the wig of the Bastis head is worn on the head of a seated statue in Cairo (CG 42041; Legrain 1906, pp. 24–25, pl. XXV; the inscription is illegible), which Alexander Scharff (1939, pp. 97–100, fig. 1) convincingly attributed to Dynasty XIII. Vandier (1958, pp. 231 and 277) discusses the statue in Cairo (CG 42041), but does not mention the wig. Elsewhere (p. 197, n. 1) he calls the wig worn by the god in the group attributed to Amenemhat III (JE 43289; his M. E. IV) "perruque en double bourse," following Boreux, and later in his life he frequently used that term in conversation. Still, in the *Manuel* he occasionally referred to it as the *khat* headdress without really explaining it (p. 310).

A good example of the striped forerunner of the bag wig is offered in the sculpture of Hetep (Cairo JE 72239; PM III,1 1974, p. 41), which may well date from Dynasty XIII rather than Dynasty XII as is generally assumed (*ZÄS* 112, 1985, pp. 87–94). Late in Dynasty XXV the bag wig occurs in the sculpture of Petamenophis, owner of Theban Tomb no. 33, in Cairo (JE 36578; seated, in calcite), and an example from the reign of King Psamtik I (664–610 B.C.; Dynasty XXVI) is illustrated in *ESLP* 1960/73, pl. 27, no. 29. It is truly amazing to what extent the sculptors of the seventh century B.C. were able to adopt certain features of Middle Kingdom statuary, and adapt them to Kushite taste so ably that even today, with the distance of thousands of years, it is sometimes difficult to distinguish works of Dynasties XII/XIII and Dynasties XXV/XXVI, a difference between them of over ten centuries. What a place Karnak must have been in the Late Period when Middle Kingdom statues were standing or lying around, unscathed in the course of a millennium, so that they could be used as models for a new school of Egyptian sculptors working for Nubian masters, the Pharaohs of Dynasty XXV, and their Saite successors.

For a Late Period example of a wise old man with a bag wig, see No. 22 below. The short paint stripe extending from the outer corners of the otherwise naturally modeled eyes is found elsewhere in Dynasty XIII (e.g. Cairo CG 408: Wildung 1984, p. 18, fig. 9, where it is attributed to Dynasty XII; and Richmond, Va., 63-29; De Meulenaere 1971, pp. 61–64; also Habachi 1985, pl. 76d, no. 27).

The presence or absence of the tabs in the Middle Kingdom has been discussed (*BMA* X 1968–69, p. 70, n. 3), but no thorough study has been made thus far. For the mouth of the Bastis head, so typically late Middle Kingdom, the new publication on Elephantine statuary (Habachi 1985) may be consulted to great profit.

◁ 2b
◁ 2c

3

KING AMENHOTEP I

New Kingdom, Dynasty XVIII
Reign of Amenhotep I
1525–1504 B.C.

Near-white Sandstone

3 b (3 a: Frontispiece)

3 c ▷
3 d ▷

It must be assumed that, during the reign of an ancient Egyptian ruler, his studios and workshops employed the best craftsmen of the time and that the quality of their work set standards by which the antiquities of the period can be judged. These standards also permit us to appreciate the arts of an era, royal as well as private, and to compare them with the products of other dynasties. Bearing all this in mind and using an eye accustomed to viewing ancient statuary critically, one can, I believe, state unequivocally that this head in the Bastis Collection is one of the outstanding royal sculptures of the early New Kingdom.

The head, in near-white sandstone, is brightly painted, mostly in red and white, with some black. It represents the lifesize features of an ancient king wearing the double crown. This crown identifies him as the ruler of Upper and Lower Egypt, and he wears it with great pride, since it was during his rule that, after a long struggle, the two lands of the Nile Valley were once more firmly united and a new era of stability, prosperity and expansion of political power began.

Although much of the crown and the back of the head are missing, the King's face and both ears are well preserved, and the same is true of the rich polychromy which lends the features such telling immediacy. The royal cobra rising above the forehead has light blue, white, and red paint preserved on it, but the serpent's head is missing.

The face was at one time painted uniformly red, while eyebrows, eyelid rims, pupils and cosmetic lines were black. The red of the face has more orange in it than the crown, the latter being carmine red. The brows are formed naturally, enhanced by the application of black paint, but the eyes are stylized, the left being faintly tilted. The eyeballs are barely convex; the upper lids have rounded rims, the lower lids are cut straight. The nose, now partly lost, was prominent. It juts out strongly from the somewhat receding forehead, so that the two form separate elements of the face; the small bump, so characteristic of the King's nose in relief, can be felt just where the break occurred. Both ears are summarily modeled, supported by the volume of negative space behind.

The face is well rounded, with full cheeks and full jowls set off against the mouth by a faint descending fold; otherwise the face is completely unlined. The philtrum is indicated; the mouth, none too wide, is slightly curved up. It has a thin upper lip, while the lower lip appears fuller, since the middle portion is tipped down. The chin, once bearded, is only partly preserved. A crescent-shaped depression separates it from cheeks and mouth; the center of the chin was cleft, a rare feature of considerable importance in identifying the pharaoh represented.

The artificial beard was tied on with a light blue strap. For most of its length the strap is contoured on the side of the face by an incised line, but not so on the underside, the side of the neck. The incised line runs directly into the contour of the crown, in front of the upper part of the ears. It thus forms the side of the tabs that usually flank the forehead.

Below the tabs two horizontal incised lines mark the slot that permits the crown to be put on, leaving the ears uncovered. In front of the lower part of each ear, the edge of the crown curves toward the back of the neck.

This mighty crown symbolizes the power of royalty, the divine kingship which elevates the ruler to god-like eminence. What renders him human as well as superhuman is the earthy personality behind the piercing eyes, determined jowls, and firmly set mouth, all impressive, convincing, and, despite the very human face, awe-inspiring.

This awe must have been greatly enhanced at one time by the fully shrouded figure of the King, dressed in white from the neck down, arms crossed on the chest under the garment, with only the fists, painted bright red, exposed. Thus far we know of only one such figure, complete with the head preserved and inscribed on the back slab with the name of King Amenhotep I (London, BM 683). It was excavated in the beginning of this century at Deir el Bahri in Western Thebes, Upper Egypt. The face, though less well preserved and partly restored, is almost identical to that of the Bastis head. It too has a cleft chin, fortunately undamaged, for it helps to establish beyond a doubt the identity of the king represented in the New York head.

While the London head is still attached to the body and back slab, the Bastis head was broken off in the distant past, and everything except the damaged crown is lost. Most of the Upper Egyptian portion of the double crown and the right part of the Lower Egyptian crown are missing; so are the head of the uraeus, left nostril, and tip of the nose. The bottom of the chin on the right is also lost. There are numerous scratches, cracks and minor blemishes on crown and face. The right ear was once knocked off (Fig. 3a, frontispiece) and replaced.

The polychromy too has suffered, and in places both paint and sizing, which was originally white, have come off. In other places only the paint has been lost while the sizing has remained, though colored white or red, depending on the original paint. The break on the uraeus shows that the hood was built up in white stucco over the sandstone core and then painted. The loss of paint has in many instances bared the now colored sizing, which explains the changes in tonality of the surface, especially of the cheeks. Originally the red paint had been thickly applied.

3e

3f Back of Head

There are white accretions in spots, especially on the upper right cheek and, nearby, on the beardstrap. They may have come from a construction above the head or from water action, which could also explain some red color on top of the white accretions.

The material is strange, a light gray to near-white sandstone, perhaps from Nubia and not from Egypt. A dark gray vein runs vertically through the left side of the head, visible on the left, back of the break, and in the cracks on the left cheek where the two planes of front and side of the face meet.

MEASUREMENTS: Height 40.6 cm.; of face now 14.2 (once 15.0) cm. Distance between outer canthi 11.5 cm. Width 22.5 cm. Depth 26.0 cm.; of break ca. 19 cm.

PROVENANCE: Not known; probably from the lost sanctuary of Amenhotep I at Deir el Bahri; see *LdÄ* I (1975), col. 1008 "D", and plan on col. 1014. Formerly in a German collection.

BIBLIOGRAPHY: None.

COMMENT: The sculpture of Amenhotep I whose head presents the closest parallel is, as mentioned above, in London (BM 683; PM II 1972, p. 343; Romano 1976, pp. 97–98, 107, n. 1–3 with additional bibliography). For the original place of the Osiride statues of Amenhotep I, the references given in PM II 1972 may be consulted, but the entire problem of the supposed brick building of Amenhotep I begs to be reconsidered.

The fundamental study of early New Kingdom royal sculpture by Vandier (1958, pp. 296–297) has been greatly improved and augmented by Romano (1976), who seems also to be the first archaeologist to have noted in print the notch above the beard, i.e. the cleft of the chin, on the statue in London. The cleft and the position of the uraeus base *above* the lower edge of the crown are among the details that make identification of the royal head in the Bastis Collection virtually certain. The summary treatment of the ears, the modeling of the eyebrows rising directly from the root of the nose, and the formation of the mouth compare well, and on both heads the lines of the beard straps are identical.

On the other hand, the modeling inside the ears of the London head differs somewhat from that of the Bastis piece. The eyeballs of the former are a little more convex, and the tilt of the left eye is more pronounced. The bright colors of the eyes were examined in the Conservation Laboratory of The Brooklyn Museum early in 1985. No modern pigmentation could be detected on the samples taken.

The brilliance of the white paint, especially on the eyes, and over the accretions formed on the surface in antiquity is surprising. It has been found, however, that not only were portions of the adjacent temple of Mentuhotep II repainted in Dynastic times, but so also was a newly discovered statue of Amenhotep I (Szafrański 1985), probably during the reign of Ramesses II.

The sketchy manner in which the slots of the crown in front of the ears are indicated is peculiar. Romano (1976, pp. 97–98) has already commented on this feature and illustrated a strikingly similar example on a royal head in Boston, which comes from an Osiride statue at Deir el Bahri and probably also represents Amenhotep I (MFA 07.583; Romano 1976, pp. 97–98, pl. XXVII:4).

The way the beardstrap is drawn, with only one incised line on the neck side and none on the face, occurs as early as Dynasty VI on the seated Osiride statuette of Pepy II in The Brooklyn Museum (39.120; Aldred 1978, p. 204, fig. 202) and again in Dynasty XI on the seated statue of Mentuhotep II in Cairo (JE 36195; PM II 1972, pp. 382–83). It is even found on an Osiris head of the Late Period (Paris, Louvre E. 10706; De Meulenaere and Bothmer 1969, p. 9, pls. I:2, II:5). Lately another sandstone Osiride pillar of Amenhotep I with double crown has come to light at Deir el Bahri (Szafrański 1985). It had been carefully cut up and buried in a trench on the nearby causeway of the funerary temple of King Mentuhotep II of Dynasty XI. The head is faceless although much of the crown is preserved, and on the back of the pillar slab the sculpture is inscribed for Amenhotep I, like its companion in London (BM 683).

As for the material – gray-white sandstone – it could have come from Gebel es-Silsila, where most of the sandstone in use since the Middle Kingdom was quarried. Although usually brown, Klemm and Klemm report (1981, p. 23) that gray-white strata have also been observed there.

It is more likely however, that the material for the Bastis sculpture came from the Island of Sai in the Sudan, between the Second and Third Cataracts, which is the origin of a much prized near-white sandstone (PM VII 1952, pp. 164–166; Sethe 1933, p. 15; Harris 1961, pp. 71–72). The presence of Amenhotep I is amply attested on the Island of Sai (*LdÄ* V 1984, cols. 353–354).

3g

4

RELIEF WITH FOWLER

White Limestone

New Kingdom
Early Dynasty XVIII
Reign of Hatshepsut or Tuthmosis III
1479–1425 B.C.

Egyptian reliefwork is basically of two types: raised and sunk. In the former the surface is cut back so that the representation stands out from the background. In the other the surface is left standing while the subject represented is cut or "sunk" into it. In both techniques a certain amount of modeling can be applied, often so subtly that it appears only in a strong raking light. This slab in fine white limestone with the representation of a man is an excellent example of the type of raised relief created in the early part of Dynasty XVIII.

It shows a man facing right and – to judge from contemporary, less fragmentary examples – standing on a light boat in a marsh or papyrus swamp. In a swamp scene, the background would have been painted green. Now all color has been lost, except for a few small traces of light red on the torso. The scene is that of a man fowling, holding in the hand of the raised arm a throwstick and in the other a captive bird as a lure, one wingtip of which is visible on the right edge of the slab.

The man, undoubtedly the owner of the tomb from which this relief was cut more than half a century ago, wears a short, bobbed plain wig which would have been black, perhaps painted so as to appear to consist of many rows of stylized curls. The wig covers the ears; it is modishly cut at an angle from back of the cheek to the base of the neck, behind which it meets the broad collar necklace of eight strands of beads. The forehead is set back from the edge of the wig. The eyebrow is a long, raised band trailing out to a point well beyond the outer corner of the eye. The upper eyelid rim is modeled as a fine raised strip; the eyeball appears to be protruding from the eyesocket; it is definitely convex, not flat.

The nose is fleshy, the mouth full, and the lips are bordered by a thin vermilion line. The contour of upper arms and shoulders indicates the man's strength, but the torso is quite flat. As is customary in Egyptian relief art, only one nipple is indicated. The upper edge of a belted loincloth appears at the bottom of the slab. The wing of the bird the man holds is probably that of a duck, most likely a pintail duck, which would have made a great deal of noise when it was held aloft. Under the elbow is the beginning of an inscription; only two hieroglyphs are left, one rounded on top like a loaf of bread, probably the letter "t", and to the left of it a vertical stroke that could be the upper part of the hieroglyph for "b".

As an example of early New Kingdom tomb relief the slab is a fine work of art, even in so fragmentary a condition. The vigor of the man's action, one arm raised and the other lowered, and the serene features of the well modeled face betray the design of a great artisan of the early fifteenth century B.C. The manner in which the owner is represented, engaged in one of the noble sports of ancient Egypt, is most compelling and renders well the skill and elegance displayed by the tomb owner at whose feet no doubt squatted the pretty female members of his family.

The stone is in sound condition, but numerous scratches and chips appear on the surface as well as on the edges of the slab. At neck and waist the reliefwork is worn, but no repairs or restorations have been made. All four edges are modern breaks or cuts. As presently mounted, the back is inaccessible.

In 1980 Mr. Bastis presented the relief to The Brooklyn Museum (80.38) in honor of Bernard V. Bothmer. It had been on loan to the Museum since 1970.

MEASUREMENTS: Height 52.7 cm.; of head 16.3 cm.; of face 8.7 cm. Width 42.8 cm. Thickness 4.0 cm

PROVENANCE: Not known; probably Western Thebes.

BIBLIOGRAPHY: Fazzini 1972, pp. 45–46, fig. 13.

COMMENT: Max Wegner (1933, p. 46) was the first to state that, with few exceptions (TT nos. 12 and 345), there were two periods in Dynasty XVIII when tombs were decorated in relief: the first during the reigns of Hatshepsut and Tuthmosis III and the second under Amenhotep III and IV. Painted tombs occur throughout the entire length of the Dynasty; tombs with reliefwork are comparatively rare. From its style the Bastis relief appears to have been carved in the time of Tuthmosis III or slightly earlier, and the figure of the anonymous owner recalls those in several relief-decorated tombs of the King's reign (TT nos. 53, 123, 125, 127, and others). For fowling scenes in Dynasty XVIII tombs, see PM I,1 1960, p. 467 17 (a). The bird in the man's hand cannot be identified with certainty, although it must be assumed to be a water fowl. The presence of hieroglyphs, probably from a name, may indicate that a member of the tomb owner's family was standing or squatting, on a smaller scale, below the forward arm. From similar representations it can be surmised that they were on a boat. For the vermilion line around the lips, see *MDAIK* 37 (1981), p. 77, n. 15.

The exact tomb from which the fowler comes has not been established, but in style it resembles fragments of hunting scenes from the same period, now in West Berlin (5/65; Berlin 1967, p.59, no. 639, ill.), in Toronto (957.218; Needler 1982, pp. 70–72, ill.), and in New York (MMA 55.92.1; Hayes 1959, pp. 164–165, fig. 90). In the last-named relief the men wear exactly the same kind of wig as the anonymous fowler.

5

KA-EM-WASET, SISTROPHOROS

New Kingdom
Dynasty XVIII
Reign of Tuthmosis IV
1397–1387 B.C.

Dark Gray to Black Granite

Whereas in the Old Kingdom (2670–2195 B.C.) statuary of private persons was relegated to sculpture chambers that formed part of the tomb complex and were inaccessible after the demise of the tomb owner, in the Middle Kingdom (2065–1780 B.C.) a new custom evolved. This permitted a person to have his or her statue set up in a temple or sanctuary, dedicated to the gods but accessible to visitors engaged in ritual or worship. This custom was generally the rule in the New Kingdom (1550–1075 B.C.), and especially in the millennium that followed since fewer people built elaborate tombs in which statues could be set up. Thus we distinguish between tomb statues and temple statues, and such a temple statue is the headless figure of Ka-em-waset on his knees.

The man once wore a double wig of echeloned stylized curls. Naked to the waist, he is dressed in a long skirt, the hem of which ends just above the ankles, while at the waist it is held by a plain belt that can be seen behind the elbows. As a man of means who did not have to work hard, he grew a paunch, which explains the folds of fat below the chest.

While temple statues of private persons first occur in the Middle Kingdom, figures of people holding a god's image or presenting a divine emblem do not seem to have been made before the New Kingdom. The man who is called Ka-em-waset is dated by the name of his king, Tuthmosis IV (1397–1387 B.C.), written in a cartouche and surmounted by two feathers, on the upper right arm. He was

5a

therefore active early in the fourteenth century B.C., as one of a group of distinguished officials of the XVIIIth Dynasty. They are often represented in the act of proffering a sacred object in the sanctuary of a deity, in this case probably that of the Goddess Mut at Karnak.

What he holds is the emblem of a female deity, a so-called naos sistrum, of which there is a fine example, though small and of a later date, in the Bastis Collection (No. 34, pp. 87–88 below). The emblem consists of the broad face of the Goddess Hathor which is always adorned by the ears of her sacred animal, the cow. A heavy plain wig frames the face, surmounted by a shrine, doorway or temple façade containing a royal cobra. Usually the shrine is flanked by two rising volutes, the whole being the stylized form of a common rattle, a kind of percussion instrument called a sistrum. It is known to have been carried by women and used since the Middle Kingdom. Thus the man presenting it is called a sistrophoros, meaning that the sculpture is of the sistrum-bearing kind. The earliest example of this type is the sistrophorous statue of the Steward Senenmut in Munich (ÄS 6265; Schoske, Wildung 1985, pp. 48, 50, no. 32, ill.), whose *floruit* lies about seventy years earlier, in the reign of Queen Hatshepsut. Here, as there, a Hathor head rests on a knot-and-tie amulet, the Isis knot, that signifies "life," "welfare" or the like (*MMJ* 5, 1972, pp. 11–13).

Although originally associated with the cult of the Goddess Hathor, the sistrum became the emblem of other female deities. Thus the Munich statue was, according to the inscription, dedicated in a sanctuary of the Goddess Iunit at Armant, south of Medinet Habu, while the text of the Bastis sculpture invokes Mut, the consort of the God Amun, whose sanctuary lies at South Karnak, facing a crescent-shaped sacred lake called Asheru which is mentioned in the inscriptions on the statue.

The sculpture is supported by a base, rounded in front, and by a broad back pillar ending just below the wig. The back pillar is inscribed with three columns of text, beginning with a plea for offerings addressed to Amun-Ra, the King of the Gods. Column 3 gives the titles of the owner who was to benefit from the blessings of his deity. Here his name is lost at the end of the text, together with the left rear corner of the base, but his chief titulary is preserved: "King's Scribe, Overseer of Cattle, and Chief Steward of the Temple of Amun."

Behind and, as side views of the statue show, between the rising volutes, royal cobras flank the shrine, and on the negative space linking the Hathor emblem to the torso of Ka-em-waset his titles are listed in a column of text, with his name fully spelled out: "Ka-em-waset," meaning "Bull of Thebes" (Fig. 5 e). This is possibly an allusion to his exalted office, because cattle were a prized possession, vital to the economics of a temple administration and, being in charge of such riches, Ka-em-waset must have profited handsomely.

A line of inscription runs around three sides of the base in two parts, one from the middle of the front to the right side, the other, somewhat damaged, to the left. And finally, there is a line on top of the front of the base, facing the observer, like a heading or announcement: "For the spirit of ... the King's Scribe and Overseer of Cattle of Amun, Ka-em-waset."

The head, except for the lower part of the wig on the left and in back, is lost. The beard too is gone, but from the remains behind the "roof" of the shrine it is evident that it was very full (Fig. 5 e). Most of the left arm is also lost, except for the hand, and so is the left rear corner of the base with the toes and parts of columns 2 and 3 of the back pillar inscription. The texts of the base are damaged on front and left side, and a few chips can be noticed elsewhere on the sculpture, especially on the right eyebrow of the Hathor face.

In 1974 Mr. Bastis presented the sculpture to The Brooklyn Museum (74.94) where it had been on loan since 1969.

MEASUREMENTS: Height 66.3 cm.; to top of back pillar 56.5 cm. Width across shoulders originally ca. 30 cm. Height of base 10.0 to 12.3 cm. Width of base 26.0 cm. Depth of base 45.3 cm. Intralinear height at left rear 4.8 cm.

PROVENANCE: Not known; probably Karnak, although the first owner of the statue was told that it had been found in the Delta. It is known to have been in Paris at least since 1968, and is the only Egyptian antiquity acquired by Mr. Bastis abroad. All others were purchased over the years in the New York market.

BIBLIOGRAPHY: *Maison et Jardin* (Paris), 149 (Dec. 1968–Jan. 1969), p. 204 ill.; Russmann, in *MMJ* 8 (1973), p. 38, n. 17 (where the original loan number should read L69.38.2); *the ART gallery* 22,2 (Dec.–Jan. 1979), p. 103; *Treasure House: Museums of the Empire State* (New York, 1979), p. 29, fig. 26.

COMMENT: Although most Egyptian statues are fairly well carved, with the back pillar perpendicular to the top of the base, there are exceptions, and some of the sculptures of kings and high-ranking officials are slightly asymmetrical and askew. The figure of Ka-em-waset, for instance, has a base higher on the right side than on the left. Also, the base level descends forward and therefore does not form a right angle with the back pillar.

Although the head is lost, the statue of Ka-em-waset constitutes an important addition to the comparatively small number of sculptures firmly dated to the time of King Tuthmosis IV, for which we have thus far only a few references (Petrie 1924, pp. xli–xlii, 171–173; Vandier 1958, pp. 510–514; and Bryan 1980). Mrs. Bryan's study of the reign of Tuthmosis IV has provided us, *inter alia,* with a most useful list of the high dignitaries of the time and their monuments, among them those of Ka-em-waset (Bryan 1980, pp. 341–344, 382, 395–396), who also had a kneeling stelophorous statue, now in London (BM 1238). There the

5b

◁ 5c
5d

5e

5f Top View, from front

owner wears the same kind of wig as does the Bastis figure, and the head is more or less intact, The face, however, is idealizing and badly damaged.

Ka-em-waset's type of double wig first becomes common usage during the reign of King Amenhotep II, and numerous private sculptures thus adorned dating from that time are now in Paris (Louvre E. 10443 and E. 27161), Cairo (CG 566), and Berlin/GDR (19286 and 19289).

There is, however, a statue well dated to the time of Tuthmosis III in London (BM 888), in which the person represented wears the double wig, and Simpson may be right in attributing an inscribed bust with double wig in Boston (MFA 1972.359; Simpson 1972, pp. 116–117) also to the reign of Tuthmosis III. These two examples would seem to constitute the first occurrences of the coiffure worn by Ka-em-waset.

Rolls of fat on the torso of important men rarely appear in Middle Kingdom seated and kneeling statuary, but are in use in the New Kingdom from the beginning; for example in a seated statue of late Dynasty XVII in New York (MMA 65.115; Wildung 1984, pp. 232, 246, fig. 201), and regularly in Dynasty XVIII, for example in the kneeling statues of Senenmut (*BMA* XI,2 1969–70, pp. 124 ff.), a contemporary of Queen Hatshepsut.

The custom of inscribing the ruling king's name on the upper arms of a private statue is first found in the New Kingdom and regularly in Dynasty XVIII. It occurs on sculptures where the chest is not fully exposed, as for example on the right arms of kneeling figures of Senenmut (*op.cit.* pp. 127, 128, 134); and whenever the second cartouche was added it is found on the right chest, as on a well known Cairo statue (CG 42123; Vandier 1958, pl. CLXVI:6). It is unlikely that a second cartouche was engraved on the upper *left* arm of Ka-em-waset, now lost. This kind of symmetrical arrangement does not occur until Dynasty XXV. The partial lack of columnar lines in the back pillar inscription seems strange.

Sistrophorous sculptures have been discussed in *LdÄ* V 1984, col. 958. They were in use from early Dynasty XVIII to Dynasty XXVI (Russmann 1973, pp. 36–37). The type of naos sistrum proffered by Ka-em-waset has often been commented upon (best by Davies 1920, p. 70; Sachs 1921, pp. 30 ff., and Klebs 1931). The authors all deal with the volutes rising to the sides of the shrine that probably represent steer or cow horns, once part of the early cattle-head amulets, and transformed the little shrine with Hathor head into a rattle when shaken. Without the wiry volutes tapping the naos, the sistrum would not have made a sound.

6

SHELL SPOON

New Kingdom
Late Dynasty XVIII
1400–1300 B.C.

Yellow to Light Brown Ivory

A timeless quality exists in the best of the minor arts from the ancient Nile Valley, and when the design is absolutely perfect such an object does not even look particularly "Egyptian." This applies to the spoonlike instrument in the form of a hand holding an oblong shell, somewhat like a large mussel. Whether the container was to be used as a ritual object to present something in a cult, or for mixing ointments, lotions, balm or scent, is much disputed. That the "handle" has the shape of a hand may mean that something is being held, given, presented, passed on, or perhaps poured out which had been prepared beforehand, not necessarily in the spoon. An idea is expressed, and this idea is perhaps more related to the hand than to what it is holding. As something abstract is meant to be conveyed, the hand is not a real hand of natural form. It is the almost disembodied reflection of a hand with four straight fingers and a thumb to one side to steady the spoon. None of the fingers are articulated and modeled to represent flesh and bone, although the Egyptians were perfectly capable of rendering any part of the body in almost *trompe l'oeil* fashion in any kind of material. And yet, fingernails and cuticles are indicated in minute detail.

As a miniature work of art, comprising the basin with lip in natural, undulating form and the hand so highly stylized, the ivory is of arresting quality. As simply a product of fine design it is a pleasure to behold, and since it is of such outstanding workmanship, it was probably made in the splendid century that has left us so many small objects of great design, the fourteenth century B.C., the latter part of Dynasty XVIII. When one considers the profusion of small works in ivory that were made in the period from King Amenhotep III to Tutankhamen, for the kings themselves as well as for their courtiers, one cannot help wondering if the Bastis spoon was not possibly created then, in one of the studios associated with the court.

The ivory shows a few dark spots and a sliver is missing from the edge of the shell, on the side opposite the thumb. The lines on the "wrist" are mere scratches where there is some slight damage, as if it had been stuck into a larger holder. Otherwise, the precious small object is in a perfect state of preservation.

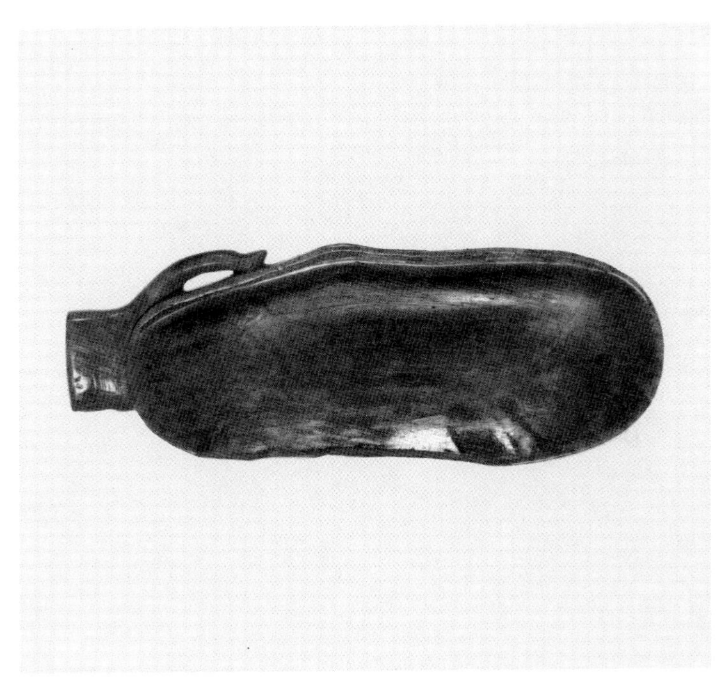

6a

6b

MEASUREMENTS: Length 8.0 cm. Width 2.6 cm. Thickness ("height") 0.9 cm.

PROVENANCE: Not known.

BIBLIOGRAPHY: None.

COMMENT: Two recent studies have contributed considerably to defining the problems that this type of usually uninscribed object presents. One deals with spoons (Wallert 1967), the other with objects attached to or forming part of a hand (Sourdive 1984). Both agree that even though they may have been used in real life, these hand-held containers are cultic. The few with inscriptions refer to wine and incense. For Egyptian ivory implements in general, see Drenkhahn 1986.

The dating of such an object is difficult unless a very similar piece has turned up in a controlled excavation. A fine assemblage of exquisite small spoons and dishes was shown in an exhibition of New Kingdom minor arts some years ago (Boston 1982, pp. 205–215, nos. 241–261). Among them were a few outstanding pieces in ivory. To them could be added the swimming-girl "spoon" in Moscow (3627; Wallert 1967, p. 129, no. M 11); the hand with a shell in Cambridge (Fitzwilliam Museum E. 429.1982; *JEA* 70, 1984, p. 133, no. 329, pl. XX:5); and several others elsewhere (Sourdive 1984, pp. 275–286). A "cosmetic palette," made of bone, not ivory, was found at Tell el Maskhuta some years ago by the ARCE-Canadian Institute in Egypt-University of Toronto Wadi Tumilat Project, and thus far is illustrated only in the *1985 Agenda* of The Chase National Bank (Egypt) S.A.E., p. 77, N 11, where it is "dated to the Saite Period, c. 525 B.C.", apparently on the basis of the stratum in which it was found. It depicts a right hand, stretched out and supporting a freshwater clamshell.

Referring back to the Bastis piece, it is obvious that it can only be compared with similar "spoons" that show the thumb to the side of the "dish", steadying it, and not adjoining the other four fingers in the most basic method of support. As it turns out, there are very few comparable objects of like or similar form: one in Cairo (JE 87868, in faience, inscribed; Wallert 1967, pp. 104–105, K 61; Sourdive 1984, pp. 282–283 ill.) and two in Paris (Louvre N. 1786, in ivory; Vandier d'Abbadie 1972, p. 27, OT 53; E. 22901, in ivory; *op.cit.*, pp. 26–27, OT 54 ill.). It is curious that two of these examples like the Bastis piece show a LEFT hand and one of them, the one in Cairo in faience, is inscribed with a dedication mentioning two Late Period, or at least Third Intermediate Period, names. Therefore it cannot date from the New Kingdom. The one in Paris also showing a LEFT hand (Louvre E. 22901) is made in ivory. Mme. Vandier attributed it to the New Kingdom, and Sourdive (p. 280) accepts it, but he is generally not very critical of the dates proposed by the owners of objects cited in his publication.

Since the object in Cairo is made in faience, obviously imitating an object in ivory, the most common material for New Kingdom "spoons" of this general type, it cannot be used for dating purposes. One is therefore inclined to follow Mme. Vandier's attribution of the Louvre piece. The quality of the Bastis ivory is such that it may well have been made in Dynasty XVIII too, specifically in the reigns of Amenhotep III or Tutankhamen.

It must be noted that Sourdive in his publication *La main*, does not seem to have mentioned the problem of "right hand," "left hand." At present, I am unable to present an explanation. Could it be that *holding* rather than *presenting* is implied by the left-handed form and that it involves the use of the right hand for picking up whatever filled the container? Perhaps it held pellets of incense that were thrown, one by one, into a flame.

The particular form of the hand, with four fingers highly stylized and only the thumb modeled in more detail, is a motif that goes back to the Old Kingdom (Sourdive 1984, p. 519). The best examples that come to mind are the expressive, yet highly stylized hands of the mature Methethy in Brooklyn (51.1; PM III,2 1981, p. 647).

7

ANCESTRAL BUST

New Kingdom
Late Dynasty XVIII
1380–1320 B.C.

White Limestone, Discolored, with Numerous Traces of Paint

Admiring the tombs and temples, painting, relief and sculpture of ancient Egypt, we marvel at the religious fervor which brought forth these forests of columns and acres of well-decorated wall space. All this is public, official, and easily visible, especially since the essentially private character of the tombs has long been lost. Little, however, is known about another aspect of Egyptian religion which was also private but is no longer evident, because the place for this kind of religion is mostly lost. That is the place of domestic worship, the cult of the family ancestors, a religious act performed in the privacy of the home. These homes, built of perishable mudbrick, have long since disappeared; hardly any secular dwellings of ordinary ancient Egyptians have survived. Only in recent years has field

7a

7b

archaeology turned to the study of domestic architecture which, as it was made in sundried mudbrick, has suffered greatly from the passage of time and, unlike the stone-built temples and tombs, has simply been washed away in the Nile Valley.

There are, however, exceptions, both for places of worship in private dwellings and for objects of such worship. The most frequently found group of antiquities relating to domestic worship are the so-called ancestral busts of which several hundred still exist. They were usually made of limestone, sometimes of sandstone or wood (Bruyère 1939, p. 168), and like the sculpture in the Bastis Collection were well painted.

This bust shows the head of a female wearing a plain tripartite wig, the lappets of which hang down in front, below the neck, while the third part, somewhat wider, extends in back to just below the shoulders. The edge of a garment is visible at the throat. In front the bust is absolutely flat; downward it increases in volume in all four directions. The bottom would have been flat, in shape somewhat between a rectangle and an oval.

The round, unlined face has a striking, alive, almost mischievous expression. The forehead recedes towards the wig; the eyebrows are prominent and naturally formed; the "buttonhole" eyes are long and slanting, the left more than the right. The upper lid is marked by a single incised line, a feature unknown before the time of King Amenhotep III. The nose was strong and broad. The philtrum is unusually wide; the mouth absolutely straight, with the lower lip somewhat fuller than the upper lip. The ears, usually long in Egyptian statuary, are extra long here, and the earlobes are nicked, indicating that an earring or ear clip was meant to be worn, as in real life. On the front of the bust at the bottom, the original edge of the sculpture is preserved, thus giving us the original height: 23.2 cm. The majority of such busts measures from 23 to 25 cm. which equals roughly half a cubit.

At one time the bust was blazing with color. The hair was black, probably with a diadem of blue lotus, as there are remains of blue visible on the right side above the ear, around both ears, and above the left shoulder. Eyelid rims and pupils were painted black, face and neck a light brown, the garment perhaps yellow, as there are spots of yellow between the two lappets.

Between and below the two lappets and on the back it is customary for such busts to have a painted broad collar (Bruyère 1939, p. 172, fig. 67). Enough traces of it can be seen on the Bastis bust to note that it must have been red and black.

7c

7d Right Back Three Quarter View

Having stated earlier that such busts come primarily from private dwellings, it should be noted that not all of the dwellings have fallen into dust (Bruyère 1933, pp. 10–11; 1934, p. 85; 1939, p. 171). Bruyère found house-walls at Deir el Medineh in Western Thebes with the remains of niches, and below them ancestral busts that had fallen to the ground. Thus there can be no doubt that they were once set up in houses, and there are representations showing that they belonged to household furnishings, such as the headrest for a bed, to be used in this life and to be taken along into the hereafter (Bruyère 1939, p. 169, fig. 65). That they were indeed worshiped may be seen from a charming stela (Vandier d'Abbadie 1946, p. 134 and fig. 1 on p. 135) that shows a woman censing and libating before an ancestral bust set up on a pedestal.

The question remains, however: who is represented? A real person or a deity commemorating a deceased ancestor? Fortunately there are a few busts with inscriptions on them, and they invoke the Goddess Hathor, and none other. This fits well with the Egyptian concept of the role of the female as "mistress of the house," a designation employed thousands of times in Egyptian texts as the title before a lady's name, and thus it is the female ancestor who was remembered in the house more than the male. The simple tripartite hairdo has regal as well as divine connotations, best seen in the dyad and triads of Mycerinus in Dynasty IV, and there is a long tradition of Hathor as mother goddess as well as guardian deity of the house wearing this hairdo. The association of Hathor with Deir el Medineh, where the Bastis bust may have come from, was very close, as the temple there which is dedicated to her shows (PM II 1972, p. 401).

The date of this ancestral bust is easily determined; it lies somewhere towards the end of Dynasty XVIII in the fourteenth century B.C. The face, especially the form of the eyes, indicates an origin between the latter part of the reign of King Amenhotep III, when the "hieroglyphic" eye was transformed into the "natural" eye of the Amarna Period, and the end of Tutankhamen's reign. As a matter of fact, the face of the bust bears a striking resemblance to that of some of Tutankhamen's shawabtis.

The preservation of head and face is very good, except for some nicks and scratches, and damage to the right nostril. The lower part of the sculpture has suffered considerably, although a bit of the original edge of the bottom front still exists. The paint is uniformly worn away, but enough is left to give a good impression of what the coloration of the little sculpture must have been.

MEASUREMENTS: Height 23.2 cm.; of head 7.1 cm.; of face 4.4 cm. Width now 9.8 cm. Depth now 8.5 cm.

PROVENANCE: Not known; probably Deir el Medineh at Western Thebes.

BIBLIOGRAPHY: None.

COMMENT: Basic studies of the ancestral bust thus far are those of Boreux 1932a, Bruyère 1939, Vandier d'Abbadie 1946, Keith-Bennett 1981, and Friedman 1985. The earlier literature can be traced through them. Ancestral busts have frequently been shown in exhibitions, and the catalogs provide further leads and discussions (Metz 1979, no. 129; Boston 1982, p. 300, no. 409). None of them, however, have speculated on the connection to Hathor and Ptah.

The nick in the earlobe made exactly in this fashion is also found on other busts of this kind; one in Cairo (JE 43980) and one in West Berlin (20694), both from Möller's excavations at Deir el Medineh (Anthes 1943, p. 58, pl. 16 d [Cairo] and 16 c [Berlin]; Berlin 1967, no. 783). The wig of the Berlin bust is blue, not black. In addition to his own findings, Bruyère draws attention also to the fact that some busts have been found at Karnak, in private houses dating from antiquity (Bruyère 1939, p. 171, n. 3). So far as is known, none has ever turned up in an ancient sanctuary or temple.

The bust in West Berlin cited above bears an inscription invoking the Goddess Hathor. The coiffure of the Bastis bust (Vandier 1958, p. 105; Staehelin 1966, pp. 180–181 3.b) is typical of the Goddess Hathor as early as Dynasty IV (Reisner 1931, pls. 38–45; see also Allam 1963, *passim*). For her role as mother goddess and deity of the house, one may consult *LdÄ* II 1977, cols. 1024–1033. It should be added that some busts represent males (Brooklyn 1956, pl. 25 no. 11 B; Boreux 1932a, pl. 63 b, Keith-Bennett 1981, figs. 1, 3, 9–12; Bierbrier 1982, p. 95, fig. 69), and three or more have two heads, one male, one female, in Cairo (TR 6/2/37/1, JE 87846), in Paris (Louvre E. 14702), and in London (BM 49735). In each case the male has a shaven pate or a tight-fitting cap which may indicate short-cropped hair. They bear a striking resemblance to standard representations of the God Ptah, who in the New Kingdom is sometimes closely associated with Hathor (*ASAE* 3, 1902, p. 100; PM II 1972, p. 201). Both were originally Memphite deities, and their appearance at Thebes West is an anomaly that awaits further study.

Despite Ms. Friedman's statement that ancestral busts represent males (Friedman 1985, p. 97), the association with undoubted males and the use of a modius (never worn by men) clearly mark the majority of the busts – those with a tripartite wig – as female.

The "buttonhole" eye is essentially two-dimensional, "written", like the "hieroglyphic" eye, into the face of a sculpture or relief as the hieroglyph of the eye is written in a formal Egyptian text (Romano 1983, pp. 105, 108, 111). The naturally formed eye, however, with a depression between eyebrow and eyelid, which protrudes over a convex eyeball, is found in the latter part of the reign of Amenhotep III in, for example, the fine wooden statuette of the King in Brooklyn (48.28; Vandier 1958, p. 618), throughout the Amarna Period and its aftermath to the time of King Ramesses I, occasionally also in the reigns of Sety I and early Ramesses II. The shawabtis of Tutankhamen that the face of the Bastis bust resembles so strikingly are T.906 and T.1086–1087 (Cairo JE 60823, 60820, and 60822), which would certainly indicate that a number of ancestral busts could be attributed to the latter part of Dynasty XVIII, both pre- and post-Amarna. For a unique ancestral bust with inlaid eyes, see Cairo JE 64911 (*ASAE* 35, 1935, p. 119, fig. 8).

The statement that almost all these busts are of Ramesside date (Boston 1982, p. 300, comment to no. 409) undoubtedly goes too far, as hitherto no one has been able to attribute the majority of them to a period later than the beginning of the reign of Ramesses II. For the Dynasty XVIII date of the first village at Deir el Medineh, see Valbelle 1985, pp. 4, 7, 20 and passim.

8a

8 QUEEN NEFERTITI

New Kingdom
Dynasty XVIII, Amarna Period
About 1350 B.C.

Brown Sandstone, Painted

Among all the queens of ancient Egypt, none has been more frequently represented in relief than Nefertiti, wife and consort of King Amenhotep IV who, after his fifth year of reign, assumed the name Akhenaten. That she, who was not a monarch, but co-ruler with her husband, appears so very often is solely due to the fact that her presence was required as part of the formal image of the royal family at functions, official and private, religous and secular, that the King attended. Their worship of the supreme deity, the living sun disk Aten, was all-pervading, and as an outstanding personality in her own right who, by herself also worshiped the Aten, Nefertiti is always shown with a strong, determined face and an expression that somewhat resembles that of her spouse.

Nefertiti was no beauty, as is evident from well over a hundred representations dating to the first five years of the royal couple's reign. During this early period a highly realistic style was developed which, in keeping with the new theology's aim for the ultimate truth, was supposed to render all humans, plants, animals and everything else in nature as they were and as they looked, devoid of the traditional idealization. Although the Queen was still young then, her features show, with great mastery on the part of the artisan, a harshness and determination that make this slab of sunk relief one of the finest representations of her personality.

The raised arms indicate that Nefertiti was making an offering to the Sun God Aten. He is sending a single ray towards her face; the ray terminates in a stylized hand holding the sign of life to her nose. She wears a long wig with stylized curls set *en echelon*, surmounted by a diadem. To the front of it, just above her forehead, a uraeus, the royal cobra, has been affixed. The naturally formed brow surmounts a half-closed eye that gives her face a dreamy, fervent look, quite appropriate to the religious act in which she is engaged. An empty cartouche has been drawn on the near forearm. Another cartouche has been erased from what might be an armlet on the upper part of the far arm.

Nefertiti was accompanied by her eldest daughter Meryt-aten who, on a smaller scale, stood behind her and to whom the column of inscription refers. It describes the little girl as being a daughter of the King's own body. Her name, Meryt-aten, is written with a curious sign, often used as a determinative in the spelling of the name of the Aten, a miniature sun disk perched on a simple plus-like cross, the whole representing a modified *ankh*-sign.

On the left the original edge of the slab is preserved; all the other sides are chipped and fragmentary. On the right, about one fifth of the standard size of the block, called in Arabic *talatat,* is lost. The back was cut off in modern times, and the relief is now set in plaster and framed. There is still much red color on face and neck, and a few specks of blue can be found on the wig. In a few places the surface of the relief is slightly marred.

In 1978 Mr. Bastis presented the relief to The Brooklyn Museum (78.39) in honor of Bernard V. Bothmer. It had been on loan since 1969.

MEASUREMENTS: Height 20.9 cm. Width 42.3 cm. Thickness 3.8 cm. Height of face 8.3 cm. Intracolumnar width 9.4 cm.

PROVENANCE: Not known, but undoubtedly from a lost shrine of the Aten at Karnak.

BIBLIOGRAPHY: *MW* 1 (1972), pp. 46–48, fig. 16; Aldred 1973, pp. 34, 66, 83 (ill.), 111 no. 25 (ill.), 113; *Archaeology* 26 (1973), p. 301; *BCMA* 64 (1977), p. 292, fig. 9; *the ART gallery* 22,2 (1979), pp. 103–104, ill.; Luxor 1979, p. 117 (same page in German ed. 1981; p. 59 in French ed. 1985); *Archaeology* 35 (1982), p. 2; *Art.Aeg.* 1983, p. 132 n. 17.

COMMENT: In the beginning of his reign King Amenhotep IV undertook at Karnak the construction of temples on a large scale in honor of his god, the Aten. He introduced a standard building block that could be carried by one man. It measured about nine inches in height by twenty-one inches in width. Hundreds of thousands of these blocks were cut, and almost 45,000 of them, decorated with relief and painted, have been found in the last sixty years. The slab in the Bastis Collection is just one of them. The blocks are called *talatat*, more correctly *thalathāt*, a unit of measurement from Islamic architecture. The term was first used by Egyptian workmen when such blocks turned up at Karnak in large numbers half a century ago (Luxor 1979, p. 104, ill.). Thanks to the long wig there is no doubt that this royal likeness represents Queen Nefertiti and not her husband, but there are a number of representations where King and Queen are hard to distinguish since their features are so very much alike (Werner 1979, pp. 324–331, 4 pls.).

Queen Teye, Nefertiti's mother-in-law, was also frequently represented, both at Karnak and at Tell el Amarna, dressed in the long lappet wig with echeloned stylized curls, and Nefertiti herself wears it on many occasions (West Berlin 89/66 and Cleveland 59.186). From other representations it is known that the wig did not extend over the upper arm, but behind it. Also, judging from a more complete representation of Queen Nefertiti (*ATP* 1976, pl. 21), the plain circlet on her hair held the uraeus. This circlet in turn was surmounted by a modius of uraei bearing

8b

the long-horned Hathor crown with sun disk, two uraei, and two tall plumes (Rammant-Peeters 1985, pp. 21–48, variant a on pl. I).

When Nefertiti raises her arm as high as in the Bastis relief she is making an offering, always without the King being present, and usually she is accompanied in these scenes by one of her daughters (*ATP* 1976, pl. 19).

The curious manner in which the determinative of the name of the Aten has been written, as a cross surmounted by a disk, is found frequently in inscriptions of the Amarna Period at Karnak and Tell el Amarna, but no philologist or epigraphist has thus far commented on the sign which probably alludes to the *ankh*, the sign of life.

Since temple construction in sandstone at Karnak was abandoned after Year 5 when the court moved to Tell el Amarna in Middle Egypt, where temples as well as palaces were decorated in limestone, the likeness of the Bastis queen represents the early style, as Aldred (1973) has so ably demonstrated. He has shown that it was during the terminal phase of the so-called Amarna Period when a less realistic, more idealizing, style evolved, that Nefertiti became the beautiful Queen as, though inaccurately, she is known. In the Bastis relief the fine ornamental line descending from the nostril and running past the mouth differs greatly from a similar but straighter incision denoting the maturity of the King's face (Aldred 1973, p. 94, no. 6).

9a

9

FACE OF OSIRIS

Third Intermediate Period
Dynasties XXI–XXIII
1000–800 B.C.

Bronze, Inlaid with
Faience and Glass

Hundreds of bronze figures representing Osiris, god of the dead, the underworld, the hereafter, are preserved in collections all over the world. Very few of them are inlaid with glass or faience, a technique that seems to have originated and flourished in the Third Intermediate Period (1075–750 B.C.) and never again. Therefore the deity's face in the Bastis Collection is of a certain rarity. It is also most attractive, with its pleasing, not at all otherworldly, expression and with its polychromy. Apart from the bronze which is brown with green and copper-red spots, there are blue glass inlays around the eyes and a remnant at the end of the right eyebrow. The eyes are inlaid with black and white opaque glass.

The face is not really a fragment; it must have come

from a hollow-cast composite figure of the God Osiris, because it is in itself an individually cast object, preserved from head to chin; only the beard is broken.

Parts of the beardstrap are preserved on either side of the chin. A tiny restoration is visible at the tip of the nose. The bronze is slightly corroded in a few places, but on the whole it is in excellent condition. The back of the face is filled with a modern matrix for support and has been fitted with a metal bar for mounting.

MEASUREMENTS: Height 4.2 cm. Width 4.0 cm. Depth 2.4 cm.

PROVENANCE: Not known.

BIBLIOGRAPHY: None.

COMMENT: Judging from the size of the face, the original statue of Osiris must have been about 50 cm. high (Roeder 1937, p. 208). Roeder was the first to do research on Osiris bronzes with inlays, (followed by Anthes 1938, pp. 69–76), and there have been other useful observations on the subject of inlays (Brooklyn 1956, pp. 46, 49).

Although the largest number of Osiris bronzes date from the Late Period, Dynasty XXV to early Ptolemaic times, none of them is inlaid with faience, glass, or the like. Therefore a dating to the Third Intermediate Period is quite acceptable, although Anthes (*op.cit.*, p. 74) hesitantly attributed such an inlaid bronze figure of Osiris in Berlin to the late Ramesside Period.

The working hypothesis that the Osiris beard in the eighth and seventh centuries B.C. fully envelops the chin (*Kêmi* 19, 1969, pp. 14, 16) and only in the latter part of Dynasty XXVI slips to the tip of the chin and eventually under it, applies primarily to stone sculpture, not necessarily to bronzes. Statuary in the Third Intermediate Period has its own rules and standards, quite different from those of the Late Period.

9b

10

FALCON GOD

Late Period
700–300 B.C.

Bronze, Solid Cast

The art of metal casting was introduced into Egypt, probably from Western Asia, towards the end of the third millennium B.C. First copper was used, later bronze, and there are a dozen or so Egyptian examples that can be attributed with reasonable certainty to the period between 1900 and 1000 B.C.

During the Third Intermediate Period and the beginning of the Late Period, in Dynasties XXI–XXIII, great progress in bronze casting was made, and several stunningly beautiful, large bronze figures, some inlaid with gold, silver, and electrum, were made. They range in date from Dynasty XXII to the beginning of Dynasty XXVI. Never again would such marvels of metal casting be created in ancient Egypt. Instead, beginning with the seventh century B.C., bronze figures of gods, goddesses, sacred animals, and emblems were produced on a smaller scale in great numbers; also, though more rarely, little figures of kings and private persons were cast. Their date is mostly uncertain, which is especially regrettable where pieces of very fine craftsmanship, like the falcon statuette, are concerned.

Since the figure has a tang under the feet one must assume that it was once attached to a base that may have borne an inscription naming the donor. Or it might have been the crowning piece of a scepter or staff, or one of many ornaments on temple furniture. Be that as it may, it is a delightful little object, delicately made and in fine condition.

Many falcon deities are known to have been worshiped in ancient Egypt, and although immediately the great God Horus, embodied by a falcon, comes to mind, this figure does not necessarily represent him, especially since it lacks the sun disk on top of the head with which the God Horus is usually endowed; there is no trace of a break at the top.

The details of head and feathering are carefully modeled and drawn. Only the large feet are somewhat summarily formed. Unlike the real bird the bronze bird wears a neatly incised necklace. The falcon also carries an engraved mark under the eye, best seen on the left side, denoting the divine nature of the bird.

The condition of the bronze is excellent. The light brown color is enlivened here and there by spots of green patina.

MEASUREMENTS: Height with the tang 7.9 cm.; without the tang 6.5 cm. Width 3.6 cm. Depth 6.1 cm.

PROVENANCE: Not known.

BIBLIOGRAPHY: None.

COMMENT: For falcon gods one may consult *LdÄ* II 1977, cols. 94–95. Similar small bronze figures of falcons are in many collections of Egyptian antiquities (Roeder 1937, pp. 61–62; Roeder 1956, pp. 395–399).

The largest bronze figures of the Third Intermediate Period are in Athens (NM 110), Berlin/GDR (2309), West Berlin (71/71), Lisbon (Gulbenkian Museum 52 and 400), London (BM 43373), and Paris (Louvre E. 7693, E. 10586, and N. 500). For an excellent, concise study of metal statuary in ancient Egypt, see Ziegler 1987, pp. 85–93. The earliest occurrence of bronze figures in Egypt seems to lie in the time of King Mentuhotep II of Dynasty XI (Arnold 1981, pp. 55–56, pls. 79, 86:c–d).

11

PRINCESS OR PRIESTESS

Late Period
Dynasty XXV
Eighth Century B.C.

Bronze, Solid Cast

Among the thousands of Egyptian bronze figures cast in the last millennium B.C. there is much repetition, as most of them were votive sculptures dedicated to a deity in his or her shrine, sanctuary, or temple. Rare indeed are the statuettes representing a type known only in a few examples. The well-modeled female in the Bastis Collection is one of them.

The lady is wearing a full, long wig, a so-called enveloping wig that covers the shoulders and, in front, falls down to the breasts. The hair is indicated by fine, incised striations; it is surmounted by the feathering of a bird, probably a vulture, whose wings embrace the head protectively and end below the cheeks at neck level. A uraeus, the royal cobra, was once above the lady's forehead; the tail of the cobra hangs down at the back of her head. On top of the head sits a modius with a rectangular depression in the center; undoubtedly it once bore a divine emblem.

The youthful face is pleasant, round, even a bit plump, with naturally formed, but sharp eyebrows, and plastic eyelid rims. The lips are contoured by a fine incised line. The body is slim and elegant and shows a deep median line. The lady wears a simple necklace of six incised strands and a tight-fitting garment that reaches below her calves. The left foot is slightly advanced; the left arm hangs down, with the fist clenched. The fist is hollow in front, but probably held nothing. The lower left arm, now missing, was presumably raised and held a scepter or staff.

The lady's identity is somewhat difficult to establish, since crown and hand-held accoutrements are missing, and the base that would have been inscribed is lost. The feathered headdress could be the vulture cap of the Goddess Mut, but the fact that she wore a uraeus seems to indicate blood royal rather than divine. She may be Shepenwepet I, daughter of the last native King of Thebes, Osorkon III (788–760 B.C.) of Dynasty XXIII, before the conquest of Egypt by the new rulers from Kush in the south. She is known to have surrendered peacefully her powers as Divine Consort of the God Amun, a kind of chief priestess at Thebes, to Amenirdas I. Amenirdas I was the sister of Piye of Nubia, who became King of Egypt in 745 B.C., and was adopted by Shepenwepet I as her daughter. There is, however, the possibility that the bronze represents Amenirdas I, rather than Shepenwepet I, as both are shown in wall reliefs at Karnak with the long enveloping wig that went out of fashion with their generation.

Tenons under the feet and the base to which they were affixed are lost. The bronze is worn in places and shows a few hairline fissures, but is in sound condition.

MEASUREMENTS: Height 19.4 cm.; of head to modius 2.5 cm.; of face 1.6 cm. Width across wig 5.3 cm. Depth 4.4 cm.

PROVENANCE: Not known.

BIBLIOGRAPHY: *Apollo* 1978, pp. 153–154, fig. 2.

COMMENT: The lady's distinctly round face associates her with the ideal of beauty prevalent in Dynasty XXV when the Kushites from Nubia ruled Egypt. On the other hand, her figure is not plump enough to identify her safely as Amenirdas I whose ample form is best known from her calcite statue in Cairo (CG 565; PM II 1972, pp. 14–15).

Perhaps the key to the identity of the person represented by the Bastis bronze lies in the long enveloping wig. It never occurs in any of the inscribed stone sculptures of the Kushite princesses, either Amenirdas I or Shepenwepet II, her successor, but only in the statue of an anonymous lady in Cairo (CG 654; PM II 1972, p. 284) that probably represents Shepenwepet I or a late Ramesside queen. This kind of wig is already known in the Middle Kingdom (Hayes 1953, p. 221, fig. 137:5; Vandier 1958, pl. LXXXI:1). It reappears in the very beginning of Dynasty XVIII when it is worn by Queen Ahmes Nefertary, wife of King Ahmose, on a well known relief from Karnak (PM II 1972, p. 73), now in the Luxor Museum.

It is in the chapel reliefs of Osiris-Onnophris and of Osiris-Heka-Djet at Karnak that both Shepenwepet I and Amenirdas I appear in this wig with a single uraeus (PM II 1972, pp. 202–206), the only ones to be so adorned in relief representations of the Third Intermediate and Late Periods; this narrows the dating of the Bastis bronze to the eighth century B.C.

There are, however, a few undated bronze figures with the same wig, foremost among them a very fine one in Paris (Louvre N. 3808, from the Salt Collection), inlaid with gold thread, that is crowned above the modius with sun disk, two uraei, and tall plumes. Others are in Cairo (CG 39325; Daressy 1905–06, pl. LXII, p. 332) and elsewhere (Roeder 1956, pls. 32 i, l, 68 g, 80 a, c), but only the figure in the Louvre can be dated with any degree of certainty because of the gold inlays. This kind of inlay technique flourished in the Third Intermediate Period and Dynasty XXV, but after that it seems never to have been employed again.

Iconographically the bronze has few close parallels. A very similar figure, only 7 mm. shorter, was sold at Sotheby's in London (11 July 1983, lot 173, p. 54, ill.). The lower right arm, held forward, is preserved on that bronze, and so is the uraeus above the forehead, but the nearly identical striated wig lacks the vulture feathering. The hole above the forehead in the Bastis figure bore the hood of a single uraeus, not a vulture head, which precludes the possibility of its being identified as the Goddess Mut. The only exception seems to be Cairo CG 38917, a bronze of Mut adorned with a single uraeus. Very useful are Vandier's remarks (*Revue du Louvre* 11, 1961, pp. 248–53) on problems of identification with regard to female figures of the Third Intermediate Period.

11 a

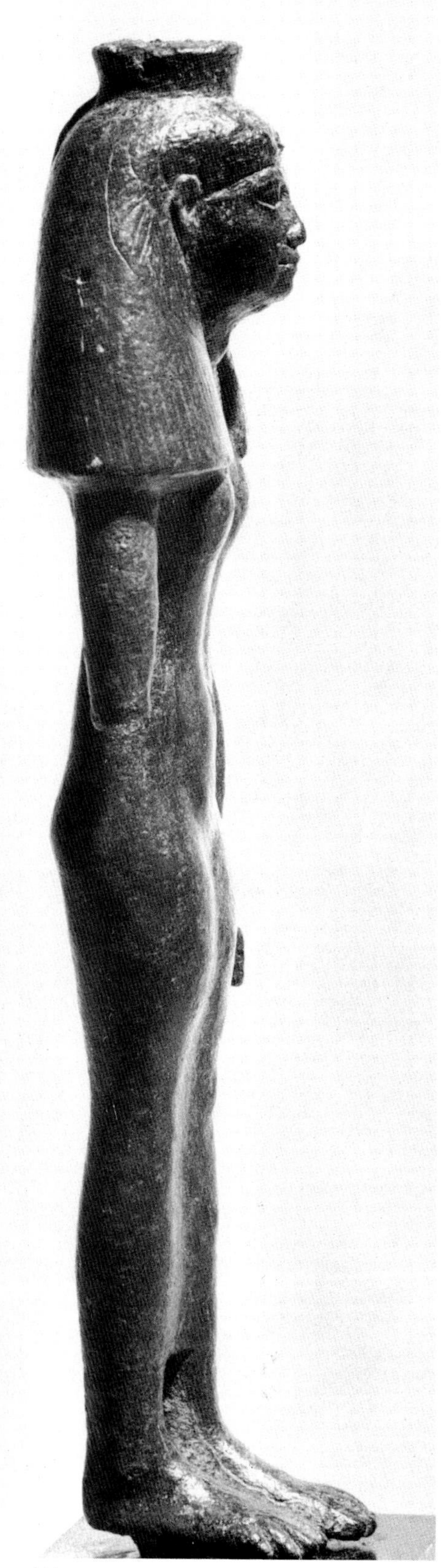

11b

11c

11d

12 a

12

NUBIAN KING

Bronze, Solid Cast

Late Period
Dynasty XXV
Early Seventh Century B.C.

In the eighth century B.C. when the rulers of Kush, the legendary kingdom of Nubia on the Upper Nile, invaded Egypt, they only knew of Pharaonic arts and crafts from what had been left behind in their own country by the kings of Dynasties XVIII–XX. After Dynasty XX, that is, after the eleventh century B.C., Egyptian domination of the Nubian heartland between the First and Fifth Cataracts ceased, and the Nubians were left to their own devices. All contact appears to have been lost between the former master, Egypt, and the slave, the land of Kush.

Thus, it was not until the Nubians conquered Egypt in about 745 B.C., that they came to know the riches of the

12b

12c

lower Nile Valley, and they quickly adopted, and adapted to their taste, Egyptian sculpture, relief, and many of the minor arts, among them jewelry making and bronze casting. Following a long-established Egyptian custom, the Kushite rulers had their own images carved in stone, or cast in bronze, and set up in temples, not only in Egypt, but also in their homeland.

Although technique and attitude are Egyptian, the little bronze figure of a kneeling king is typically Nubian by virtue of the cap crown, the double uraeus, the streamers hanging down in back, and the pendant and necklace trappings that once decorated chest and neck. They are all Kushite characteristics, although the kilt the king wears is genuinely Pharaonic, a model that remained the same for two thousand years.

The king is represented as kneeling in humility before a god, probably offering two vessels which he held just above his knees. His headcover may have been a Kushite cap studded with disk beads or his natural hair with stylized curls. Be that as it may, it is crowned with a circlet to which two royal cobras, representing a double uraeus, were attached. They indicate the king's rulership over Upper and Lower Egypt, and in relief representations the two serpents sometimes wear the white and red crowns of the two lands. Two streamers descend from the circlet at the back of the head.

The king's necklace, now erased, once held a ram's head amulet which hung down in front, while the two pendants on right and left, apparently the loose end of the necklace tie, also ended in ram heads. The torso modeling is vigorous but simple and the round, full face highly expressive, enhanced by the narrow eyes and small mouth with protruding lips. For lack of an inscription one wonders which Nubian king of Dynasty XXV cold be represented: Piye, Shabaqo, Shebitqo, Taharqo, or Tanwetamani? From the number of inscribed bronzes similar to the Bastis statuette, King Taharqo (690–664 B.C.) appears to be the likeliest candidate. It should be noted that there are traces of gilding on cap and kilt.

Although the lower arms and toes are lost and the

12 d

12 e

bronze has some minor blemishes, the main damage seems to have been caused intentionally, not more than a hundred years after the figure was made. Such damage may be noticed on the heads and hoods of the uraei, at the root and sides of the nose and on the necklace and pendant insignia. Someone obviously tried to deface the little king's Nubian accoutrements, probably in Dynasty XXVI, during the reign of Psamtik II (595–589 B.C.). While the Kushites around 656 B.C. withdrew, apparently peacefully, from Egypt to their homeland in Upper Nubia and a truce existed between them and Egypt during the reigns of Kings Psamtik I (664–610 B.C.) and Necho II (610–595 B.C.), Psamtik II mounted a campaign against the Nubians. During his reign all Kushite royal representations were altered and the names of their kings who ruled Egypt were erased and replaced by those of Psamtik II.

MEASUREMENTS: Height 7.2 cm. Width 3.3 cm. Depth 3.7 cm.

PROVENANCE: Not known; probably North Saqqara.

BIBLIOGRAPHY: *Apollo* 1978, p. 153, fig. 1; *the ART gallery* 22,2 (1978), p. 103; *AiA* I 1978, p. 33 R; II, pp. 49, 53, 171, no. 82 ill.

COMMENT: The iconography and identification of the various Kushite rulers who served as kings of Egypt in Dynasty XXV has been fully discussed (Russmann 1974; *AiA* I 1978). Several bronze figures which had Nubian trappings have been similarly defaced (Brooklyn 69.73; West Berlin 35/74 and 1/75; Cairo TR 8/4/70/10). As, except for the Cairo bronze, they all appeared in the market at about the same time, they may well have come from one of the then newly discovered shrines and sanctuaries of North Saqqara where similar kneeling royal bronze figurines were found (*JEA* 57, 1971, pl. VII:4–5). Having been set up by the Kushite kings as ex-votos, by themselves or as part of the pieces of liturgical equipment, they could have remained undisturbed until the iconoclasm of Psamtik II took place. At the Persian invasion in 525 B.C. they may have been put into hiding and thus survived. The face of the Bastis bronze, with narrow eyes set high on the head, bears a resemblance, not altogether surprising, to the head of Petamenophis (No. 14).

After the Kushites conquered Egypt and learned, or discovered on their own, the art of bronze casting, they endowed their newly built temples at Kawa (Macadam 1955), a little south of the Third Cataract, and at Napata (Dunham 1950, 1955, 1970), near the Fourth Cataract, with numerous royal bronze statuettes, some of which were found to be fully gilded (Boston MFA 21.3096; Dunham 1970, p. 43, pl. XLVIIE).

Whether the Kushite royal "cap crown" represents a cap or natural hair has been amply dealt with by Russmann (1979, pp. 49–53; 1981, p. 151). But since then others have dissented, and scholarly discussion of the problem will continue.

13

AEGIS

Late Period
About 700–300 B.C.

Bronze and Gold

In Egyptian archaeology the term "aegis," originally borrowed from Greek mythology, describes a broad collar with the head of a deity on the front. The broad collar is an item of personal adornment, made of beads in semiprecious stones, faience, or glass, worn around the neck and resting on the shoulders and the upper part of the chest. The head of the deity can be male or female, human or animal. The small aegis in the Bastis Collection is of the latter type and shows, in bronze, a simplified broad collar surmounted by the exquisitely modeled head of a lioness in a striated lappet wig.

This wig, however, covers only the back of the head. The protruberances on the sides of the lappets are rudimentary falcon heads, usually part of the aegis. On a real broad collar they form the spacers that gather in, on either end, the multiple strands of beads of which the broad collar is composed.

The striations of the wig were once inlaid with gold thread, while the exposed part of the lioness' head is covered with sheet gold. The aegis is a precious little ornament of amuletic character. A piece in the back shows that it was once attached to something else, possibly a larger bronze figure. As an example, the cat-headed goddess in the Bastis Collection (No. 33, Pp. 85–86, Figs. 33 a–c) holds an aegis in the left hand.

Some of the gold inlays are now missing, and a break on top of the head indicates that the lioness' head was once crowned by a sun disk, perhaps with uraei, as in other, better preserved examples. The broad collar is slightly damaged, and the left falcon head is broken off. Here and there on the bronze are slight signs of corrosion, but the piece itself is in sound condition.

MEASUREMENTS: Height 2.8 cm.; of head 1.5 cm. Width 3.1 cm. Depth 2.2 cm.

PROVENANCE: Not known.

BIBLIOGRAPHY: None.

COMMENT: Although the *Lexikon der Ägyptologie* ignores "aegis," there is an excellent discussion of the type in Bonnet 1952, pp. 8–9. Since then, two important studies have been published (Parlasca 1953, pp. 128–131, with inserts on pp. 43–45, and pl. XI; and Leclant 1963, pp. 77–81, figs. 2–5 on p. 77). Both authors stress that the term "aegis" for that kind of an object is a misnomer. Parlasca proposes "collar protome" ("Kragenprotome" in German), but as the term is cumbersome it has not been accepted, even in his native land. Both studies provide numerous references for aegises with the head of a lioness, although the deity represented by the fearsome beast is still uncertain.

13 a

13 b

13 c

14

PETAMENOPHIS

Late Period
Late Dynasty XXV
680–660 B.C.

Green-glazed Steatite

When the Kushite rulers of Upper Nubia conquered Egypt and ascended the throne of the Pharaohs as kings of Dynasty XXV (750–656 B.C.) they adopted much of the art of Egypt, but suited it to their own style and appearance. Thus we have in sculpture and relief of their time a countenance that, while entirely Egyptian, has a distinctly Kushite "look" which can be unerringly attributed to the period when non-Egyptians reigned in the lower Nile Valley. Their ideal of representation was highly realistic, and the Egyptians who served the Kushite rulers, or who simply enjoyed some prominence at that time, also sported the Kushite look. One of these Egyptians was a man named Petamenophis, for whom this little head was made.

Petamenophis was a Chief Lector Priest, not a particularly prominent member of the clergy, and a royal official. He was also a man of immense means who built for himself the largest rock-cut tomb ever constructed in ancient Egypt for a private person. With the funerary equipment were a number of shawabtis, little inscribed figures of the dead in mummiform; they usually hold farming tools so as to function as agricultural laborers in life after death. Many thousands were made in Egypt over several thousand years. While most of them are idealizing, with standard features reflecting the youth and beauty of their time, those of Petamenophis are exceptional in showing a mature sly face, not at all kind and benign, with small lidless eyes set high up in the head. Most of these shawabtis look alike, many wearing the same expression and, what is quite special, were carved by the same hand in steatite and covered with, an originally green, copper silicate glaze.

From complete shawabtis where the name of Petamenophis is preserved in the inscription we know him well. Therefore there can be no doubt that the little head in the Bastis Collection represents him and no one else. He wore a tripartite wig that pushed the large ears forward. The brows are sharp, the cheeks full, the nose unmodeled, and the mouth small but pouting.

14a

Steatite is a soft material, and the green glaze, which is well preserved on the face and on the left side of the wig, inadequately covers traces of the tool with which the sculpture was carved. The break is clean and fresh, not worn, and should make it possible some day to find the rest of the body to this little head.

MEASUREMENTS: Height 5.6 cm. Width 6.2 cm. Depth 4.3 cm. Height of face 3.2 cm. Width of face 3.5 cm.

PROVENANCE: Not known, but almost certainly Theban Tomb 33 (PM I,1 1960, pp. 50–56).

BIBLIOGRAPHY: None.

COMMENT: The personality of Petamenophis is strangely elusive. He is known from a number of fine statues (*LdÄ* IV 1982, cols. 991–992), among which the block statue in West Berlin (23728; Berlin 1967, p. 94, no. 942, ill.) is truly outstanding. It has the same lidless eyes, described by archaeologists as "buttonhole eyes" (*ESLP* 1960/73, pp. 79R, 182L), like the majority of Petamenophis' shawabti heads. Complete examples in the same material with the same glaze are in Brooklyn (60.10; *BMA* I, 1959–60, p. 69), in the British Museum (Málek 1977, p. 137), and elsewhere (Aubert 1974, pp. 201–202). There is a note on the high positioning of the eyes in *BdE* XCVII/I, 1985, pp. 101–102.

For Petamenophis' tomb, TT 33, see, more recently, Eigner 1984, pp. 46–48, 210, and passim. Although none of the many inscriptions of Petamenophis' tomb, statues, or other monuments makes any direct reference to the Kushite kings by name, there is one little-known connection which A. Piankoff pointed out many years ago (Piankoff 1947, p. 78, n. 1). Petamenophis' so-called sarcophagus ("Corridor XIII" of PM I,1 1960, p. 54) has a text paralleled only on the sarcophagus of the Nubian King Aspelta (593–568 B.C.) who is buried at Nuri, south, i. e. downstream from the Fourth Cataract (Allen 1950, pp. 14–15 & passim).

That Petamenophis owed his position as Chief Lector Priest and his good fortune, which permitted him to have the largest private tomb ever carved in the bedrock of the Western Necropolis at Thebes, to the favors of a king residing at Thebes is not doubted. He often refers to this anonymous king in the texts of his tomb, and it is evident that he was Kushite, either Taharqo (690–664 B.C.) or Tanwetamani (664–653 B.C.). In the inscriptions of Petamenophis' contemporary, Mentuemhat, owner of TT 34, no royal Kushite names appear either, but the cartouche of Psamtik I, first King of Dynasty XXVI, who took over Thebes in 656 B.C., is found. For more references to shawabtis of Petamenophis, see Málek 1977.

14b

15

LADY OF THEBES

Late Period
Late Dynasty XXV to early Dynasty XXVI
670–650 B.C.

Near-white Limestone
with Traces of Color

In the large repertory of ancient Egyptian reliefwork there are so many different styles and modes of representation that fragmentary, decorated pieces of stone are often hard to attribute to a given period or to a definite monument, with very few exceptions. This lady's image in the Bastis Collection is one of them; it comes undoubtedly from Theban Tomb no. 34, the burial place of the Fourth Prophet of the God Amun, Mentuemhat, Count of Thebes and Governor of Upper Egypt in the last years of Dynasty XXV and the first of Dynasty XXVI.

It is a vast place, among private tombs second only in size to that of Petamenophis (see No. 14 above), and contains a large number of wall decorations, both in sunk and in raised relief. While the sunk relief is fine, the work in

raised relief is finer, and for the degree of height above the background, for the exquisite detail of carving, and for the rich variety of subject matter it is unsurpassed among the Late Period tombs of the Theban Necropolis.

The fragmentary slab shows the head of a lady facing left, wearing a tripartite wig, one part of which falls forward below the ear, the other part behind her shoulder. The third portion of the tripartite hairdo is presumably on the other side of the head. She has a delicately sweeping, raised eyebrow, and the upper eyelid rim ends in a short cosmetic line. The long ear is modeled in some detail; the nose is straight, with just a faint indication of the nostril, while the ala is strong and fleshy and set off against the upper cheek by a deep fold. The lady wears a broad collar around her neck, once brightly painted, and above the head are two columns of inscription which give a clue to her identity. The first, on the left, states "[whom] he [loves], the royal acquaintance, mistress of the house," and the second reads ". . . . *nebyt*, blessed" which is the end of her name with an indication that she is deceased.

Many members of Mentuemhat's family, his retainers and servants are well known from the walls of his tomb and from fragments of its decoration, now dispersed in collections all over the world, but not all the fragments have been recorded; large portions of the walls are empty, and the fate of the relief that decorated them is not known. Furthermore, some portions of the tomb have not yet been excavated, much less published. The formality of the inscription here seems to indicate that the woman had been a valued member of the house of Mentuemhat, possibly a daughter, that she had been married, with her own house to look after, and that she was probably no longer alive, although "blessed" is not always a sure indication.

Unless the fragment comes from one of the rooms not yet fully explored, it is possible that it once formed part of the decoration of the back (west) wall of the portico at the west end of the first court. Müller assumes, with sound reasoning, that here were once represented Mentuemhat and his wife at a table piled high with offerings and, facing them, other family members, possibly even his ancestors (Müller 1975, p. 16R). Since some of the scenes in the tomb were inspired by representations in nearby tombs of Dynasty XVIII, painted a good seven to eight hundred years earlier, which often show funerary feasts and banquets attended by numerous family members, this noble lady may well have been part of such a festive group.

The relief, cracked in several places, is now composed of five pieces and mended. It is much chipped, but there is no restoration. The surface is light brown overall, like many reliefs still extant on the walls of the tomb. Traces of green and dark brown paint are left on some of the hieroglyphs and on the broad collar. The back is a modern cut.

MEASUREMENTS: Height 24.0 cm.; of head 6.5 cm.; of face 4.1 cm. Width 16.8 cm. Thickness 2.1 cm. Intracolumnar width 6.1 cm.

PROVENANCE: Not known; almost certainly Theban Tomb 34.

BIBLIOGRAPHY: None.

COMMENT: Present knowledge of the life and times of Mentuemhat has been summarized in *LdÄ* IV 1982, col. 204, for which Leclant furnished the basis with a major study a quarter of a century ago (Leclant 1961). Since then numerous contributions have been made. Those that are of interest here deal mainly with the relief work in the tomb (Müller 1975; Manuelian 1982, 1983, 1985). Its architecture has recently been discussed by Eigner 1984, pp. 44–46, 209.

The name of the lady is puzzling and has not yet been established since the beginning of the inscription is missing. None of the names known thus far from the tomb of Mentuemhat, however, ends on . . . . *nebyt*. There have been reports that the Egyptian Antiquities Organization, which has been conducting work in the tomb since the summer of 1984, has now discovered decoration in raised relief in the room at the foot of the sloping entrance corridor (Manuelian 1985, p. 121). It is quite possible that the Bastis relief was removed a long time ago from one of the rooms now being systematically explored.

16

ATUM AS COBRA AND EEL

Late Period
Dynasties XXV–XXVI
About 670–590 B.C.

Bronze

16 a

The forms in which the ancient Egyptians represented their deities were manifold; their vivid imagination thus shown was eventually outdone only by the Greeks. For purposes of worship and adulation the Egyptians invented phenomena that did not exist in nature. Their gods could take the form of humans, animals, inanimate objects, or a combination of all three. One such shape that owes its existence solely to religious belief and a fertile mind is this cobra with a human head endowed with beard, wig, uraeus, and a divine crown, as protome of the body of an eel. The whole is an emblem, or better a personification, of the God Atum.

Atum is one of the primordial gods of Egypt, a member of the earliest ennead of Heliopolis. His name is derived from the verb *tem*, meaning "to be complete." Atum is a cosmic god, a creator, and, in the Pyramid Texts, is sometimes called the "Father of the Gods." In remote antiquity he was thought to have manifested himself as a serpent; hence in the Late Period his appearance as a cobra.

The Bastis bronze consists of the raised hood of the royal cobra of Egypt, the οὐραῖος of the Greeks, from which the term uraeus is derived. In the middle of the hood, in low relief, the spinal column is depicted, crossed by a curving line, above which the dorsal scales are marked by cross hatching. Instead of the expected serpent's head a human head appears. It is adorned with a tripartite striated wig, a braided beard that can be royal as well as divine, with the ensign of the uraeus at the forehead and the *atef*-crown on the head. The features, especially the ears, are summarily modeled on a minute scale, but most interesting are the eyes, the left one very narrow and on a slant, both heavy-lidded.

The crown is basically that of the God Osiris, originally a harvest god. It consists of a bundle of plant stalks tied together to form a kind of tall hat. It is flanked by two ostrich feathers, emblems of the Goddess Ma^{c}at, spiritual embodiment of eternal truth and harmony. The feathers rest on two ram's horns, emblems of an ancient creative deity. By the time the bronze was modeled and cast, the sheep with horizontal horns had long since died out in the

Nile Valley. They are reflections of a distant past, when gods and myths came into being. The *atef*-crown with horizontal ram's horns, often worn by the king and the God Osiris, eventually became a divine crown used in the iconography of numerous gods.

The fragmentary attachment underneath, indicates that the bronze once formed part of an object, now mostly lost, but well known from a few intact examples. The clue is the roll-like form in the back, first thought to be the cobra's body, but in fact being part of an eel that decorated the top of an oblong box. The whole once formed the coffin for a sacred eel; part of the eel's body and a fragment of the top of the coffin are still preserved.

The eel, as dweller of the primordial morass, was sacred to the God Atum. Complete examples of box coffin, eel figure, the god's image and inscription are preserved in several collections. At the back of the cobra hood a slanting *maʿat*-feather provides support.

The bronze, a fragment of a much larger eel coffin, is in sound condition. Some scratches and pitmarks appear in several places. The color is a deep brown, with patches of dark red and green all over the surface. The underside is rough.

MEASUREMENTS: Height 14.3 cm.; of head 2.2 cm.; of face 1.5 cm. Width 3.7 cm. Depth 7.4. cm.

PROVENANCE: Not known.

BIBLIOGRAPHY: None.

COMMENT: The fundamental study of the God Atum, his physical form and spiritual role, has been written by Karol Myśliwiec 1978–79, who also lists the monuments on and in which the god appears. His catalog of bronze figures (Myśliwiec 1978, pp. 191–196, 279–283, pls. XXXVI–XLII, nos. 36–39) includes four complete bronze coffins fronted by the cobra hood with divine head and crown, surmounted for the whole length of the box by the body of the fish. To judge from their size, the coffin of the Bastis eel would have been at least 30 cm. long. All of the eel coffins Myśliwiec cites, however, show the eel with the head of the God Atum wearing the double crown.

The only close parallel to the Bastis Atum is found in the Cairo Museum (CG 38704; Daressy 1905–06, p. 180, pl. XXVIII). It consists of a bronze box coffin, 44 cm. long, surmounted by two eels with two cobra busts bearing the head of the God Atum, whose identity is confirmed by the inscription. Each head wears exactly the same crown as the Bastis bronze, including the ram's horns. The Cairo bronze was dedicated to Atum by one Tesh-nefer, son of Amenirdas, names that unfortunately do not help to date the piece. It is not listed in the Myśliwiec catalog, although it clearly pertains to his subject.

The attribution of such an object within the last millennium is notably hard to establish. The only feature that contributes to a possible date is the god's face, and with it the general form of mouth and eyes which bear a certain resemblance to Kushite features, as for instance those of Petamenophis (No. 14 above, Pp. 43–44, Figs. 14a–b). The plastic lids too could belong to the period from late Dynasty XXV to early Dynasty XXVI (*ESLP* 1960/73, nos. 8, 17, and 20). On the other hand, the extreme slant of the left eye occurs as late as the reign of King Psamtik II, 595–589 B.C. (*ESLP*, no. 49). Thus a range in date between 670 and 590 B.C. is acceptable for the Bastis bronze.

16 b

17

GODDESS WADJET

Late Period
Dynasty XXVI
About 650–550 B.C.

Bronze, Solid Cast

17 a

Here, for once, is a bronze figure from ancient Egypt that is virtually intact, from the tangs that held the statuette to an ancient pedestal or other support, from the base with the inscription of the donor, to the accoutrements on the deity's head. Only the papyrus scepter that she would have held in her left hand and the *ankh*-sign in her right hand are missing.

Several goddesses with the head of a lioness are known from ancient Egypt; among them two are outstanding. One is Sakhmet, the other Wadjet, also known by the Greek version of her name as Uto or Buto. Sakhmet, who can be represented standing or seated, is more prominent in the New Kingdom than in the Late Period. In the Late Period she is shown, in bronze or faience, as striding, not seated.

The Goddess Wadjet, on the other hand, is never represented in sculpture in the round in the New Kingdom and the Third Intermediate Period. We know her in Late Period sculpture, in bronze and also in relief, and in faience as an amulet. Normally she is shown seated. A seated lion-headed goddess in the Late Period is almost always considered to be a Wadjet, and one standing or striding to be a Sakhmet. The Bastis deity, however, is the exception to the rule, because, as we learn from the inscription on the base, she represents Wadjet and is asked to give life, meaning everlasting life in the hereafter, to a man named Padyhor-enpe. The names of his parents, although now illegible, had also been given.

The goddess is shown striding, the left foot well advanced, and on her lion's head is the sun disk fronted by

17 b Right Side

17 c Front

Base

a cobra with rising hood, the uraeus. The cobra's tail hangs down in back, over the tripartite wig decorated with an incised pattern. In front, under the face, the lion's mane is also shown.

The right arm hangs by the side, the fist pierced, probably to hold the sign of life, the *ankh*. The left arm is bent and would formerly have held a papyrus plant, emblem of the Goddess Wadjet. Armlets and wristlets are engraved on both arms. The goddess is dressed in a well-fitted sheath over which she wears an ornamental collar, visible between the breasts. Her body is lithe, slim, and well proportioned; abdomen and pubic mound are modestly indicated under the garment that ends well below the calf.

The statuette was undoubtedly a votive figure in the temple of the goddess at Buto in the northwestern Delta. The owner's name is composed with that of the God Horus of Pe, the name of one of the sanctuaries of Buto.

The bronze is in sound condition, though somewhat discolored in places. Numerous very minor casting faults can be noticed.

MEASUREMENTS: Height with tangs 25.7 cm.; without tangs 23.5 cm.; of base 2.3 cm. Width of base 4.2 cm. Depth of base 7.7 cm.

PROVENANCE: Not known, but most likely Buto (Tell el Fara'in).

BIBLIOGRAPHY: None.

COMMENT: The hieroglyphic text begins on the front of the base, continues on the right side, and ends on the back, Except for the names of the parents it is clearly legible. It is always surprising how poorly such inscriptions are written on the bases of bronze figures that present such a high degree of artisanship as well as craftsmanship. Unfortunately, these dedications very rarely give us the title of the donor, so that a commonplace name can hardly ever be identified on another, better dated, monument as both referring to the same person. That is one of the reasons why bronzes are notably hard to attribute to a specific dynasty, period, century, or king's reign.

The Goddess Wadjet does not always appear with the head of a lioness. Entirely human and holding the papyrus scepter, she is shown on the reliefs of Ptolemy I from Terenuthis (*BMFA* 50, 1952, no. 281, p. 50, figs. 2–3). That bronze figures of a seated lion-headed goddess represent not Sakhmet but Wadjet may be gleaned from Bothmer 1949, pp. 121–123, pls. XII–XIV, figs. 1–13. A major find of figurative bronzes was made at Buto (*ASAE* 24, 1924, pp. 169–177, with one plate illustrating a fragmentary base in bronze. The base bears two feet, side by side. It probably belonged to a seated figure of the Goddess Wadjet who is addressed in the inscription that runs around the four sides of the base).

For Wadjet in general, see *LdÄ* VI 1985, cols. 906–911; to the paragraph on bronze figures of the goddess (col. 907), add Vandier 1967, pp. 58–63, and Vandier 1971, pp. 126–129, pls. VII–IX. For the site of Buto, see *LdÄ* I 1975, cols. 887–889, and more recently Redford 1983.

17 d

17 e

18

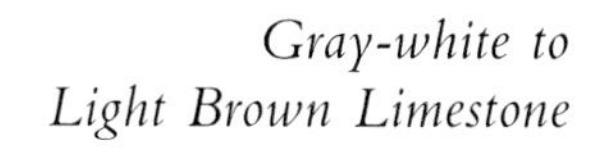

LION-HEAD PROTOME

Late Period
Dynasties XXVI–XXX
650–350 B.C.

Gray-white to
Light Brown Limestone

18 a

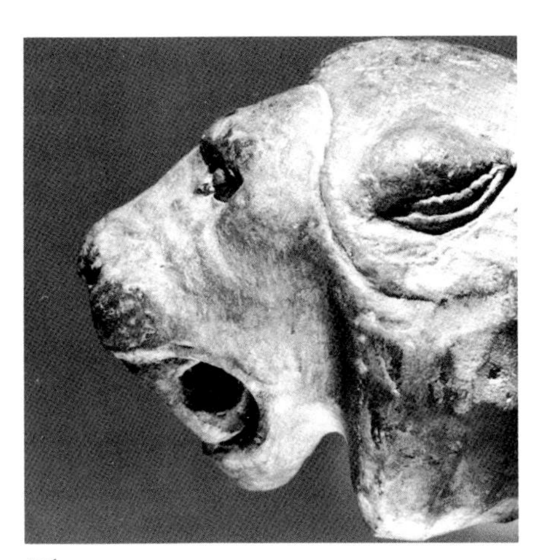

18 b

There are still many antiquities from the fields and sands of the Nile Valley whose original purpose, place of origin, and manner of ancient display are not known. A good example is the lion protome in the Bastis Collection.

A protome is the foremost part of a figure, from Greek *protemnein*, "to cut off in front," but the original purpose is still in doubt. It is the head of a snarling rather than roaring lion, with an open mouth that, despite the small scale, shows the menacing teeth. The sculpture is hardly more than two inches high.

The mane on top of the head is smooth, while below the ears it is left unfinished, as if that part of the head had been partly inaccessible or invisible. The forehead is deeply depressed in the middle; the brows bulge. Much attention has been lavished upon the eyes where the upper eyelid rims have been worked out in detail, as are the deeply contoured, bulging, highly convex eyeballs. The left ear is summarily modeled except for the dentilation that shows along the lower flap. The right ear could be unfinished or worn down. The creases on the upper lip are well indicated, thus lending credibility to the gaping muzzle that is characterized by the teeth, modeled in openwork, the upper and lower on each side fashioned as one. They too seem to lack the sculptor's final touch. Tool marks are visible on the chin which is set off against the open mouth.

The stone is discolored, and there are slight blemishes here and there. The tip of the muzzle was damaged at one time and has been smoothed down or worn off; the same holds true for the right ear.

MEASUREMENTS: Height 5.7 cm. Width 5.3 cm. Depth now 5.4 cm.

PROVENANCE: Not known.

BIBLIOGRAPHY: None.

COMMENT: The piece has been so firmly glued into its present support that it cannot be removed to study the back. If it shows any gridlines, the head may well have been intended as an ex-voto (*LdÄ* IV 1982, cols. 170, 177, n. 73), and the entire surface may have been worn down through the touch of many hands.

Since most Egyptian lions are represented with the mouth closed, the open-mouthed snarling (or occasionally roaring) lion's head has long been attributed to Achaemenid influence, thought to have come to Egypt with the Persians in Dynasty XXVII, 525–404 B.C. (Cooney 1953, p. 29; Brooklyn 1956, p. 55; Cooney 1965, p. 40; Kozloff 1983, p. 61, and others). This, however, is not quite correct, as the motif of the lion with wide-open mouth already occurs on figures dated by inscription to Psamtik I, 664–610 B.C. (Scharff 1941, p. 199, n. 22), and Necho II, 610–595 B.C. (Parlasca 1979, p. 318), both antedating the Persian invasion of Egypt by at least seventy years.

The dentilation of the hairtufts on the lion's left ear can also be observed on rhyta terminating in lion heads, such as Brooklyn 48.29 (Riefstahl 1968, pp. 63, 107, no. 61) and Brooklyn 65.3.1; (*op.cit.*, pp. 64, 107, no. 62). The ribbing, resembling a Pan's pipe, often seen protruding from lions' ears of the Late Period, as on Brooklyn 53.174 (Cooney 1953, pp. 28–30, figs. 7–8; Brooklyn 1956, pp. 55–56, pl. 86, no. 69), is probably a stylized version of the dentilated hairtufts, first found in the Middle Kingdom; see the lion on a relief attributed to Sesostris I, 1974–1929 B.C. (Schweitzer 1948, pl. VI:3).

19 a

19 b

19 c

19

BRACHYCEPHALIC PATAIKOS

Late Period
Sixth Century B.C.

Green Faience

Behind the high-sounding caption hides a humble and amusing, dwarflike creature which, as indicated by the loop at the back of the neck, was at one time suspended from the neck of a human being as an amulet. It is not clear whether the wearer was a man or a woman, but whoever it was must have loved the creature, for these talismans have also been found in graves to furnish protection for the owner in the hereafter.

Pataikos is a Greek name, first employed by Herodotus. It is the name of the dwarf genie who was always considered to represent the creator-god Ptah of Memphis. Brachycephalic is a technical term for the form of the wide and squat head. On it sits a scarab, in itself a protective deity, but what he sits upon is not easy to determine. It could either be hair, following the form of the misshapen skull, or a cap like a Basque beret that covers his head. A cap is more likely, because his lord and master, the God Ptah of Memphis, is himself almost always shown wearing at tight-fitting headpiece.

Pataikos has overly large ears that stick out, set back and high on the head. He bends his head forward as if to contemplate his feet and what they are stepping on, and thus the eyes, set at a slant, are overly strained and popping. The nose is very long and pointed; the mouth protrudes unduly. Neck and chest are decorated with a large ornamental collar that reaches from one raised shoulder to the other.

On either side of the pot belly with its deep navel, the fists seem to be holding something, probably stringy serpents that were often tightly held by protective deities. Pataikos' buttocks are grotesquely deformed; he is visibly naked, spreading his bow-legged limbs apart while standing on two crocodiles. Their tails overlap in the rear, right over left. They are resting on a thin round base.

The creature is amusing, yet awe-inspiring, more a household deity than a mighty god residing in a splendid temple. The amulet is, however, on a small scale a real masterpiece of modeling and appears to have been made with a sense of humor, creating something at once highly comical and yet divine.

The condition is excellent. Some tiny casting faults and blemishes are hardly noticeable to the naked eye.

MEASUREMENTS: Height 5.6 cm.; of head without the scarab 1.6 cm.; of face 1.1 cm. Width across the elbows 2.4 cm. Depth 2.5 cm.

PROVENANCE: Not known.

BIBLIOGRAPHY: None.

COMMENT: The figure of pataikos as it appears in this amulet is not known before the last millennium B.C. (Bonnet 1952, pp. 584–585; *LdÄ* IV 1982, cols. 914–915). The bow-legged pygmy is frequently found in Kushite graves, and he is definitely the one who holds the evil serpents that sometimes even rest their heads to the side of his mouth (*AiA* II 1978, pp. 189–191, nos. 106 and 109). Horus-the-Child, too, captures snakes and stands on crocodiles, as can be seen on the Metternich Stela in New York (MMA 50.85; Scott 1951, p. 206 ill.).

As to the question whether pataikos is a pygmy, a dwarf, or a child crippled by rickets, most authorities now agree that he is a dwarf, and since dwarfs were always recognized as skilled workers in jewelry and metals, their association with Ptah is easily explained. Ptah was the deity of workshops, of mechanics as a whole.

Similar pataikoi appear in the royal tombs of the Napatan kings of Nubia, a scarab on the head, and also standing on crocodiles (*AiA, loc.-cit.*), which may be used as dating criteria since one such figure was excavated from the burial of a queen of King Piye of Dynasty XXV. A pataikos with the sidelock of the Child Horus is in The Brooklyn Museum (71.85; height 9.3 cm., green faience, unpublished). He too wears a cap, has a scarab on his head, and holds his arms, worked in the round, by his sides.

20

BRONZE CAT

Late Period
600–300 B.C.

Hollow Cast

Among the hundreds of bronze cats cast in Egypt's last millennium B.C., only one is dated by inscription. It was made in the time of the Saite King Psamtik I (664–610 B.C.) of Dynasty XXVI. Like all others of a certain size, the Bastis cat was cast hollow and originally housed the mummy of a kitten sacred to the Goddess Bastet, originally an angry spirit who eventually became a symbol of beauty and gaiety.

The cat in the Bastis Collection is seated on its haunches, with the tail curled around the right forepaw. At the front and back of the figure are the two tangs which held it to a base. Gold earrings once adorned the pierced ears (see No. 33, Pp. 85–86, Figs. 33a–c); they bear the incised image of the ostrich feather of eternal truth, emblem of the Goddess Maᶜat. The eyes, formerly inlaid with glass, are now empty. Above them, between the ears, the engraved contour of a scarab is faintly visible.

Around the neck the cat wears an incised ornamental collar from which a series of drop-shaped pendants descends. Below that a sacred eye is suspended on a double string. The entire body is engraved with a comma-like design well rendering the furry aspect of the cat's coat.

Scratches appear in a few places on the surface of the bronze, and minor damage is evident on tail and paws.

20 a

Otherwise the figure is in sound condition. The earrings and eye inlays are lost.

MEASUREMENTS: Height with tangs 17.8 cm.; without tangs 15.7 cm. Width 6.9 cm. Depth 11.5 cm.

PROVENANCE: Not known; perhaps Saqqara or Tell Basta.

BIBLIOGRAPHY: None.

COMMENT: Tell Basta is not the only well known provenance of cat representations; Saqqara too had a vast cat cemetery, and this bronze could have come from either place. The cat bronze dated to King Psamtik I is in Paris (Louvre N. 3933; Wiedemann 1884, p. 621; Pierret 1889, p. 16, no. 26; Yoyotte 1968, p. 201 ill., and 203; Ziegler 1987, p. 93 ill.). The Louvre cat, however, is much larger than the Bastis cat and was formed individually, before mass production of bronzes had begun.

People having been fond of cats since time immemorial, and statuettes of Egyptian cats having survived in large numbers in wood, stone, faience and especially bronze, there is a an extensive literature on cat figures (Roeder 1937, pp. 46–53; Bonnet 1952, pp. 371–373; Riefstahl 1952, pp. 1–15; Roeder 1956, pp. 344–357, and *LdÄ* III 1980, cols. 367–368).

A cat bronze in Berlin/GDR (8299; Roeder 1956, p. 348, par 450 f, pl. 51 d), of exactly the same height as the Bastis cat, is so similar that both may well have been cast from a mold made from the same wax model. Another one, too, recently sold at auction in London (Christie's, 16 July 1986, lot 201), corresponds so closely in measurements and attitude to the Bastis and Berlin cats that it too may have descended from the same model.

Since the Bastis cat is hollow, it could have served as a coffin for a cat or kitten mummy (Roeder 1956, p. 344, par. 444), but it is also possible that it sat on top of an oblong bronze box, the mini-sarcophagus of a sacred animal (Roeder 1956, p. 350, par. 453 a).

20 b

21

GODDESS SERKET (?)

Late Period
Late Dynasty XXVI
About 530 B.C.

Gray-green Schist

Although probably as many female as male images were made throughout the long history of ancient Egyptian statuary, there is a curious gap in the sequence. From the time of King Psamtik I (about 650 B.C.) to the reign of King Ptolemy I (about 300 B.C.), with one or two exceptions, we know of no stone sculptures of private ladies. Every female representation in the round is that of a goddess or princess, and of the latter there are fewer than half a dozen, as if for nearly four centuries there had been a taboo against modeling the image of a woman in durable material. Therefore this female likeness is a rare find, even if it represents a goddess and not a commoner.

That she is a goddess, with features lovely and yet serene, is evident from the remains of the emblem on her head and from the companion head, still part of a statue, that reflects her image, trait by trait. The face of the Bastis head is an exact replica of that of the Goddess Isis whose complete figure is in the Cairo Museum (CG 38884; PM III,2 1981, p. 670), and since this statue forms one of a group of three sculptures, all inscribed, we know that their donor was a man named Psamtik, an Overseer of the Seal and Chief Royal Steward in the time of King Amasis (570–526 B.C.). All three are made of the same material as the Bastis head; so there can be no doubt that it belonged to a fourth statue by the same sculptor. Like the Cairo Isis, the crown of the head is covered by a modius which bore the emblem of the goddess. From its scanty remains it is evident that the emblem was a rising scorpion, sacred to the tutelary Goddess Serket, a protectress of life.

Hers is a fine face, with natural eyebrows and just a touch of makeup in the cosmetic lines extending beyond the plastic eyelids. The ear is more stylized than the rest of the face, and there is a hint of individuality, hardly noticeable at first glance, in the high cheekbones. The goddess once wore a tripartite wig.

The head is very fragmentary, but the condition is sound. On the left side a piece including the left ear was broken off and has been glued back. The scorpion, uraeus, right ear, and tip of the nose have been knocked off, and there is slight damage to the lower lip. The break at the front of the neck has now been squared off in plaster.

MEASUREMENTS: Height 21.2 cm.; of face 8.3 cm. Width 13.2 cm; of face in front of ears 8.6 cm. Depth 14.9 cm.

PROVENANCE: Not known; probably Saqqara. Formerly in the collection of Lord Amherst.

BIBLIOGRAPHY: Sale Catalogue, London, Sotheby, 13–17 June 1921, p. 27, no. 257, pl. VIII; *ESLP* 1960/73, pp. xi, 63–64, 144, pl. 52, figs. 127 and 129, no. 55; von Bothmer 1961, p. 17, pls. 22 and 25, no. 81.

COMMENT: The head was fully published in *ESLP* loc.cit., and there is hardly anything to add. Attribution to the latter part of King Amasis' reign has remained undisputed, but now additional evidence has been discovered in a bust of the Goddess Isis in Florence (Museo Archeologico 313). Her face was undoubtedly fashioned by the same sculptor as the Bastis head, and this Isis bust bears an inscription on the back pillar that includes the cartouche of Amasis. The tentative identification published in *ESLP*, namely that the Bastis head was that of the goddess Serket (*LdÄ* V 1984, cols. 830–833), may now be regarded as confirmed.

21 b Back of Head

21 a

21 c ▷
21 d ▷

22 a

22

BURDEN OF AGE

Late Period,
Early Dynasty XXVII
About 500 B.C.

Fine-grained Black Basalt
with Brown Vein

One of the great achievements of Egyptian art is that in the course of twenty-five hundred years it developed in sculpture in the round a range of human features that surpasses anything produced elsewhere in the ancient world. The range extends from bland idealization to veristic portraiture and encompasses such an amazing scale of nuances between those extremes that practically any type or form of human likeness can be found. It is, however, mainly in the crafting of the human face that the mastery of the Egyptian sculptor shows at its best, rendering not only skin, flesh, and bone in durable material for the hereafter, but also imbuing the features with the reflection of a person's intellect, character, wisdom and, occasionally, sorrow and age.

All these elements combined are found in the head of an old man in the Bastis Collection, a head that – little known thus far – already ranks among the great portrait-like representations of outstanding personalities in Egypt's Late Period: Petamenophis in West Berlin (23728; Berlin 1967, p. 194, no. 942, ill.), the "Bust of Sorrows" in Paris (Louvre N. 2454; *ESLP* 1960/73, no. 67), the Boston "Green Head" (MFA 04.1749; *op. cit.* no. 108), and the Brooklyn "Black Head" (58.30; *op. cit.* no. 132). It once formed part of a statue, but until the torso has been found the man immortalized will have to remain anonymous, for the beginning of the two columns of inscription on the back pillar does not provide a clue; it merely contains an appeal to the "local god" and the title "mayor". That the owner was a person of rank, however, is best shown by his face; it bears the marks of dignity, age, character and experience.

The man is represented wearing a bag wig which leaves the ears uncovered; it circles them, but does not force them forward as is often the case. Here the ears – long but not wide – rest against the wig, which has no tabs in front of the ears. The forehead, receding toward the edge of the wig, is marked by two sinews rising from the nose and leveling off, right and left, on the sharp brows of which they form a part. The upper lids are full and fleshy, the rims bordered by an incised line. Although the eyes are small the eyeballs bulge strongly.

A depression under the eyes sets them off against the high cheekbones that mark the upper limits of the fat cheeks. The latter are emphasized below by a deep nasolabial furrow that swings back just above the corners of the lipless mouth. The cheeks recede, unmarked, at right angles to the frontal plane towards ears and wig. The mouth is just a slash, a deeply carved line, descending left more than right, giving the face an expression of both determination and sadness. There was once a prominent double chin, rarely found in Egyptian likenesses of the Late Period. Underneath, a roll of flesh which looks like a neck-band marks the old man's aging skin.

A brown vein in the black stone rises from the left cheek in front of the ear, loops over the top of the head and runs down into the right eye. In the back a second, narrower vein goes from the top of the head to the top of the back pillar. The back pillar is beveled off at the upper corners in a fashion typical of the Persian Period (*ESLP*, p. 71R, no. 60); this has been noticed many times more since it was first mentioned in print.

With the acquisition of this head Mr. Bastis added to his collection a remarkable sculpture, remarkable in the sense that it evokes the memory of a late Middle Kingdom representation which had already been part of his collection for some time (No. 2, Pp. 2–6, Figs. 2a–d). Although two different people, twelve hundred years apart, are portrayed in the two heads, it is evident that the artisan who modeled No. 22 drew on an age-old tradition of which the other head, No. 2, is one of the finest examples. In each one a kind of maturity has been captured, common to man all over the ancient world, but finding in Egyptian sculpture from 2400 B.C. to Roman times its finest, most profound expression. The Bastis head, with its thin-lipped realism, is the newest and most outstanding example of the kind.

The sculpture is damaged on eyebrows and eyes; the nose is lost, and the mouth has suffered severe chipping in the middle. The chin is also heavily marred, and scratches and small damage marks appear elsewhere on the face, right ear and back pillar.

MEASUREMENTS: Height 16.0 cm.; of head 12.0 cm.; of face 8.0 cm. Width 17.7 cm. Depth 15.2 cm. Width of back pillar 9.0 cm. Intracolumnar width 3.9 cm. (col. 1), 3.6 cm (col. 2). Width of break 17.5 cm; at neck 7.5 cm. Depth of break 11.2 cm.

PROVENANCE: Ashmunein (Tuna el Gebel?).

22 b

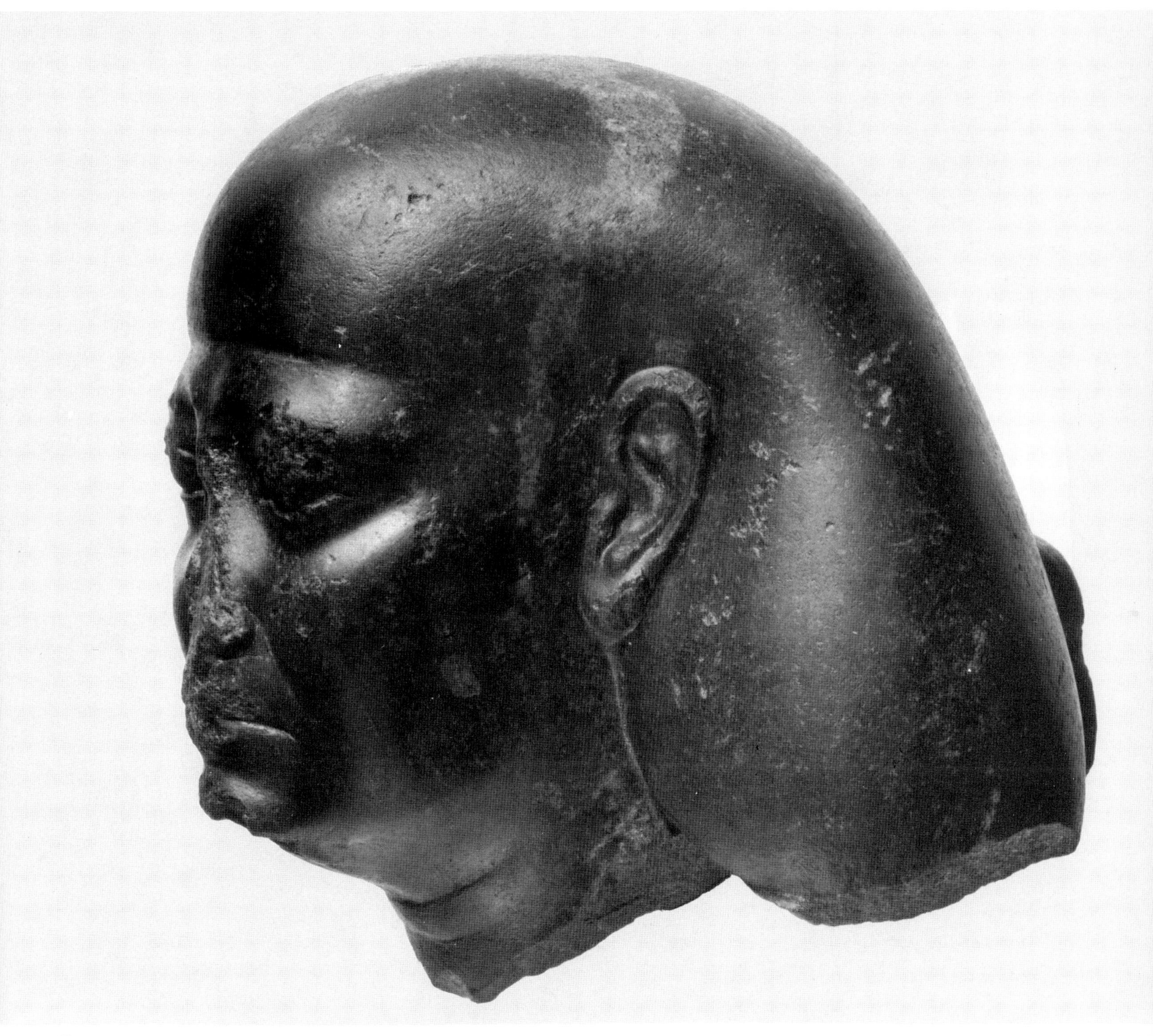

22 c

22 d Back of Head

BIBLIOGRAPHY: Thurgau 1985, pp. 44–45, no. 20, ill.

COMMENT: The head probably came from a striding or kneeling naophorous statue, such as one in Paris (Louvre A 93; Sauneron 1957, p. 110, ill.), or in Cleveland (3955.20; *ESLP* 1960/73, no. 61). For the origin of the bag wig, see the Comment above on No. 2. It reappears in the seventh century B.C. as one of the many archaizing elements of Late Period sculpture (*ESLP*, p. 35). It continues into the second half of the fourth century B.C. (*ESLP*, no. 21, now attributed to Dynasty XXX or slightly later [*MDAIK* 37, 1981, p. 76, n. 10]). Three other heads with bag wigs and realistic features are approximately contemporary with the Bastis head, in Paris (Louvre A. F. 6314; *BMA* IV 1962–63, p. 48, fig. 7), in Boston (MFA 37.377; *ESLP,* no. 60), and from the Hartmann Collection (Sale Catalogue, London, Christie's, 10 Dec. 1981, p. 78, no. 377, ill.), but none of them shows the profound human character expressed in the features of the Bastis head. Its high polish seems to be particular to black or near-black stone as early as Dynasty XXVII, the Persian Period, while this treatment of the surface rarely occurs in green schist until a century later, in the fourth century, B.C.

A fleshy upper lid is found in Egyptian statuary as early as Dynasty IV; the best example being on the head of Mycerinus in the pair statue in Boston (MFA 11.1738; not visible in photographs, but clearly noticeable on the original), and in a Late Period bust in Paris (Louvre N. 2454; *ESLP,* no. 67, now well illustrated by Aldred 1980, p. 155, fig. 136).

An outstanding likeness with overly pointed chin, of the Late Period, is the head of an old man in Paris (Louvre E. 8060; Lange and Hirmer 1961, pl. 253). As for the roll of fat on the neck, one would be tempted to identify it as the band at the top of a round-necked garment of the Persian Period as, for instance, on a statue in Baltimore (WAG 149; *ESLP* no. 68), but the "band" on the neck of the Bastis head sits so high that it could never have been the top of a garment. The Louvre bust cited above has a comparably fat neck, more delicately indicated.

23 IDEALIZING HEAD

Persian or Post-Persian Period
500—300 B.C.

Near-black Basalt
with Brown Sheen

There are basically two types of human heads in Egyptian art: one is idealizing, the other realistic, with many stages in between (see above No. 22, Page 61 L). This fine little sculpture in the Bastis Collection is a classic example of the best in Late Period idealization.

The youthful male head, with an evenly formed somewhat extended skull, is covered with a tight-fitting cap; or the contour line visible over the forehead indicates the natural, short-cropped hair ending in a tab in front of the ears. The face is smooth and pleasant looking; the eyebrows are natural, and so are the eyes. The upper eyelid rims are contoured; the lower rims are plain. The narrow mouth turns up at the corners; there is a small philtrum. Chin and transition to neck are full.

The broad back pillar is uninscribed; it ends squarely just below the level of the tips of the ears which are unusually slim and lacking in volume.

The head is broken off at the neck. Much of the right ear and part of the nose are missing. The cap or hair contour is chipped, and there is a certain amount of damage to philtrum, mouth and left ear.

MEASUREMENTS: Height 8.1 cm.; of head 7.6 cm.; of face 4.7 cm. Width 6.5 cm. Depth 9.9 cm.; of break 7.7 cm. Width of break at neck 4.2 cm.; at back pillar 4.4 cm.

23 a

23 b

23 c

23 d

PROVENANCE: Not known.

BIBLIOGRAPHY: *Apollo* 1978, pp. 154–155, fig. 5.

COMMENT: It is not easy to establish the approximate date of an idealizing head of this type, and the form of the back pillar does not assist us either. The fact that the back pillar is uninscribed merely indicates that the head could date from Dynasty XXVII or later, because earlier sculptures always bears a text on the rear support. The only aid we have in attributing the head to a definite period is the cap, or cap-like short-cropped hair, rarely found in Egyptian statuary in the Late Period. The earliest examples can be attributed to Dynasty XXVI, the reign of Amasis (Edinburgh RMS 1956.134; *ESLP* 1960/73, no. 66, pl. 63, where the date should be corrected to ca. 550–525 B.C.), and to Dynasty XXVII (New York, MMA 25.2.10; Hornemann 1951, pl. 286; *ESLP* 1960/73, pp. 86, 149; Desroches-Noblecourt 1981, p. 299, no. 35), but it also occurs occasionally in the fourth century B.C. (Paris, Louvre E. 11414; Boreux 1932 b, p. 397, pl. LIII; Hornemann 1951, pl. 299).

The problem of attribution is, however, not entirely resolved since in Late Period representations the demigod Imhotep (*LdÄ* III 1980, cols. 145–148) wears the same cap as the Bastis head – in stone in Paris (Louvre N. 4541; Wildung 1977 a, pp. 37–38, no. 15, pl. III; Wildung 1977 b, fig. 28), and also in bronze in Munich (ÄS 5314; München 1976, pp. 184–185, ill.). Although the God Ptah too is often represented wearing this "cap", in Late Period stone sculpture he is always bearded. Thus the head in the Bastis Collection may be either that of the demigod Imhotep or of an unknown man.

24

Late Period
Fourth Century B.C.

Gray to Light Brown,
Hard, Homogeneous Stone

One of the great abilities of Egyptian artisans in the Late Period was to carve hard stone and apply inscriptions on a very small scale. This kind of craftsmanship was much in evidence during a limited period, from the early fourth to the early third century B.C., when a type of miniature statuary was developed from only the hardest stone. The little head, less than two inches high, is a superb example, both for its sculptural features and decorative details.

It is the head of a mature man, originally dressed in a bag wig, much like that of No. 22 above (Pp. 60–64), except that the forehead is cut back more strongly so that the wig stands out as an alien attribute, rather formally, not simulating hair. All elements of the face are naturally formed, but the ears are stylized and summarily modeled. Eyebrows and eyes are very fine, and so is the mouth. The most interesting aspect of the head, however, is the decoration. It consists of figures of deities and divine emblems, all known as part of a sizeable body of magical texts and illustrations that are to benefit the person represented and protect him against evil in life after death.

The statuette to which the head once belonged, except for face, hands, and feet, must have been completely covered with this kind of decoration. A number of complete sculptures bear this out. Directly above the forehead a scarab is engraved with wings that, now slightly rough, were once probably covered with gold leaf. Behind it, on top of

24 a

24 b

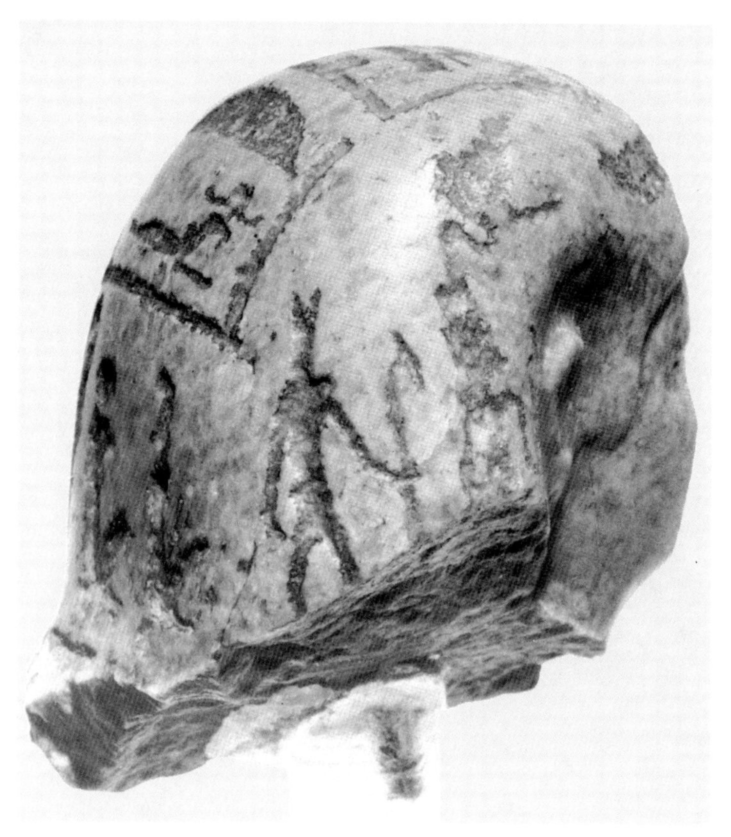
24 c

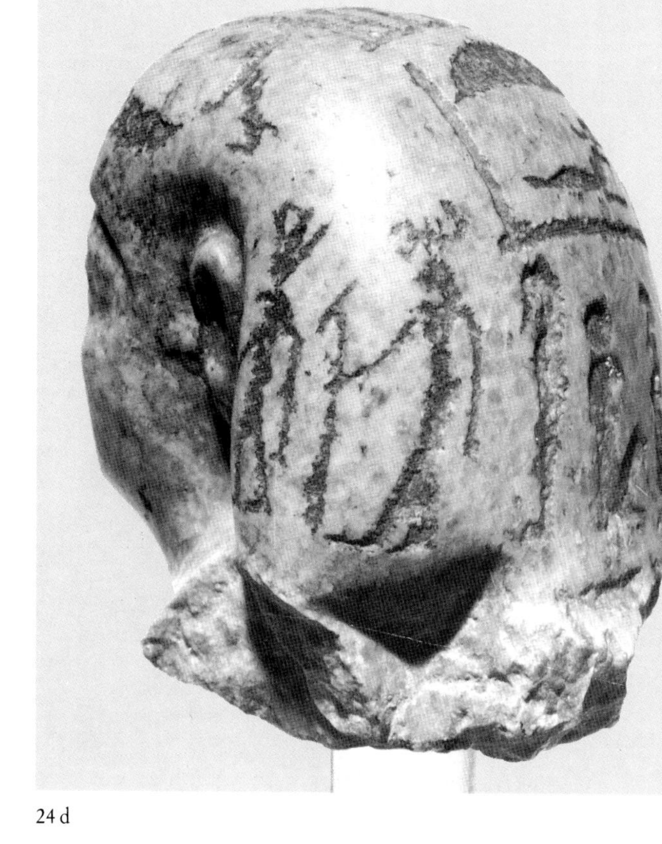
24 d

24 e

24 f

the head, is a temple shrine in which a crocodile hovers facing right, and below it, at the back of the head, is a mound within an enclosure with a legged serpent wearing the *atef*-crown (see No. 16, Page 47, Fig. 16a). Below that are several deities, some squatting, some striding, with more of them on the right and left sides of the wig, behind the ears. A tiny bit of the back pillar is preserved. It too bore magical illustrations.

The condition of the head is good, except that most of the nose is missing and parts of the face are slightly chipped.

MEASUREMENTS: Height 4.5 cm.; of face 2.0 cm. Width 3.7 cm. Depth 4.4 cm; horizontal depth of break ca. 3.3 cm.

PROVENANCE: Not known.

BIBLIOGRAPHY: None.

COMMENT: The stone is intriguing; at first it was thought to be a kind of marble. Examination in the Conservation Laboratory of The Brooklyn Museum, however, showed that it contains carbonates, but lacks calcium; also the hardness is 6 on the Moh Scale. Therefore it is not marble, but it may possibly be a feldspathic rock, rarely chosen for sculpture in the round.

Some examples of minute inscriptions applied to fine-grained hard stone are well dated (Scott 1951, pp. 201–217; *Fs. Parker* 1986, p. 10). The manner in which the wig juts out above the forehead is very typical for the fourth century and the early Ptolemaic Period (*ESLP* 1960/73, nos. 80, 89, 102, to give only a few examples).

Several magical sculptures were said to benefit those who approached them for their healing powers; for example, the striding figure in Paris (Louvre E. 10777), called the "Statue Tyskiewicz" (Aldred 1980, pp. 158–159, fig. 141) of Dynasty XXX (380–342 B.C.), and the block statue of Djed-hor in Cairo (JE 46341; PM IV 1934, p. 66) dated to the reign of Philip Arrhidaeus (323–317 B.C.). The finest magical monument, however, is the Metternich Stela in New York (MMA 50.85; Scott 1951) which bears the cartouches of King Nectanebo II (360–342 B.C.).

The manner in which the bottom of the wig slopes off in the back, covered with a hieroglyphic sign flanked by two columnar lines, represents the kind of transition which could indicate that the head comes from a sphinx. This, however, is not the case; a similar condition is found on a magical sculpture in Berlin/GDR (7554; badly damaged in WW II); the old photographs bear this out.

Rows of squatting as well as of striding deities only occur occasionally as wig decoration on magical figures; for example, on a head fragment in Paris (Louvre E. 4898 = A.F. 1657; PM VII 1951, p. 383), but they are frequently carved elsewhere on sculptures and other magical monuments of all types, almost always without captions, so that individuel deities are hard to identify. The two squatting gods on the back of the wig are undoubtedly Ma'at and Ra. On the left side the second figure represents a scorpion goddess with the insect on her head, perhaps it is Serket, or possibly Ta-bytet (van de Walle 1967).

25

Late Period
About Fourth Century B.C.

Papyrus, Painted

Book illustrations of today have their origin in ancient Egypt. Some time in the middle or second half of Dynasty XVIII a standard type of funerary text, known to us as the Book of the Dead, had a few illustrations interspersed. Later, that is from the end of the fifteenth century B.C., in increasing measure papyrus rolls containing these texts for perusal in the hereafter were illustrated, chapter by chapter, with vignettes making pictorial reference to the text. The fragmentary manuscript in the Bastis Collection comes from one of these Books of the Dead and, judging from the penmanship, may be attributed to the middle of the last millennium B.C. or shortly thereafter. Thus it is the result of a tradition going back a thousand years.

The representation is set in a rectangle on top of a text from Chapter 40 of the Book of the Dead and parts of Chapters 39 and 42 on either side, written in hieratic.

The caption, somewhat damaged, is written in red; it reads "A Spell for Repelling the Eater of the Ass." The vignette shows a striding man spearing a cowering donkey or wild ass. The faceless man is drawn in a black outline filled with red for his skin and white for his loincloth. Except for the line marking the foldover of his garment, there is no interior design. His thumbs and the raised heel of the near foot are somewhat enlarged, emphasizing the swiftness of his action.

Far more skill has been lavished on the beast. It too is drawn in a black outline, in this case filled with gray, but one ear shows interior striations; mane and tail are bushy, the turned head is endowed with some detail, and the eye is well marked. Also the overlap of head over rump is expertly handled on such a minute scale; the neck folds are indicated by single lines. In contrast to the dynamism of the advancing man, the calm repose of the animal has a static quality that underscores its malign nature. From the contents of the chapter below, the donkey is the symbol of sin.

The text is written in black; only the beginning words, like the chapter heading over the vignette, are given in red for emphasis. The same holds true for the fragmentary Chapter 39 on the right and the equally incomplete Chapter 42 on the left. The owner of the papyrus is unknown, because the places where his name is expected, line 1 of Chapter 40 and lines 11 and 18 of Chapter 42,

25a

have been left empty. Just before them is written the name of the God Osiris with whom the deceased was to become one in the hereafter. Alas, he never did become Osiris! Otherwise we would know his name.

In addition to the obvious lacunae in lines 1–3 of Chapter 39 and in the heading of Chapter 40, the fragment is somewhat abraded in several places. There has also been some damage to the man's skirt and upper far leg.

In 1981 Mr. Bastis presented the papyrus fragment to the Institute of Fine Arts of New York University for the Egyptian study room.

MEASUREMENTS: Height 23.5 cm.; of man, from head to foot 3.0 cm.; of donkey, from eartip to ground 2.1 cm. For details, see the Fig. 25c below.

PROVENANCE: Not known.

BIBLIOGRAPHY: Sale Catalog, New York, Sotheby Parke Bernet (no. 3635), 4 May 1974, p. 43, no. 158, ill. [but was not sold at the auction].

COMMENT: The only study at present on the beginnings of Egyptian papyrus illustration is the unpublished M. A. thesis (Institute of Fine Arts, N.Y.U., 1980) of Bannon McHenry, "The Vignettes of Early New Kingdom Papyri: Composition and Style." The history of Egyptian book illustration, from Dynasty XVIII to the Roman Period, remains to be written. It is inextricably connected with the study of Egypt's funerary papyri, the texts of which have been analyzed and discussed over and over again, without a serious study of the subject and changing character of the illustrations ever being made.

25b

Still worse, with hundreds of examples on hand, research into the palaeography has not yet resulted in a reliable body of dating criteria, and the only comprehensive tool (Möller 1912) is over seventy years old. Securely dated papyri of the last millennium B.C., such as the one published in *ASAE* 63 (1979), pp.. 51–78, are very rare. For a long time, Brooklyn 47.218.3 (Parker 1962) was the one exception, as it bears the only historical vignette that has come down to us from ancient Egypt. It relates an event that took place on October 4, 651 B.C., during the reign of Psamtik I; it has nothing to do with the Book of the Dead. There is one Book of the Dead in hieratic dated to the same king, namely that of Bakenrenef, Vizier of Psamtik I (Pernigotti 1985), but it is written on linen, not papyrus. A list of New Kingdom Book of the Dead manuscripts, chronologically arranged, has been published (Luft 1977, pp. 67–74), but it ends with Dynasty XX.

For donkeys and wild asses in ancient Egypt, see *LdÄ* II 1977, cols. 27–30. Known first from representations of the late Predynastic Period (*WM* IX 1985, pp. 157, 158, 162, 165–167, fig. B 5 on page 154), the donkey, almost unchanged, remains the same breed throughout Egyptian history (Nibbi 1979). The long ears recall those of the *equidae* which Tutankhamen is hunting on his painted box in the Cairo Museum (T. 324, JE 61467; PM I,2 1964, pp. 577–78).

Probably the finest vignette of Chapter 40 of the Book of the Dead is that on the "papyrus", actually a vellum, of Nakht and Thuyu in London (BM 10471/16; Faulkner 1985, pp. 61–62, ill.; Shorter 1938, p. 13). There, as on all pre-Late Period Book of the Dead illustrations of Chapter 40, the man is shown spearing a snake whose wiggly body hovers over the back of a cowering donkey. There are other versions of the Book of the Dead in which the snake is only faintly indicated (Lepsius 1842, pl. XVIII; Barguet 1967, p. 82). In the Bastis version of later date, the snake has been entirely eliminated, and instead of the snake the donkey is being attacked as the symbol of evil against which the deceased was to be protected in the hereafter.

A Book of the Dead in London (BM 10558; Faulkner 1985, pp. 9, last entry, 61, lower right) has vignettes by a draftsman, not a painter, in which that of Chapter 40 is well preserved. The illustration shows the donkey peacefully on the ground, facing the man who attacks it with his spear. The snake of the early papyri is not in evidence. Thus it seems that what we have there is a close parallel to the Bastis fragment. The Book of the Dead in London belonged to a man named Ankh-wah-ib-ra; it is being attributed to post-Persian times. James calls it Ptolemaic (James 1979, p. 172), but because of the current lack of palaeographical research (Limme 1983, p. 96) this does not solve the vexing question of the date of the Bastis vignette. There seems to be general agreement among competent philologists, however, that the fragment is post-Persian in date and that the hieratic hand is fairly close to that of the Papyrus Bremner-Rhind in London (BM 10188; Jankuhn 1974, p. 32), dated to 312 B.C. (Faulkner 1936, p. 121).

Thus the Bastis vignette opens a new field of inquiry. It seems that there are two different versions of the illustration to Chapter 40 in the Late Period, one with the snake that bites the donkey being speared and another one, without the snake, in which the man attacks the donkey with his spear. The caption of the Bastis version certainly implies that the evil serpent and not the ass is being repulsed. As to the spaces left empty for the insertion of the owner's name, see the recent study of *spatia* in *ASAE* 70 (1985), p. 389; also *GM* 27 (1978), pp. 33–37. To facilitate piecing together the *disiecta membra* of the papyrus which may, unrecognized, lie in storage somewhere, the scheme of detailed measurements is given below.

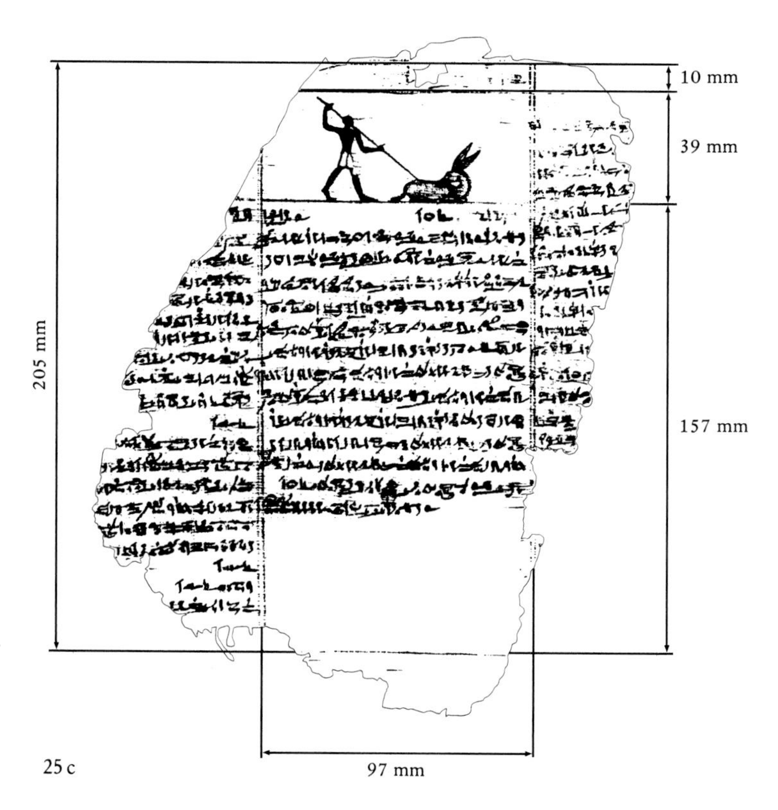

25 c

Just before this catalog went to press two other fragments of the Bastis Book of the Dead did indeed turn up, namely in the collection of the University of Heidelberg (Ägyptologisches Institut 566; Feucht 1986, p. 148, no. 333 ill.; in color on p. 91). They are of unknown provenance, the first containing vignettes and portions of Chapter 17 of the Book of the Dead, the second parts of Chapters 94, 104 and 105. On both the name of the owner has been left empty in the appropriate places. Perhaps the publication of the Bastis fragment will bring other pieces of this richly illustrated document to light.

Although the hieratic hand of the Heidelberg and Bastis fragments seems to be the same, the painter of the former may not have been the artist who illustrated the Bastis papyrus of the Book of the Dead.

26

FOUR-HEADED RAM

Late Period
Fourth to Second Century B.C.

Light Blue-green Faience

There is no such quadruped in nature, a sheep with four rams' heads, two looking fore and two looking aft. But here it is, an amulet of fine modeling, representing the body of a breed known in zoology as *Ovis platyra aegyptiaca*. The fat tail, when properly roasted, was a great delicacy. The sheep has the four heads of the horned male of the species to identify it clearly as supernatural, a divine being – perhaps not a real deity, but a representative, a messenger of the gods. It is modeled on a base, both left legs advanced, apparently minding its own business. Behind the outward calm lies a world of cosmic forces and mythology of which this mini-monster is the emblem.

In ancient Egypt numerous ram gods were worshiped under different names in several parts of the Nile Valley. They go back to an early creator deity whose male prowess embodied the procreative forces of nature. As Khnum he formed human beings on a potter's wheel.

The name of the ram in ancient Egyptian is *ba*, undoubtedly onomatopoeic, imitating the bleat of the sheep. *Ba*, however, can also mean "soul" in Egyptian, and as the representative of the soul, or spirit, of several major gods, the four-headed ram was thought to represent all of them as one. On the other hand, he is also mentioned in connection with the four deities of wind, standing by himself for the wind from the North (de Wit 1957, pp. 29–32). The four-headed ram was truly the symbol of many forces in nature.

Aside from some tiny cracks in the glaze of the animal and the base, the condition of the little figure is perfect.

MEASUREMENTS: Height 3.8 cm. Width 1.9 cm. Length 4.8 cm.

PROVENANCE: Not known. At one time in the collection of the Comtesse R. de Béarn in Paris, later in that of the Comtesse de Béhague.

BIBLIOGRAPHY: Froehner 1909, p. 62, no. 11, pl. XI.

26 a

26 b

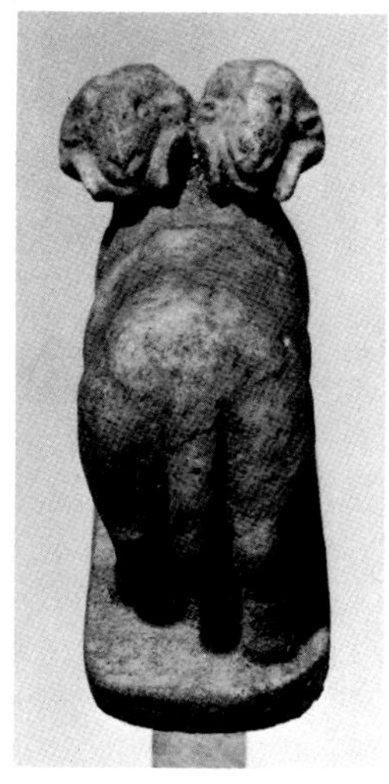

26 c

26 d

COMMENT: For another *Ovis platyra aegyptiaca*, see below No. 31 (Pp. 82–83). Information on the ram with four heads is scattered through numerous essays on Egyptian religion (Bonnet 1952, p. 870; Wild 1960, esp. pp. 61–66). Bonnet summarizes the older literature; Wild deals extensively with the subject in an article on the Palermo-Cairo statue of Bes, Prince of Mendes (*ESLP* 1960/73, no. 20), whose place, Mendes in the Delta, was the home of a god known only as the "Ram of Mendes." The back pillar inscription of the Bes statue has four columns, each of which is preceded by the invocation of the Ba, namely Ba – soul of Osiris, Ba – soul of Geb, Ba – soul of Shu, and Ba – soul of Ra. These are the gods to whom the four giant naoi of Mendes were dedicated, representing the hereafter (Osiris), earth (Geb), sky (Shu), and life (Ra), a theology particular to this cult center in Lower Egypt.

In another, probably older theology, the four-headed ram acquired the properties of Osiris and Ra and those of Ra's two children, Shu and Tefnut. Out of this identification grew the doctrine of the tetrad in which the ram personified a group of four other deities (*LdÄ* s.v. "Mendes," "Schaf," and "Widder").

There are several four-headed ram figurines of lapis lazuli in other collections: in Brooklyn (37.1325E, 37.1326E), in Cairo (CG 12344, CG 12345, JE 48073), and in London (BM 35409, 57889), and another one (BM 57907) in blue faience. All of them are smaller than the Bastis piece. Only one of the figurines has a known provenance, namely Cairo JE 48073, which comes from near Mazourah, west of el Fashn (Wainwright 1925, pp. 145–147, ill.) in Middle Egypt.

27

ISIS AND HORUS

Late Period
Fourth to Third Century B.C.

Pale Green Faience

Mother and child, an eternal subject, is here embodied in a colorful miniature sculpture of great intricacy. It represents the Goddess Isis with the naked infant son, the God Horus, on her lap. The Goddess wears on her head the emblem that renders her name: a straight-backed chair. She is crowned with the feather skin of a vulture over a beaded tripartite wig. She also wears a broad necklace, and with her right hand offers her left breast to the infant Horus.

Horus, though sitting on his mother's lap, has a separate base for his feet. Both hands rest by his sides on the Goddess' thigh. Her block seat has side panels decorated as matting and a short, narrow backrest.

The statuette is a complex piece of casting, and the maker of the mould must have been a master, as both arms and legs of the two figures are completely in the round. To judge from the color of the faience and the Goddess' fine face, the group may have been made at the end of the Pharaonic or early in the Ptolemaic Period. The preservation is good, except for Isis's lower left arm and hand and Horus' head which are lost, as is also the beak of the vulture head. The faience is somewhat discolored in places.

MEASUREMENTS: Height 13.5 cm.; of head 1.9 cm.; of face 1.3 cm. Width, elbow to elbow 3.6 cm. Depth of base 6.4 cm. Height of base 7 mm. Width of base 2.5 cm.

PROVENANCE: Not known.

BIBLIOGRAPHY: None.

COMMENT: The fundamental essay on the motif of Isis and Horus, mother and child, was written by H. W. Müller, and to this day it remains the most valuable art-historical study of the subject (Müller 1963 a). It also contributes an extensive bibliography. Close parallels to the Bastis Isis are found in Cairo (CG 39353; Daressy 1905–06, pp. 338–339, pl. LXII), and especially in Paris (Louvre E. 3503; Müller 1963 b, p. 4, fig. 2); and several in other collections offer similar examples, though very few are of this size.

To establish a date for almost any faience figurines of the Late Period is notably difficult. From the goddess' face and the color of the faience, which is found on shawabtis of the Post-Persian Period and on Hellenistic vessels of the early Ptolemaic Period, a date somewhere between 400 and 200 B.C. seems convincing.

27 a

27 b

27 c

28 a

28 b

28 c

28

TWO-SIDED TABLET WITH KINGS' HEADS

Late Period
Dynasty XXX
King Nectanebo II (?)

White Limestone

Among the votive objects deposited in shrines and temples by the faithful as gifts to the gods, often with a plea in writing attached, are pictures of deities, kings, queens, and various animals in raised relief. These relief-decorated tablets are usually one-sided and the back is flat, but a very few, always of superior quality, are two-sided, and among them is this royal image. Actually there are two royal images, because a second one, very similar to the first, is on the reverse. The front of the plaque shows the head of a king wearing the so-called Blue Crown, a kind of war helmet probably made of leather. On the front, just above the forehead, rises the royal insignia, the uraeus with the hood fully displayed, while behind it the body extends in two loops, one above the other, with a long tail. Between ear and uraeus the helmet itself has a double border; a third one below belongs to the helmet liner. The ear is very naturalistically modeled, whereas eye and face are idealizing, even stylized. The mouth, however, shows a personal feature. It is drawn up at the corner and presents a distinct smile. The chin is round and somewhat chubby. Two streamers hang down from the crown in back.

For lack of an inscription the identity of the king is at first hard to divine. The two loops of the uraeus, however, never occur in reliefwork of Dynasties XXVI–XXVII. They are found, with one exception, only in post-Persian times, in the fourth century B.C., and then only on votive plaques such as the Bastis piece.

The exception just mentioned is on a granite relief in Cairo (CG 70016; Roeder 1914, pp. 49–50, pl. 12 b) of King Nectanebo II (360–342 B.C.) of Dynasty XXX, and its detail that provides the clue to the identity of the pharaoh on the Bastis tablet is well illustrated in Myśliwiec

1979, pl. XV:a. It shows not only the two loops of the uraeus but also the mouth distinctly drawn up at the corner, thus producing the same kind of smile as the Bastis king. Furthermore, the streamer at the back of the head on the granite relief is similar to those on the obverse of the plaque and resembles even more that on the reverse. On both sides of the plaque the chubby chin is unmistakably that of Nectanebo II of the granite relief.

The identification of the king on the Bastis plaque helps to attribute a number of other pieces to the same ruler, among them a second tablet in this collection (No. 29 below), one in Lisbon, Gulbenkian Collection, another in Milan, Museum of the Castello Sforzesco, and others in Baltimore, Walters Art Gallery, in Copenhagen, and elsewhere.

The reverse of the Bastis plaque shows the same king as on the obverse, in an unfinished state, but the two loops of the uraeus' body were already worked out. The ear has also been fully sculpted, and the head is in all details, as may be expected, very close to the head on the granite relief of King Nectanebo II in Cairo. Although the kind of helmet, the Blue Crown, is frequently shown in relief during the Ptolemaic Period, not once does the uraeus appear with *two* loops, one above the other, after Dynasty XXX.

The condition of the little ex-voto is very good. It suffers from minor discolorations, and in a few places it is chipped and scratched. All four edges are original.

MEASUREMENTS: Height 7.7 cm.; of face on obverse 2.7 cm.; on reverse 2.3 cm. Width 5.4 cm. Thickness 1.6 cm.

PROVENANCE: Not known.

BIBLIOGRAPHY: *Apollo* 1978, pp. 154–55, fig. 6.

COMMENT: Fundamental for the study of these votive plaques is Liepsner 1982; for those with inscriptions, see his col. 173. In col. 171 he makes a good point for the creation of these ex-votos *before* the Ptolemaic Period. The Gulbenkian plaque is illustrated by Edwards 1937, p. 10 no. 15, pl. XIX. Curiously, it seems to have been overlooked that it, or an identical replica elsewhere, is mirrored by a stucco relief in Hildesheim (2086; *Ergänzungen* 1979, no. 197 C). It renders the Gulbenkian plaque in every detail as part of a worshiping king with raised arms. The date given for it ("Späthellenistisch, 1. Jh. v. Chr.") is untenable, especially since other stucco reliefs from the same lot date to the fourth century B.C. (Reinsberg 1980, pp. 293–297, nos. 2–9, to cite just a few).

The tablet in Milan (Castello Sforzesco 920; Lise 1981, pp. 128, 130, fig. 61) has a mouth straighter than that on the Bastis piece, and so does the one in Copenhagen (AEIN 1537; Mogensen 1930, pl. LXXXIV, no. A 645) which has a natural eyebrow and a distinct smile. The piece in Baltimore (WAG 331; Steindorff 1946, p. 95, pl. LXII) faithfully reproduces the facial features of the Bastis tablet, and there are more in other collections.

The Gulbenkian plaque cited above has not only details of the crown indicated by a multitude of incised circles, presumably representing the faience disks sewn onto the leather helmet, but also shows at the back of the helmet part of a falcon with spread wing, holding the *shen*-ring of protection in its claw. Another, somewhat fragmentary piece with similar decoration, is in Baltimore (WAG 333; Steindorff 1946, p. 96, pl. LXIV). The presence of the falcon behind the crown, also found on the stucco relief in Hildesheim, alludes to the fact that, in the funerary cult of Nectanebo II, he is referred to as "the falcon." The cult lasted as late as the reign of Ptolemy V at the end of the third century B.C. (Wildung 1969, p. 16). The possibility that the Bastis plaque represents King Nectanebo II, but was made in the early Ptolemaic Period, deserves further study.

29

ONE-SIDED TABLET WITH KING'S HEAD

Late Period
Dynasty XXX
King Nectanebo II (?)

White Limestone

Votive plaques commemorating kings are not rare. Few, however, show a Pharaoh wearing the war helmet, the so-called Blue Crown. It is surprising therefore that the Bastis Collection includes two examples, the better preserved being No. 28 above. While that one is two-sided, another rarity, this one, somewhat fragmentary, is one-sided. It is also unusual that the royal cobra rising above the forehead is represented with two loops behind the hood – another feature in common with the two heads on No. 28.

The king's face is well preserved. Here he has a different personality, leaner and slightly more sophisticated. In the other examples the eye is horizontal; here it is set at a slant. The nose seems more pointed, but that impression may be incorrect, since the ala of the nostril has been damaged and looks more open than it was meant to be.

Again the ear is well articulated; this may have to do with the fact that the ear as an ex-voto by itself, or as part of an ex-voto, played an important role for the faithful who fervently hoped that their pleas would he heard. The earlobe may be nicked. The eyebrow is sharp, but not plastically rendered in relief.

The tip of the uraeus head has been damaged, and a chip missing from the nostril has been mentioned. Three break lines at the back of the helmet are visible on the front surface of the slab; they do not go through. The top edge of the tablet is ancient. The right side is probably ancient too, although the tool marks differ from those on the top. Since top and right side form an exact right angle, it is possible that the right edge was cut back in modern times to minimize the appearance of damage. The cut of the left edge is not ancient. The surface is somewhat discolored by accretions of lime. The back is rough and has not been worked.

MEASUREMENTS: Height 13.5 cm.; of face 5.8 cm. Width 13.2 cm. Thickness 2.9 cm.

PROVENANCE: Not known.

BIBLIOGRAPHY: None.

COMMENT: For ex-voto plaques with royal heads wearing the Blue Crown, see the text of No. 28 above. This type of Pharaonic headgear has been extensively discussed (Davies 1982). Following the terminology standardized by Sally B. Johnson (1988), we call the bend of the serpent's body a loop. Thus the equivalent in sculpture in the round of the type of uraeus appearing on the Bastis tablets would be described as "two double loops, one above the other, placed behind the cobra hood." The term "figure eight" can no longer be used, because a cobra body never forms a true figure eight.

Two loops in relief, one above the other, are occasionally found on other crowns, for instance on the Upper Egyptian crown worn by King Alexander II (or IV, 317–310 B.C.; PM V 1937, p. 227), but this never occurs in relief on a Blue Crown during the Ptolemaic Period. The Blue Crown, however, with uraeus (one loop or none) appears in relief all the way through the Ptolemaic Period to the end of the first century B.C.:
Alexander the Great, Luxor Temple Sanctuary (PM II 1972, p. 325)
Ptolemy I, temple relief in Cairo (TR 5/3/25/1; Derchain 1961, pl. X)
Ptolemy V, Bucheum stela in Cairo (JE 54313; PM V 1937, p. 158)
Ptolemy XII, colossal statue base in Cairo (JE 40643 and 49103; PM V 1937, pp. 131–132).

The king represented on the Bastis plaque is probably Nectanebo II. Although it differs from the two likenesses of the king on No. 28, the corner of the mouth is drawn up as in those representations. As for the naturally formed eyebrow, it occurs in the same manner on a very similar ex-voto in Amsterdam (Coll. W. A. van Leer; Janssen 1957, p. 14, no. 3, pl. II:3), and there the king's head is protected by a falcon in relief at the back of the Blue Crown. Since this is considered an allusion to Nectanebo II (Wildung 1969, p. 17), the plaque in Amsterdam is meant to represent this very king and, by analogy, he may also be represented on the Bastis tablet.

The role of the ear in Egyptian cults furthered the production of numerous ex-votos on which only ears are shown (Habachi 1954, p. 536, pl. XXXIV:B; Anthes 1965, pp. 72–77, pls. 24–25; Liepsner 1982, col. 173; Schulman 1981, pp. 165–166, figs. 3–4). They have given references to the role of the ear in cult representations; tablets on which in a human face the ear is emphasized by detailed modeling may also be included among those devoted to the cult of the ear (Habachi, *loc.cit.*).

Although a dating to King Nectanebo II of Dynasty XXX seems justified, there is still the possibility that these plaques were made in the Ptolemaic Period as signs of worship of a ruler of the fourth century B.C. who, characteristically for the earlier era, is represented with the double loop uraeus. It was not in use under the Ptolemies, but had once been employed in Dynasty XXVI, and then as a neo-archaism (*Fs. Parker* 1986, p. 8) was featured again in the post-Persian Period in Dynasty XXX.

30a

30

SACRED FISH

Ptolemaic Period
300–100 B.C.

Bronze, Solid Cast

The number of bronze cats cast in Egypt's Late Period (ca. 800 to 30 B.C.) is probably exceeded only by the number of bronze fish made at the same time. Hundreds are preserved, and most of them, like the Bastis fish, have a tang underneath that permitted the donor to set it on a wooden or bronze base or attach it to a chair, shrine or even larger pedestal in a sanctuary and then deposit it as an ex-voto in a holy place. In such a sanctuary large numbers of fish must have stood in rows to fend off evil and to please the gods.

With its soulful eyes and the lively pattern of scales and fins, this fish is unusually fine. It is a Barbel, *Barbus bynni* in Latin, *Lepidotos* in Greek, a carp of the Cyprinid family, common in ancient Egypt and still found in the Nile today. Its chief characteristic is the steep, triangular-shaped dorsal fin. It was perhaps sacred to the lion-headed Goddess Mehyt of This, but according to Strabo, it was worshiped elsewhere in Egypt as well.

The bronze is in good condition, with minor corrosion on top fin, tail and belly.

30 b

MEASUREMENTS: Height with tang 5.4 cm.; without tang 5.2 cm. Length 10.0 cm. Thickness 11 mm.

PROVENANCE: Not known, perhaps Lepidotonpolis, in the eighth Upper Egyptian nome, the nome of This, where the Goddess Mehyt resided.

BIBLIOGRAPHY: None.

COMMENT: There is a fundamental study on fish and fish cults in ancient Egypt by Gamer-Wallert 1970; on the *Barbus bynni* pp. 9, 19, 37–38, 95–98, 121, 130, pl. IX:4. Gamer-Wallert also wrote the entries for "fish" in the *LdÄ* II 1977, cols. 223–234. Except for Ayrton *et al.* 1904, p. 51, where three fine *Barbus bynni* bronzes, illustrated on pl. XXI:4, are wrongly attributed to Dynasty XXII, no attempt seems to have been made to date this type of votive figure beyond assigning it to the "Late Period" in general, or to the "Epoque Saïte" in particular. Of the Late Period the fish surely is, but Saite probably not. In view of the mass production of animal bronzes, it is more likely that their overwhelming number dates from the period after 500 B.C., and most likely from the fourth to second century B.C.

A bronze fish of almost identical size – the difference amounts to 2 mm. – is in Baltimore (WAG 709; Steindorff 1946, p. 156, pl. CIII). How to worship the fish *Barbus bynni* is well illustrated on a bronze plaque in Cairo (JE 4591; *ZÄS* 95, 1969, pp. 96–97, fig. 2) where it is addressed as Mehyt, Mistress of This, by an adoring lady who faces it. The outsized fish rests on top of a shrine, dwarfing it as well as the female worshiper.

31 a

31

RAM'S HEAD PLAQUE

Ptolemaic Period
300–100 B.C.

White Limestone

The custom of placing images of objects, deities, and royalty in holy places in Egypt seems to have been as old as Egyptian history; it may have begun in the Archaic Period. However, it is only in the Late Period, and specifically in the seventh century B.C., that the production of votive gifts for the gods increased to major proportions.

First there were bronzes (see above, Nos. 9–13, Pp. 33–42), but beginning with the fourth century all sorts of items were made for such purposes in limestone, erroneously labeled "sculptor's models". It was not until 1953 that the first dissent to this traditional misnomer appeared in print.

There can be no doubt that the fine plaque with the head of a ram in the Bastis Collection was at one time placed in a sanctuary, near a shrine where the sacred image of this powerful animal was worshiped, as a token of the faithful person appealing to a deity for help, healing, or other support.

The plaque is beautifully carved in very high, bold relief, representing the head of a ram, with underslung horn, of the breed *Ovis platyra aegyptiaca*. It was introduced into Egypt in the Middle Kingdom when the earlier breed with horizontal horns, *Ovis longipes palaeoaegyptiaca*, died out. The possibility, however, is not excluded that the plaque also showed the horizontal horns above the ram's head, because a modern cut has created a new top edge which may have had traces of the decoration above, now lost, and many representations exist of the ram deity with both types of horns on his head. Eyebrows and forehead exhibit unusually fine modeling; the eyeball is highly convex.

Which deity was meant is hard to say; it depends on the findspot, as ram gods were worshiped at Assuan, Herakleopolis, and Mendes, to name but a few places. It is even harder to attribute such a plaque to a definite date, except to state that it was surely made in the Post-Persian Period, after 400 B.C., and probably under the Ptolemies when such tablets were dedicated in large numbers in the temples of the Nile Valley.

The plaque must originally have been larger, as all four edges were cut in modern times, probably to square it off. Only the back appears to have been left untouched, and of course the ram's head itself is entirely ancient. Fig. 31 b shows the condition before restoration. The upper and lower left corners are worn and chipped; also a break ran through the beard, and a chip was missing.

31 b Before Restoration

MEASUREMENTS: Height 14.4 cm. Width 21.9 cm. Thickness 3.0 cm.

PROVENANCE: Not known.

BIBLIOGRAPHY: von Bothmer 1961, p. 18, pl. 22, no. 83.

COMMENT: For lack of information from controlled excavations the dating of such relief plaques is still very much in the air. For some time they were thought to have originated in Egypt after Alexander the Great, but there is now evidence that at least one type may have been made earlier in the fourth century B.C.; see also the Comment on No. 28. For a brief history of models of objects deposited as ex-votos, see Liepsner 1982, col. 172. One could also add the models of food offerings in Dynasty VI (Smith 1946, p. 93, figs. 22–23, and p. 99, fig. 24).

The article that attempted for the first time to single out the pieces that, often by their inscriptions, could truly be considered as ex-votos and not sculptors' studies appeared in *BMFA* 51, 1953, pp. 80–84. figs. 1–7. It deals with a plaque representing a ram's head in Boston (MFA 51.274) with two sets of horns of the earlier and later race of sheep domesticated in Egypt (*LdÄ* V 1984, cols. 522–524, s.v. "Schaf"). There is another fine ram's head plaque in New York (MMA 18.9.1; Young 1964, pp. 250–251, fig. 8).

The Liepsner (1982) study, based on about two thousand ex-votos in more than one hundred collections all over the world, has clarified considerably the problem of identifying and dating many of these votive gifts.

32

Ptolemaic Period
300–100 B.C.

LITTLE OWL
(Athena Noctua Glaux)

White Limestone, Discolored

The well-modeled upper portion of an owl in relief is apparently complete, and not a fragment. Several similar pieces are found in American and European collections, some flat in back, others – like the Bastis owl – rounded off, as if the piece had been cut out of a monumental inscription where each hieroglyph was carved with loving attention to the smallest detail.

The owl, when complete, represents the hieroglyph for "m" which may originally have been an ideogram for the concept "to see" (*LdÄ* II 1977, cols. 37–40: "Eule"). What we have here may be the so-called Barn Owl (*Tyto alba alba* or *Tyto alba pratincola*), as common in the ancient Nile Valley as it still is today. The tear-shaped protuberance on the inner corner of each eye was in reality a third eyelid, a nictitating membrane (Pasquier 1977, p. 104), no longer found on owls. The two folds between brow and upper eyelid are rows of stylized feathering.

MEASUREMENTS: Height 12.4 cm. Width 11.8 cm. Thickness 3.4 cm.

PROVENANCE: Not known.

BIBLIOGRAPHY: None.

COMMENT: Although votive plaques are known that show an entire owl from head to tail and feet (Capart 1931, pl. 94:A and F), there are others equally complete on which only the forepart of an owl is reproduced (*op.cit.*, pl. 94:B), and a third group which consists only of the head and chest of the owl. The Bastis piece belongs to the third group of which several examples are known (*op.cit.*, pl. 94:D and E), but those illustrated are flat in the back and originally square or rectangular. This would indicate that, like the first two groups, they are complete as preserved today.

The back of the Bastis owl, however, is convex, so that the piece is thickest in the middle and thinnest at the top, right and left edges. It had been dressed down anciently so that the back shows some of the tell-tale tool marks known from Egyptian tombs (Bietak 1982, p. 221L: "Flachmeissel"), while the finer tool marks are the same as on the front. The owl is much too thick to have come from a typical rectangular votive plaque.

The piece fits well into one's right hand, the middle finger resting in the concave space below the owl's right eye. Were this and other owls of similar shape perhaps to be carried in processions or used in some other ritual?

The Bastis owl is not unique. A second piece of similar shape and thickness exists in Chicago (Oriental Institute Museum 17972; *LdÄ* IV 1982, col. 170: "Eulenkopf").

The definitive article on ancient Egyptian owls by Louis Keimer (1951) leaves the correct identification of this owl still open. It could also be the Barred Owl (*Strix varia*) or the Little Owl (*Athena noctua glaux*). We prefer the last-named in view of the present owner's origin. Since owls were sometimes mummified (Keimer 1951, p. 75 n. 1), they must have been sacred at one time to a deity or divine spirit, but nothing is known about it thus far. For owl deities outside Egypt, see Marinatos 1968.

33 a

33 b

33

CAT GODDESS

Ptolemaic Period
Third Century B.C.

Bronze, Solid Cast

In the early part of the last millennium B.C. the craft of bronze casting had become a fixed part of the repertoire of the arts of Egypt. Although the mass production of standard figures of the most prominent gods constituted the major output of the studios and foundries, from time to time unusually fine statuettes were made in bronze which did not duplicate others all cast from the same mold. They are usually quite small and are either without a close parallel of exactly the same size or represent a type of which only a few examples of great quality are known. This figure is of the latter group.

The statuette is that of a young woman with the head of a cat. Both ears are pierced; each one is adorned with a gold ring. She wears a short-sleeved, patterned dress with a border at the neck, nearly round in front, and V-shaped in back. The garment ends halfway between calf and ankle. In the raised right hand she carries a looped sistrum decorated with a stylized Hathor head, but lacking the customary wires and rattles, and in the left hand she holds an aegis, a kind of protective emblem (see No. 13, Page 42, Figs. 13 a–c). It consists of a broad collar and a lion head topped by a sun disk with uraeus. Near the bend of the left arm hangs a little basket, now empty, with a looped handle that swings freely on the lower arm. The feet are set side by side on a tiny base.

The figure with all its accoutrements is a masterpiece of casting. A charming motif of unusual playfulness is combined with the eternal wish of the Egyptians to please a deity, in this case probably the Goddess Bastet who is usually represented as a cat or as a woman with a cat's head. The condition is excellent.

MEASUREMENTS: Height 10.3 cm. Width 3.1 cm. Depth 2.7 cm. Height of base 5.5 mm. Width of base 2.2 cm. Depth of base 2.7 cm.

PROVENANCE: Not known; perhaps Tell Basta. Among similar pieces at the Cairo Museum, however, there is a comparable statuette (JE 71746) that was found at Tell el Maskhuta in 1939, and others turned up in recent years in Emery's excavations at North Saqqara (*JEA* 55, 1969, p. 31, pl. VII; 56, 1970, p. 6, pl. VII).

BIBLIOGRAPHY: None.

COMMENT: Statuettes of this type, but not quite as fine as the Bastis figure, have long been known (Daressy 1906, pp. 250–52; Roeder 1937, pp. 34–36), but the closest example is in Berlin/GDR (11354; Roeder 1956, pp. 224, 267, 270, pl. 40:c–d), which is related in many details to the Bastis bronze. There is also a very similar figurine, although much less well preserved, in New York (MMA 15.43.5; *BMMA* 12,3 1953, p. 78 ill.).

Although at first the dress of the Bastis figure appears to be unusual, it is found on several similar bronzes. Patterned garments of this kind, with sleeves, are known only from reliefs of the Ptolemaic Period, which makes one think of a date late rather than early in the last millennium B.C. for the cat-headed bronze. The statuette seems closer to the fourth and third centuries B.C. than to an earlier period. For cat goddesses, see Bonnet 1952, pp. 371–373. The looped sistrum carried by the deity (Anderson 1976, pp. 40–52; Manniche 1976, pp. 5–6) is known since the Middle Kingdom (see No. 34, Page 88). The types and meaning of the aegis have been discussed by Bonnet 1952, pp. 8–9, and especially by Parlasca 1953, pp. 127–131.

The tight-fitting, long, patterned dress, best paralleled in Ptolemaic relief, appears on a stela in Cairo (CG 22114; Kamal 1904, pls. XXIV and LXXXVII:137, from Akhmim), where it is worn by both Isis and Hathor. Thus the date of the Bastis bronze appears to be well established.

33 c

34

VOTIVE SISTRUM

Ptolemaic Period,
300–100 B.C.

White Limestone, Discolored

Among the multitude of ex-votos with which the ancient Egyptians filled their temples, shrines, and sanctuaries to glorify, mollify, please, and appeal to, their gods, there were in the Late Period an increasingly large number of small objects, mostly fabricated in bronze or limestone. One such ex-voto is this Hathor-headed slab that, despite its stylized form, represents a common musical percussion instrument, the sistrum.

Basically a sistrum is a rattle, usually, but not always, carried by women. It consists of a loop through which stiff wires bearing metal disks are stuck, and underneath is a handle surmounted by the cow-eared face of the Goddess Hathor.

Another type of sistrum, known since the Old Kingdom, has instead of a loop the image of a shrine, a naos, set above the handle. On the sides of the shrine rise two volutes, like the spiral on the Lower Egyptian Crown. First shown in painting in a Middle Kingdom tomb at Beni Hasan, the naos sistrum undergoes slight modifications over many hundreds of years, but always incorporates the head of the Goddess Hathor with the cow ears. Eventually this instrument, used in religious processions, acquires in itself a sacred character and, devoid of handle and rattle, is transformed into a shrine over the head of the Goddess Hathor, to be set up in a sanctuary on behalf of the donor.

The Bastis plaque is the ultimate form since, unlike similar ex-votos, the shrine is solid, except for a small niche filled by a uraeus with a sun disk on the head. The front of the shrine is surmounted by a bar over which the typical Egyptian cavetto cornice is raised and on the sides of which are the volutes, rising like the antennae of a curious insect.

The Hathor head, as always, is decked out with a plain wig descending on either side of the face. The auricles of the cow ears are deeply channeled, each with a knoblike plug protruding from the auditory canal. The eyes are long and narrow, iris and pupil marked in black, with long thin eyebrows and cosmetic lines. Although the small curved mouth is fully modeled, it looks as if the space below it still lacks the sculptor's final touch. A beaded necklace graces the throat.

All four edges of the slab were cut anciently; some of them are chipped and so in places are the volutes, the shrine, and the goddess' wig. The back is dressed absolutely flat but not smoothed, and tool marks are visible there and on the wig. Tool marks are also visible below Hathor's mouth. The lower right hand corner of the ex-voto is missing. On top of the cavetto cornice, 11 mm. from the front and 23 mm. from the back, is a sharply incised guideline. In several places bits of mud still adhere to the stone.

MEASUREMENTS: Height 23.4 cm. Width 13.5 cm. Depth 4.4 cm. Thickness of backslab 1.5 cm.

PROVENANCE: Not known.

BIBLIOGRAPHY: None.

COMMENT: This ex-voto belong to the group listed by Liepsner 1982, col. 170. The two types of sistra, the loop type and the naos type, were well described by Klebs 1931, basing herself in part on Davies 1920 and Sachs 1921. Manniche 1976, pp. 5–6, calls the loop type "arched sistra."

The prototype of the naos sistrum is the calcite instrument of King Tety, 2345–2333 B.C., in New York (MMA 26.7.1450; Davies 1920; Hayes 1953, pp. 125–126, fig. 76). There, instead of a loop, a hollow housing in the form of a shrine or naos was pierced laterally to take the wires with the disks, and at the sides two volutes rose that banged against the housing when shaken. Most scholars agree with Davies' interpretation (1920, p. 70) that the volutes were derived from the horns of cattle-head emblems, amulets, and the like. This makes good sense in view of the Hathor head decoration with cow's ears above the handle. Davies was the first to call them antennae.

The tomb at Beni Hasan in which the naos sistrum with volutes was first shown is that of Amenemhat of the time of Sesostris I, 1974–1929 B.C. (Newberry 1900, pl. XXV:5, p. 8), and there is another representation of about the same time in Tomb B 2 at Meir (Blackman 1915, pl. XV). For the association of Hathor with the sistrum and for the use of sistra in the cult of the Goddess Hathor, see George 1978.

The long thin eyebrows and cosmetic lines of even width from one end to the other have a long tradition. They appear already in exactly this form on the naos sistrum which the kneeling Senenmut holds in his statues in Cairo (CG 579) and Munich (ÄS 6265), while his own eyebrows are in the style of his time, increasing and decreasing in width, and ending in a fine point. Thus they cannot be used as dating criteria, and the huge ornamental Hathor head capital from Tell el Rub^ca, now in Cairo (JE 50039; *Mendes* II 1976, p. 194, pl. 13, no. 25), with the same eye decorations may well be earlier than the Late Period.

35

PTOLEMAIC KING

Ptolemaic Period
About 150–100 B.C.

Light Brown, Discolored Limestone

Very little has been done in the last twenty years to clarify the chronology of the heads of Ptolemaic rulers in Egyptian style although numerous examples are on view or in storage in many collections all over the world. The lack of chronology is due in part to the continued absence of well inscribed, and thus dated, royal statuary from the end of the fourth century on, and in part to the scarcity of any new material, be it a statue with the head intact, or just a head by itself. It is therefore a great pleasure to encounter a new unknown head of a Ptolemaic king that, apart from

35 a

35 b

35 c

its fine quality, offers a number of exceptional features, the study of which may advance the iconography of the Ptolemies to a certain, if only minor, degree.

This royal head in the Bastis Collection is most impressive, both for its lifesize scale and its good state of preservation. It represents a king wearing the traditional headcloth, the *nemes*, surmounted by a protruberance, probably the remnants of a tenon on which a separately worked accoutrement rested, an emblem or a crown. The *nemes* is adorned with parallel bands, while the lappets are ribbed in evenly spaced striations. There is a frontlet to the *nemes* over the forehead; from its upper edge and slightly overlapping it rose the royal cobra, the uraeus, with two loops, one on either side of the missing hood. The cobra body and tail continue in relief on the central band of the *nemes* up to the disk surrounding the lump on the crown of the head. Fairly wide tabs, rudimentary indications of the hair partly covered by the frontlet, are set in front of the ears. The ears, naturalistically modeled, are quite small, but the eyes are stylized. The eyebrows were indicated as low, narrow stripes in relief. The upper eyelid rims are contoured and trail out to a fine point just beyond the outer canthi.

The most arresting element of the face, however, is the

35 d

35 e

barely damaged mouth. It is very small, somewhat pouting, and the thick lips have a kind of rosebud appearance. The corners of the mouth are deeply cut, not drilled. The chin, also relatively small, is pointed and on the underside quite full. The queue at the back of the headdress falls straight down to the break, an indication that the back pillar ended well below the shoulder blades, as in a number of royal statues of the Ptolemaic Period.

The face wears a pleasant expression, idealizing and not at all stern. Since few elements in this royal sculpture give a clue to the identity of the king represented, only a general attribution is possible at present; all one can say is that it must have been made after the middle of the second century B.C.

The stone is in sound condition, but the sculpture suffered some damage in the distant past. The head and hood of the uraeus are missing, as are also portions of the ears, nose, philtrum and left lappet. The tenon on top of the head and the mouth are damaged, also the wings of the *nemes* and the sides of the queue in back. The condition of the plastic eyebrows is strange; they look as if they had been partly worn off. The entire surface of the head shows discoloration and small pit marks and in some places lime accretions.

MEASUREMENTS: Height 31.8 cm.; of head without stump ca. 25.0 cm.; of face 14.8 cm. Width 27 cm.; of break at front of neck ca. 11.0 cm.; at queue ca 5.2 cm. Depth 24.4 cm; of break through queue ca. 16.5 cm.; through neck only ca. 12.0 cm.

PROVENANCE: Not known.

BIBLIOGRAPHY: *Apollo* (London) 115, no. 243, May 1982, p. 3 ill.

COMMENT: The limestone appears to be nummelitic; it is very hard. In the break it is almost marble-like. This kind of material is rare in the Ptolemaic Period. It may therefore be possible some day to identify the missing torso, even if no direct contact with the break at the neck can be established. The surface shows petrified calcareous deposits, as for example at the lower edge of the frontlet, above the right eye. They are quite old.

In recent years several new studies of royal Ptolemaic iconography have been made (Müller 1955, *ESLP* 1960/73, Aldred 1962, Myśliwiec 1973, Parlasca 1978, and Kyrieleis 1975, although the last-named work, very substantial in its own right, deals mainly with Hellenistic, not Pharaonic portraiture).

At first the tenon on top of the head was thought to provide a lead because it is known from late Ptolemaic (Cairo TR 13/3/15/3; Essen 1978, no. 130) and Roman Period sculptures (London, Sir John Soane's Museum 114; Massner 1986, pl. 10:1). It was discovered, however, that a tenon on the *nemes* also occurs on the over lifesize statue of King Nectanebo I (380–362 B.C.) in Mansura (E.A.O. 25; Bakry 1971, pp. 13–15, pls. XIII–XV); as a matter of fact, the Great Sphinx at Giza, dating from Dynasty IV, once had a tenon on the crown of the head as well – a rare bit of information which I owe to the kindness of Mr. Mark Lehner in Cairo. The tenon may have held the double crown, worked separately, or more likely the four-feathered crown frequently worn with the *nemes* in Ptolemaic relief (Chassinat and Daumas 1972, pl. DCXLI).

The back pillar ending well below the shoulder blades is more of a help for dating purposes, because this particular type does not occur on sculptures of the early Ptolemaic rulers (New Haven 1.1.1953; *ESLP* 1960/73, pl. 101, fig. 271, no. 109), at least not before Ptolemy III. On the other hand, the small thick-lipped, pursed mouth may give some guidance, since it appears only very rarely in this form and with this bitter-sweet expression. It was pointed out many years ago (*ESLP* 1960/73, no. 114, p. 148 R) that the small pouting mouth is found on the two giant granite sphinxes at the Serapeum of Alexandria (*ESLP* 1960/73, pp. 147, 148; Michałowski 1970, pls. 39–41), generally attributed to Ptolemy VI Philometor (180–164, 163–145 B.C.). The prototype of this mouth occasionally appears on lifesize heads from then on (Brundage Collection 2/97, *ESLP* no. 114; Brussels E. 1839, Vandersleyen 1975, fig. 229). Thus, the new royal head in the Bastis Collection may be attributed either to Ptolemy VI or to one of his successors (Ptolemies VII–IX) in the second half of the second century B.C.

35f

35g Back View

36

MAN OF EXPERIENCE

Late Ptolemaic Period
First Century B.C.

Black Basalt with Brownish Sheen

36 a

In nearly three thousand years of sculpting the human form, the Egyptians made an overwhelming number of likenesses showing men and women at their youthful best, idealizing, with a pleasant, though somewhat remote expression, often bland. At the same time, however, an undercurrent of realistic modeling flowed that aimed at showing man as a mature, even ageworn being, whose face reflected the burden of years and the wisdom, or bitterness, of experience. And while in idealizing statuary there is often very little variation within a given period, in realistic sculpture an amazing number of diverse expressions were produced.

The fragment of a head in the Bastis Collection demonstrates well this great diversity of expression; as a realistic likeness it is unique. It does not render a type of which several replicas exist, but portrays the features of one man, and of him alone. He wears a plain wig that covers the skull and ends in front of the ear with the well-known tab that simulates a sideburn. The forehead wrinkles are indicated by two incised lines, with a third set directly above the eyebrow. Like eyesocket, lid, and eye, the brow is naturally formed. The upper eyelid has a fold, and neatly engraved crow's-feet appear at the outer canthus.

The nose is extraordinary, long and strong, with fleshy alae that – a most unusual feature – are set off against the broad nostril. The mouth too has an individual peculiarity inasmuch as, under a small philtrum, the narrow upper lip

36 b

36 c

is exceeded by the full, protruding lower lip with a vertical incision in the exact center.

The wrinkled upper eyelid, the fleshy nose, and the protruding lower lip lend the face a character that is exceptional. The sculptor had a great model for this likeness and made the attempt to render a true portrait, combining outer features with the personality of an older man, wise to the ways of the world and somewhat disdainful of it.

The fragment consists of part of the wig and the right side of the face; the left side, apart from the nose, is entirely gone, and there is a blemish on the wig above the forehead and damage to the left side of the chin.

MEASUREMENTS: Height 7.8; of break at back of head 7.55 cm. Width of break at back of head 3.9 cm.; of break on left side of face 1.55 cm.

PROVENANCE: Kom Abu Billo (Terenuthis) in the Western Delta.

BIBLIOGRAPHY: *Apollo* 1978, p. 155, fig. 7.

COMMENT: For realistic representations in the Old Kingdom, see *Expedition* (Philadelphia) 24,2 (Winter 1982), pp. 27–39. Lines on the forehead, a subject recently discussed by Vandersleyen (*CdE* 60, 1985, pp. 365 ff.), can be found not only in the Old Kingdom, but especially in the Middle Kingdom, on which the Late Period tradition is based: see for instance a head in London (UCL 16451; Benson and Gourlay 1899, pp. 76–77, pl. VII; Page 1976, p. 94, no. 105, where unbelievably the head is mistaken for one of Dynasty XXV/XXVI and, still worse, is attributed to Mentuemhat). Other Middle Kingdom heads show fewer wrinkles on the forehead (Strasbourg 1392; although invisible in the publication by Spiegelberg 1909, frontispiece, pp. 4–5, fig. 2, pl. IV:7. Cairo JE 43928; Corteggiani 1986, p. 75, no. 38, ill.). Then this feature disappears, not to be employed again until Dynasty XXVII (*ESLP* 1960/73, p. 83R); after that it occurs, intermittently, to the late Ptolemaic Period.

Although the crow's-feet at the outer corners of the eyes are not unusual in the Late Period, the notch in the middle of the lower lip as a definite mark of identity, not as the casual blemish of an aged face, is found in two other outstanding likenesses, both in West Berlin (1/65 and 12500 [the Berlin "Green Head"]; Kaiser, in *JbBerlMus* 8, 1966, pp. 5–31. figs. 14–16), that in my opinion are datable to the first century B.C.

To attribute the fragment of so small a head, actually only part of a face, presents a great deal of difficulty, considering our still very sketchy knowledge and understanding of Late Egyptian portraiture. For reasons based more on experience, feeling, and hunch than on hard facts, the piece is tentatively assigned to the end of the Ptolemaic Period, somewhere close to the aforementioned Berlin "Green Head", which also has a heavy protruding lower lip with a center incision.

37 ISIS EX-VOTO

Ptolemaic Period
Second to First Century B.C.

Pale Yellow to
Light Brown Limestone

While fragmentary, this little plaque preserves the face and part of the headdress of an eminent Egyptian deity, the Goddess Isis, wife of Osiris, mother of Horus. Her worship spans the millennia of Egyptian history, and many queens had themselves represented in the guise of the great lady of the Egyptian pantheon. As such she often assumes the outfit of other goddesses, and although her emblem is the stool or chair, the hieroglyph with which her name is written (*aset*) and which she balances on her head (as in No. 27, Pp. 74–75, above), in later times she is often shown with the cow horns of Hathor, the mother goddess, or with the vulture cap of Mut, consort and wife of Amun, king of the gods, at Thebes.

Here she was bedecked in a curly lappet wig, traces of which appear on her forehead, at the back of the head, and just below the ear. Over the wig she wears the vulture headdress, with the head of the powerful bird jutting out above her face. The Goddess' ear and eyebrow are naturally formed, but the eye is curiously slanted and narrow; yet the eyeball is very convex, a feature that is found on other Isis plaques as well. That this relief truly shows Isis, and not any of the other goddesses wearing the same coiffure and headdress, is attested by the plaques to Isis in other collections, bearing in Demotic or Greek an address by the suppliant who dedicated the image in her honor.

While most votive tablets with the image of Isis have the idealizing features of a young girl, the Bastis relief renders the face of a mature woman. One wonders who, in the guise of the great goddess, may have been portrayed – a private donor or a ruling queen?

Although badly cracked and fragmentary, the object has not been restored or repaired; the face is entirely ancient. The back, now covered, appears to have been cut straight in ancient times. A guide line on the top edge of the slab extends across between front and back.

MEASUREMENTS: Height 7.3 cm; of face 3.0 cm. Width 6.9 cm. Thickness 2.3 cm.

PROVENANCE: Not known.

BIBLIOGRAPHY: None.

COMMENT: The best synopsis of the vast literature on the Goddess Isis is found in *LdÄ* III 1980, cols, 186–203. For ex-votos dedicated to deities, see Liepsner 1982, cols. 170 and 173, and a plaque of the goddess with vulture cap, inscribed to Isis, *ibid.* col. 173, fig. 2, n. 151. Of course, numerous collections of ex-voto tablets all over the world include one or two plaques with the head, bust, or entire figure of Isis. Only a few show this particular slanting, narrow eye with the highly convex eyeball. Among them are one tablet in Paris (Louvre E. 16603; *Siècle* 1981, p. 299, no 324) and another in Lucerne (Kofler Collection A 163; Seipel 1983, no. 112). Both show idealizing faces, but the eyes are similar. Like the Bastis plaque they are based on temple representations such as a relief in Hildesheim (Pelizaeus-Museum 1025; *Nofret* II 1985 pp. 154–155, no. 176).

As for true portraiture of women in Late Period relief, there is practically none; almost all are represented in an idealizing manner. For the best parallel to the Bastis piece one must repair to sculpture in the round. Among the heads of queens or goddesses with a similar profile is a limestone head in Alexandria (21992; Essen 1978, no. 117). Undoubtedly a portrait, the head is considered to be the prototype of an important series of replicas in Florence, Paris, and New York. The date has not yet been definitely established, although Classical archaeologists now attribute the Alexandria head to the century after 150 B.C. It greatly resembles a coin of Cleopatra VII (Sboronos III 1904, pl. LXIII:10), although later Ptolemaic queen representations on coins tend to reproduce modified versions of those of the great ladies of the early Ptolemaic Period.

38–42

FIVE AMULETS

Late Period
Dynasties XXVI–XXX
About 650–350 B.C.

Pale Green Faience

Like all highly cultured peoples of the ancient world the Egyptians believed in magic, and magic could produce the benefits humans needed in life as well as in afterlife. Various means were employed to assure those benefits, and one of them was the adornment with amulets, worn as jewelry in life or taken into one's tomb for life after death.

In the appeal for beneficial protection various deities had to be addressed, and this was achieved primarily by representing them in their most characteristic form. Thus, from left to right we have first a bull *passant* with the sun disk between the horns, undoubtedly the God Apis, representing fertility and male prowess (No. 38).

Next, as number two, comes Thoeris, a female deity composed of the head of a hippopotamus, human breasts, arms, legs and pregnant belly, with the back of a crocodile – surely a frightening monster (No. 39). She is, however, benign as protectress of motherhood and symbol of life-giving nourishment.

The center figure is the God Shu who represents the principal of eternal life (No. 40). He supports the sky, here identified as the sun that rests on his head. Next on the right sits the cat-headed Goddess Bastet who brings joy to the universe, to man and beast (No. 41). On the far right is a lion *couchant*, symbol of fortitude, as the God Mahes and as the Sun God's son, Pharaoh (No. 42).

MEASUREMENTS AND CONDITION:

No. 38 Height 2.0 cm. Base: Height 2 mm.; width 7 mm.; depth 2.2 cm. There is a great deal of detailed modeling to this tiny bull, and fat folds and ribs are well indicated. A ring for suspension is molded in one piece on the back. The preservation is perfect.

No. 39 Height 3.0 cm. Base: Height 2.5 mm.; width 8 mm.; depth 1.1 cm. A protuberance, pierced sideways, below Thoeris' wig in the back serves as a ring for suspension. There are a few impurities in the glaze, and the right front corner of the base is chipped.

No. 40 Height 4.0 cm. Width 2.5 cm. Base: Height 3 mm.; width 1.1 cm.; depth 1.9 cm.

The asymmetric squatting figure of the god is exceptionally well sculpted on so small a scale. He is bearded, wears a tripartite striated wig, and his heavy-lidded eyes seem to express the weight of the burden he is bearing. A suspension ring protrudes from the back of the wig. Although the negative space between arms and wig was meant to prevent breakage, Shu's left hand is damaged and the right hand is broken off. Beard and base are slightly chipped, and the glaze, which has few blemishes, is somewhat discolored in places.

No. 41 Height 2.5 cm. Width 1.0 cm. Depth 1.5 cm. The ears are unusually large. At the back of the head, well above the level of the ears, is a big suspension ring. The right arm is modeled partly in the round. The glaze of the figurine shows a green deeper than that of the other amulets; this may indicate that it is the earliest piece in the group.

No. 42 Height 1.8 cm. Base: Height 4 mm.; width 1.1 cm.; depth 3.5 cm. The lion's base is square in front and rounded in back. Mane, skin folds, and ribs are well articulated; the scrotum is showing. Some chipping that must have occurred before the piece was fired has changed the color at the left ear, right cheek, at the nose, at the right front corner of the base, and on top of the back where a small break indicates the loss of a suspension ring.

PROVENANCE: Not known.

BIBLIOGRAPHY: None.

COMMENT: The world of small amulets is a field of study entirely of its own. The overwhelming majority of them were made in the last millennium B.C., and then – unlike those of earlier periods – they were crafted mainly in faience which gives them a fairly uniform appearance. Although large numbers of amulets were found over the years in controlled excavations at datable levels, the study and pictorial reproduction in scholarly publications of recent date are usually so poor that even well-dated finds (e.g. Bresciani 1977) cannot be used for comparison. Also, few reports ever indicate the disposition of such minor finds, so that further research on well documented amulets is stymied for lack of information.

These five amulets in green, mostly shiny, faience represent a cross-section of the mini-cosmos of the talisman. A man god is present (Shu), two animals (Apis and Mahes) are shown, also a woman with an animal's head (Bastet), and a monster (Thoeris). The presence of the last-named deity is a reminder that apotropaeic forces in many cultures take the form of the frightful, the superhuman creature. Thus this small collection of amulets encompasses the whole range of sentiment, faith and belief that the ancient Egyptian expressed in the making of such tiny sculptures in a material most pleasing to the eye.

38 39 40 41 42

BIBLIOGRAPHY AND ABBREVIATIONS – PART I

ÄA — *Ägyptologische Abhandlungen* (Wiesbaden)

ÄS — Ägyptische Staatssammlung

ÄF — *Ägyptologische Forschungen* (Glückstadt, Hamburg)

AiA 1978 — *Africa in Antiquity, The Arts of Ancient Nubia and the Sudan* I–II (Brooklyn, 1978)

AJA — *The American Journal of Archaeology*

Aldred 1962 — Aldred, C. Review of *ESLP*, in *AJA* 66 (1962), pp. 207–09

Aldred 1973 — Aldred, C. *Akhenaten and Nefertiti* (Brooklyn, 1973)

Aldred 1978 — Aldred, C. "Statuaire," in *Le temps des Pyramides*; ed. J. Leclant (Paris, 1978) = *Le monde égyptien; Les pharaons* I, pp. 170–225 ill.

Aldred 1980 — Aldred, C. "Statuaire," in *L'Egypte du crépuscule*; ed. J. Leclant (Paris, 1980), = *Le monde égyptien; Les pharaons* III, pp. 120–167 ill.

Allam 1963 — Allam, S. *Beiträge zum Hathorkult (bis zum Ende des Mittleren Reiches) = MÄS* IV (1963)

Allen 1950 — Allen, T.G. *Occurrences of Pyramid Texts with Cross Indexes of These and Other Egyptian Mortuary Texts* (Chicago, 1950)

AM — *Mitteilungen des Deutschen Archäologischen Instituts, Athenische Abteilung* (Berlin)

Anderson 1976 — Anderson, R.D. *Musical Instruments = Catalogue of the Egyptian Antiquities* III (London, 1976)

Anthes 1938 — Anthes, R. "Technik und Datierung einiger ägyptischer Bronzen mit farbigen Glaseinlagen," *Berliner Museen* 59 (1938), pp. 69–76 ill.

Anthes 1943 — Anthes, R. "Die deutschen Grabungen auf der Westseite von Theben in den Jahren 1911 und 1913," *MDAIK* 12 (1943), pp. 1–68 ill.

Anthes 1965 — Anthes, R. *Mit Rahineh 1956* (Philadelphia, 1965)

Apollo 1978 — "Egyptian Art from the Bastis Collection," *Apollo* (London) 108, no. 199 (September, 1978), pp. 153–155 ill.

ASAE — *Annales du Service des Antiquités de l'Egypte* (Cairo)

Archaeology — *Archaeology, An Official Publication of the Archaeological Institute of America* (New York)

Arnold 1981 — Arnold, D. *Der Tempel des Königs Mentuhotep von Deir el-Bahari III = AV* 23 (1981)

Art.Aeg. 1983 — *Artibus Aegypti, Studia in Honorem...* (Brussels, 1983)

ATP 1976 — *The Akhenaten Temple Project* I, *Initial Discoveries* (Warminster, England, 1976)

Aubert 1974 — Aubert, J.-F. and L. *Statuettes égyptiennes, chaouabtis, ouchebtis* (Paris, 1974)

AV — *Archäologische Veröffentlichungen* (Mainz am Rhein)

Ayrton 1904 — Ayrton, E. R., et al. *Abydos* III (London, 1904)

Bakry 1971 — Bakry, H. S. K. "Recent Discoveries in the Delta," *RSO* 46 (1971), pp. 1–15 ill.

Barguet 1967 — Barguet, P. *Le livre des morts des anciens égyptiens* (Paris, 1967)

BdE — *Bibliothèque d'Etude* (Cairo)

Benson and Gourlay 1899 — Benson, M., and Gourlay, J. *The Temple of Mut in Asher* (London, 1899)

Berlin 1967 — *Staatliche Museen Preussischer Kulturbesitz, Ägyptisches Museum Berlin* (Berlin/BRD, 1967)

BES — *Bulletin of the Egyptological Seminar* (New York)

Bierbrier 1982 — Bierbrier, M. *The Tomb-builders of the Pharaohs* (London, 1982)

Bietak 1982 — Bietak, M., et al. *Das Grab des ʿAnch-Hor, Obersthofmeister der Gottesgemahlin Nitokris* (Vienna, 1982)

BIFAO — *Bulletin de l'Institut Français d'Archéologie Orientale*

Blackman 1915 — *Blackman, A. M. The Rock Tombs of Meir* II (London, 1915)

BM — The British Museum

BMA — *The Brooklyn Museum Annual*

BMB — *The Brooklyn Museum Bulletin*

BMCA — *The Bulletin of the Cleveland Museum of Art*

BMFA — *Bulletin of the Museum of Fine Arts* (Boston)

BMMA — *Bulletin of the Metropolitan Museum of Art* (New York)

Bonnet 1952 — Bonnet, H. *Reallexikon der ägyptischen Religionsgeschichte* (Berlin, 1952)

Boreux 1932 a — Boreux, C. "À propos de quelques bustes égyptiens," in *Studies Presented to F. Ll. Griffith* (London, 1932), pp. 395–401 ill.

Boreux 1932 b — Boreux, C. *Département des Antiquités Égyptiennes, Guide-catalogue sommaire* II (Paris, 1932)

Boston 1982 — *Egypt's Golden Age: The Art of Living in the New Kingdom, 1558–1085 B.C.* (Boston, 1982)

Bothmer 1949 — Bothmer, B. V. "Statuettes of *Wꜣḏ.t* as Ichneumon Coffins," *JNES* 8 (1949), pp. 121–23 ill.

Bresciani 1977 — Bresciani, E., et al. *La tomba di Ciennehebu, capo della flotta del re* (Pisa, 1977)

Brooklyn 1956 — *Five Years of Collecting Egyptian Art, 1951–1956 ★ Catalog of an Exhibition Held at The Brooklyn Museum, 11 December 1956 to 17 March 1957* (Brooklyn, 1956)

Bruyère 1933 — Bruyère, B. *Rapport sur les fouilles de Deir el Médineh (1930) = FIFAO* VIII,3 (1933)

Bruyère 1934 — Bruyère, B. *Rapport sur les fouilles de Deir el Médineh (1931–1932) = FIFAO* X,1 (1934)

Bruyère 1939 — Bruyère, B. "Les bustes de laraires," in *FIFAO* XVI (1939), pp. 168–74 ill.

Bryan 1980 — Bryan, B. M. *The Reign of Tuthmosis IV* (Dissertation, Yale University, 1980)

Capart 1931 — Capart, J. *Documents pour servir à l'étude de l'art égyptien* II (Paris, 1931)

CdE — *Chronique d'Egypte* (Brussels)

CG — Catalogue Général

CGC — *Catalogue général des antiquités égyptiennes du Musée du Caire*

Chassinat and Daumas 1972 — Chassinat, É, and Daumas, F. *Le temple de Dendara* VII (Cairo, 1972)

Cooney 1953 — Cooney, J. D. "The Lions of Leontopolis," *BMB* 15,2 (1953), pp. 17–30 ill.

Cooney 1965 — Cooney, J. D. "Persian Influence in Late Egyptian Art," *JARCE* 4 (1965), pp. 39–63 ill.

Corteggiani 1986 — Corteggiani, J.-P. *L'Egypte des pharaons au Musée du Caire* (Paris, 1986)

Daressy 1905–06 — Daressy, G. *Statues de divinités (CGC)* I-II (Cairo, 1905–06)

Davies 1920 — Davies, N. de G. "An Alabaster Sistrum Dedicated by King Teta," *JEA* 6 (1920), pp. 69–72 ill.

Davies 1982 — Davies, W. V. "The Origin of the Blue Crown," *JEA* 68 (1982), pp. 69–76 ill.

De Meulenaere 1971 — De Meulenaere, H. "La statue d'un contemporain de Sébekhotep IV," *BIFAO* 69 (1971), pp. 61–64 ill.

De Meulenaere and Bothmer 1969 — De Meulenaere, H., and Bothmer, B. V. "Une tête d'Osiris au Musée du Louvre," *Kêmi* 19 (1969), pp. 9–16 ill.

Derchain 1961 — Derchain, P. *Zwei Kapellen des Ptolemäus I Soter in Hildesheim = Pelizaeus-Museum Hildesheim, Wissenschaftliche Veröffentlichung* V (Hildesheim, 1961)

Desroches-Noblecourt 1981 — Desroches-Noblecout, C. "Egypt," in *Art in the Ancient World, A Handbook of Styles and Forms*; ed. P. Amiet (London, Boston, 1981), pp. 175–317 ill.

de Wit 1957 — de Wit, C. "Les génies des quatre vents au temple d'Opet," *CdE* 63 (1957), pp. 25–39

Drenkhahn 1986 — Drenkhahn, R. *Elfenbein im Alten Ägypten, Leihgaben aus dem Petrie-Museum London* (Erbach, West Germany, 1986)

Dunham 1950 — Dunham, D. *El Kurru* = *RCK* I (1950)

Dunham 1955 — Dunham, D. *Nuri* = *RCK* II (1955)

Dunham 1970 — Dunham, D. *The Barkal Temples, Excavated by George Andrew Reisner* (Boston, 1970)

E.A.O. — Egyptian Antiquities Organization

Eaton-Krauss 1977 — Eaton-Krauss, M. "The *Khat* Headdress to the End of the Amarna Period," *SAK* 5 (1977), pp. 21–39 ill.

Edwards 1937 — [Edwards, I.E.S.] *Ancient Egyptian Sculpture Lent by C. S. Gulbenkian, Esq.* (London, 1937)

Eigner 1984 — Eigner, D. *Die monumentalen Grabbauten der Spätzeit in der thebanischen Nekropole* (Vienna, 1984)

Ergänzungen 1979 — Hildesheim, Roemer- und Pelizaeus-Museum, *Ergänzungen; Götter und Pharaonen* (Hildesheim, 1979)

ESLP 1960/73 — *Egyptian Sculpture of the Late Period – 700 B.C. to A.D. 100* (Brooklyn 1960; reprint with corrections 1973)

Essen 1978 — *Götter, Pharaonen* [exhibition catalog: Essen] (Munich, 1978)

Evers 1929 — Evers, H. G. *Staat aus dem Stein* I–II (Munich, 1929)

Faulkner 1936 — Faulkner, R. O. "The Bremner-Rhind Papyrus – I," *JEA* 22 (1936), pp. 121–140

Faulkner 1985 — Faulkner, R. O. *The Ancient Egyptian Book of the Dead* (London, 1985)

Fazzini 1972 — Fazzini, R. "Some Egyptian Reliefs in Brooklyn," *MW* 1 (1972), pp. 33–70 ill.

Feucht 1986 — Feucht, E.– *Vom Nil zum Neckar; Kunstschätze Ägyptens aus pharaonischer und koptischer Zeit an der Universität Heidelberg* (Berlin, Heidelberg, New York, 1986)

FIFAO — *Fouilles de l'Institut Français d'Archéologie Orientale* (Cairo)

Friedman 1985 — Friedman, F. "On the Meaning of Some Anthropoid Busts from Deir el-Medîna," *JEA* 71 (1985), pp. 82–97 ill.

Froehner 1909 — Froehner, W. *Collection de la Comtesse R. de Béarn, Troisième Cahier* (Paris, 1909)

Fs. Parker 1986 — *Egyptological Studies in Honor of Richard A. Parker...* (Hanover, London, 1986)

Gamer-Wallert 1970 — Gamer-Wallert, I. *Fische und Fischkulte im alten Ägypten* = *ÄA XXI* (1970)

George 1978 — George, B. "Hathor, Herrin der Sistren," *Medelhavsmuseet Bulletin* (Stockholm) 13 (1978), pp. 25–31 ill.

GM — *Göttinger Miszellen*

Habachi 1954 — Habachi, L. "Khatâ'na-Qantîr: Importance," *ASAE* 52 (1954), pp. 443–562 ill.

Habachi 1985 — Habachi, L. *Elephantine* IV, *The Sanctuary of Heqaib* (Mainz-am-Rhein, 1985) = *AV* 33

HÄB — *Hildesheimer Ägyptologische Beiträge* (Hildesheim)

Harris 1961 — Harris, J. R. *Lexicographical Studies in Ancient Egyptian Minerals* (Berlin, 1961)

Hayes 1953
Hayes 1959 — Hayes, Wm. C. *The Scepter of Egypt* I–II (Cambridge, Mass., 1953, 1959)

Hornemann 1951 — Hornemann, B. *Types of Ancient Egyptian Statuary* I (Copenhagen, 1951)

James 1979 — James, T. G. H. *An Introduction to Ancient Egypt* (London, 1979)

Jankuhn 1974 — Jankuhn, D. *Bibliographie der hieratischen und hieroglyphischen Papyri* (Wiesbaden, 1974)

Janssen 1957 — Janssen, J. M. A. *Egyptische Oudheden... W. A. van Leer* = *Mededelingen en Verhandelingen No 12 van het Vooraziatisch-Egyptisch Genootschap "Ex Oriente Lux"* (Leiden, 1957)

JARCE — *Journal of the American Research Center*

JbBerlMus — *Jahrbuch der Berliner Museen*

JE — Journal d'Entrée

JEA — *The Journal of Egyptian Archaeology*

JNES — *Journal of Near Eastern Studies* (Chicago)

Johnson 1988 — Johnson, S. B. *The Cobra Goddess of Ancient Egypt, History of the Uraeus Serpent Symbol* I; *Predynastic, Early Dynastic, and Old Kingdom Periods* (London, 1988)

Kamal 1904 — Kamal, A. Bey *Stèles ptolémaiques et romaines* II *(CGC)* (Cairo, 1904)

Keimer 1951 — Keimer, L. "Les hiboux constituant les prototypes de la lettre M de l'alphabet égyptien," *Annals of the Faculty of Arts* (Cairo) 1 (1951), pp. 73–83 ill.

Keith-Bennett 1981 — Keith-Bennet, J. L. "Anthropoid Busts II," *BES* 3 (1981), pp. 43–72 ill.

Kêmi — *Kêmi; Revue de Philologie et d'Archéologie égyptiennes et coptes* (Paris)

Klebs 1931 — Klebs, L. "Die verschiedenen Formen des Sistrums," *ZÄS* 67 (1931), pp. 60–63 ill.

Klemm and Klemm 1981 — Klemm, R. and D. *Die Steine Ägyptens* (Munich, 1981)

Kozloff 1983 — Kozloff, A. P. "Symbols of Egypt's Might," *BES* 5 (1983), pp. 61–66 ill.

Kyrieleis 1975 — Kyrieleis, H. *Bildnisse der Ptolemäer* (Berlin, 1975)

Lange and Hirmer 1961 — Lange, K., and Hirmer, M. *Egypt; Architecture, Sculpture, Painting in Three Thousand Years* (London, 1961)

LdÄ	*Lexikon der Ägyptologie* (Wiesbaden)
Leclant 1961	Leclant, J. *Montouemhat, quatrième prophète d'Amon, prince de la ville = BdE* XXXV (Cairo, 1961)
Leclant 1963	Leclant, J. "Kashta, Pharaon, en Égypte," *ZÄS* 90 (1963), pp. 74–81 ill.
Legrain 1906	Legrain, G. *Statues et statuettes de rois et de particuliers (CGC)* I (Cairo, 1906)
Lepsius 1842	Lepsius, C. R. *Das Todtenbuch der Ägypter* (Leipzig, 1842)
Liepsner 1982	Liepsner, T. F. "Modelle," in *LdÄ* IV (1982), cols. 168–180 ill.
Limme 1983	Limme, Luc "Trois 'Livres des Morts' illustrés des Musées Royaux d'Art et d'Histoire à Bruxelles," in *Art.Aeg.* (1983), pp. 81–99 ill.
Lise 1981	Lise, G. *La Civica Raccolta Egizia, Castello Sforzesco* (Milan, 1981)
Lucas 1962	Lucas, A. *Ancient Egyptian Industries and Materials,* 4th. ed. (London, 1962)
Luft 1977	Luft, U. "Das Totenbuch des Ptahmose, Papyrus Kraków MNK IX–752/1–4," *ZÄS* 104 (1977), pp. 46–75 ill.
Luxor 1979	*The Luxor Museum of Ancient Egyptian Art; Catalogue* (Cairo, 1979)
Macadam 1955	Macadam, M. F. L. *The Temples of Kawa* II (London, 1955)
MÄS	*Münchner Ägyptologische Studien* (Berlin)
Málek 1977	Málek, J. "Shabtis of Pedamenope (Theb.Tb. 33) in the Ashmolean and Fitzwilliam Museums," *JEA* 63 (1977), pp. 137–141 ill.
Manniche 1976	Manniche, L. *Musical Instruments from the Tomb of Tutʿankhamūn* (Oxford, 1976)
Manuelian 1982	Manuelian, P. D. "A Fragment of Relief from the Tomb of Mentuemhat Attributed to the Fifth Dynasty," *The Journal of the Society for the Study of Egyptian Antiquities* (Toronto) 12 (1982), pp. 185–88 ill.
Manuelian 1983	Manuelian, P. D. "An Essay in Reconstruction: Two Registers from the Tomb of Mentuemhat at Thebes (no. 34)," *MDAIK* 39 (1983), pp. 131–150 ill.
Manuelian 1985	Manuelian, P. D. "Two Fragments of Relief and a New Model for the Tomb of Montuemḥēt at Thebes," *JEA* 71 (1985), pp. 99–121 ill.
Marinatos 1968	Marinatos, S. "Die Eulengöttin von Pylos," *AM* 83 (1968), pp. 167–74 ill.
Massner 1986	Massner, A. K. "Ägyptisierende Bildnisse des Kaisers Claudius," *Antike Kunst* (Basel) 29 (1986), pp. 63–67 ill.
MDAIK	*Mitteilungen des Deutschen Archäologischen Instituts, Abteilung Kairo*
Mendes II 1976	De Meulenaere, H., and Mackay, P. *Mendes* II (Warminster, England, 1976)
Metz 1979	Musées de Metz, *Vie quotidienne chez les artisans de Pharaon* (Metz, 1979)
MFA	Museum of Fine Arts (Boston)
Michałowski 1970	Michałowski, K. *Alexandria* (Vienna, Munich, 1970)
MJb	*Münchner Jahrbuch der bildenden Kunst*
MMA	The Metropolitan Museum of Art
MMJ	*Metropolitan Museum Journal (New York)*
Mogensen 1930	Mogensen, M. *La Glyptothèque Ny Carlsberg, La collection égyptienne* I–II (Copenhagen, 1930)

Möller 1912 — Möller, G. *Hieratische Paläographie* III (Leipzig, 1912)

Mon.Piot — *Fondation Eugène Piot, Monuments et Mémoires . . .* (Paris)

Müller 1955 — Müller, H. W. "Der Torso einer Königsstatue im Museo Archeologico zu Florenz," in *Studi Rosellini* II (Pisa, 1955), pp. 181–221 ill.

Müller 1963 a — Müller, H. W. *"Isis mit dem Horuskinde," MJb* 14 (1963), pp. 7–38 ill.

Müller 1963 b — Müller, H. W. *Die stillende Gottesmutter in Ägypten = Materia Medica Nordmark* II (Hamburg, 1963)

Müller 1975 — Müller, H. W. "Der 'Stadtfürst von Theben' Montemhêt," *MJb* 26 (1975), pp. 7–36 ill.

München 1976 — *Staatliche Sammlung Ägyptischer Kunst* [2nd ed.] (Munich, 1976)

MW — *Miscellanea Wilbouriana* (Brooklyn)

Myśliwiec 1973 — Myśliwiec, K. "A Contribution to the Study of the Ptolemaic Royal Portrait," in *Études et Travaux* (Warsaw) VII (1973), pp. 41–51 ill.

Myśliwiec 1978 — Myśliwiec, K. *Studien zum Gott Atum* I, *Die heiligen Tiere des Atum = HÄB* V (1978)

Myśliwiec 1979 — Myśliwiec, K. *Studien zum Gott Atum* II, *Name – Epitheta – Ikonographie = HÄB* VIII (1979)

Needler, 1982 — Needler, W. "From a Hunt in the Desert," *Canadian Collector* 17 (1982), pp. 70–72 ill.

Newberry 1900 — [Newberry, P. E.] *Beni Hasan* IV (London, 1900)

Nibbi 1979 — Nibbi, A. "Some Remarks on Ass and Horse in Ancient Egypt and the Absence of the Mule," *ZÄS* 106 (1979), pp. 148–168 ill.

Nofret II 1985 — *Nofret – Die Schöne, Die Frau im Alten Ägypten; "Wahrheit" und Wirklichkeit* (Hildesheim, 1985)

Page 1976 — Page, A. *Egyptian Sculpture, Archaic to Saite, From the Petrie Collection* (Warminster, England, 1976)

Parker 1962 — Parker, R. A. *A Saite Oracle Papyrus from Thebes in The Brooklyn Museum* (Providence, R.I., 1962)

Parlasca 1953 — Parlasca, K. "Zwei ägyptische Bronzen aus dem Heraion von Samos," *AM* 68 (1953), pp. 127–136 ill.

Parlasca 1978 — Parlasca, K. "Probleme der späten Ptolemäerbildnisse," in *Das ptolemäische Ägypten* (Mainz, 1978), pp. 25–30 ill.

Parlasca 1979 — Parlasca, K. "Persische Elemente in der frühptolemäischen Kunst," in *Archäologische Mitteilungen aus Iran, Ergänzungsband* IV (1979), pp. 317–323 ill.

Pasquier 1977 — Pasquier, R. F. *Watching Birds; An Introduction to Ornithology* (Boston, 1977)

Pernigotti 1985 — Pernigotti, S. *Saqqara II, – Tomba di Bocchori, il Libro dei Morti su benda di mummia* (Pisa, 1985)

Piankoff 1947 — Piankoff, A. "Les grandes compositions religieuses dans la tombe de Pédéménope," *BIFAO* 46 (1947), pp. 73–92 ill.

Petrie 1924 — Petrie, W.M.F. *A History of Egypt* II (London, 1924)

Pierret 1889 — Pierret, P. *Musée du Louvre; Catalogue de la Salle Historique de la Galérie Égyptienne suivi d'un glossaire* (Paris, 1889)

PKG — *Propyläen Kunstgeschichte* (Berlin)

PM — Porter, B. and Moss, R. *Topographical Bibliography* I,1 (1960); I,2 (1964); II (1972); III,1 (1974); III,2 (1981); IV (1934); V (1937); VI (1939); VII (1951) (Oxford)

Rammant-Peeters 1985 — Rammant-Peeters, A. "Les couronnes de Nefertiti à El-Amarna," *Orientalia Lovaniensia Periodica* (Louvain) 16 (1985), pp. 21–48 ill.

RCK — *The Royal Cemeteries of Kush* (Cambridge, Mass.)

RdE — *Revue d'Égyptologie* (Paris)

Redford 1983 — Redford, D. B. "Notes on the History of Ancient Buto," *BES* 5 (1983), pp. 67–101 ill.

Reinsberg 1980 — Reinsberg, C. *Studien zur hellenistischen Toreutik, Die antiken Gipsabgüsse aus Memphis = HÄB* IX (1980)

Reisner 1931 — Reisner, G. A. *Mycerinus; The Temples of the Third Pyramid at Giza* (Cambridge, Mass., 1931)

Riefstahl 1952 — Riefstahl, E. "A Sacred Cat," *BMB* II,1 (1952), pp. 1–15 ill.

Riefstahl 1968 — Riefstahl, E. *Ancient Egyptian Glass and Glazes in The Brooklyn Museum = WM* I, (Brooklyn, 1968)

Roeder 1914 — Roeder, G. *Naos (CGC)* (Leipzig, 1914)

Roeder 1937 — Roeder, G. *Ägyptische Bronzewerke* (Glückstadt, Hamburg, New York, 1937)

Roeder 1956 — Roeder, G. *Ägyptische Bronzefiguren* (Berlin, 1956)

Romano 1976 — Romano, J. F. "Observations on Early Eighteenth Dynasty Royal Sculpture," *JARCE* 13 (1976), pp. 97–111 ill.

Romano 1983 — Romano, J. F. "A Relief of King Ahmose and Early Eighteenth Dynasty Archaism," *BES* 5 (1983), pp. 103–115 ill.

RSO — *Rivista degli Studi Orientali* (Rome)

Russmann 1973 — Russmann, E. R. "The Statue of Amenemope-em-hat," *MMJ* 8 (1973), pp. 33–46 ill.

Russmann 1974 — Russmann, E. R. *The Representation of the King in the XXVth Dynasty = Monographies Reine Elisabeth* III (Brussels, Brooklyn, 1974)

Russmann 1979 — Russmann, E. R. "Some Reflections on the Regalia of the Kushite Kings of Egpyt," in *Meroitica* (Berlin) 5 (1979), pp. 49–53 ill.

Russmann 1981 — Russmann, E. R. "An Egyptian Royal Statuette of the Eighth Century B.C.," in *Studies in Ancient Egypt ... in Honor of Dows Dunham ...* (Boston, 1981), pp. 149–55 ill.

Sachs 1921 — Sachs, C. *Die Musikinstrumente des alten Ägypten* (Berlin, 1921)

SAK — *Studien zur Altägyptischen Kultur* (Hamburg)

Sauneron 1957 — Sauneron, S. *Les prêtres de l'ancienne Égypte* (Paris, 1957)

Sboronos 1904 — Sboronos, I. N. *Ta nomismata ton Ptolemaion* III (Athens, 1904)

Scharff 1939 — Scharff, A. "Ein Porträtkopf der Münchener Sammlung," *ZÄS* 75 (1939), pp. 93–100 ill.

Scharff 1941 — Scharff, A. "Bemerkungen zur Kunst der 30. Dynastie," in *Miscellanea Gregoriana* (Vatican City, 1941), pp. 195–203 ill.

Schoske, Wildung 1985 — Schoske, S., and Wildung, D. *Ägyptische Kunst München* (Munich, 1985)

Schulman 1981 — Schulman, A. R. "Reshep Times Two," *Studies in Ancient Egypt ... in Honor of Dows Dunham ...* (Boston, 1981), pp. 157–166 ill.

Schweitzer 1948 — Schweitzer, U. *Löwe und Sphinx im alten Ägypten = ÄF* XV (1948)

Scott 1951 — Scott, N. "The Metternich Stela," *BMMA* 9 (1951), pp. 201–217 ill.

Seipel 1983 — Seipel, W. *Bilder für die Ewigkeit; 3000 Jahre ägyptische Kunst* (Konstanz, 1983)

Sethe 1933 — Sethe, K. "Die Bau- und Denkmalsteine der alten Ägypter und ihre Namen," *Preuss. Akad. d. Wiss., Philos.-hist. Klasse, Sitzungsberichte* (Berlin, 1933), pp. 864–912

Shorter 1938 — Shorter, A. W. *Catalogue of Egyptian Religious Papyri in the British Museum* I (London, 1938)

Siècle 1981 — *Un siècle de fouilles françaises en Égypte, 1880–1980* (Paris, 1981)

Simpson 1972 — Simpson, Wm. K. "Ahmose, called Patjenna," *BMFA* 70 (1972), nos. 361–362, pp. 116–117 ill.

Smith 1946 — Smith, W. S. *A History of Egyptian Sculpture and Painting in the Old Kingdom* (London, 1946)

Sourdive 1984 — Sourdive, C. *La main dans l'Égypte pharaonique* (Berne, New York, 1984)

Spiegelberg 1909 — Spiegelberg, W. *Ausgewählte Kunst-Denkmäler der Aegyptischen Sammlung der Kaiser-Wilhelms-Universität Strassburg* (Strasbourg, 1909)

Staehelin 1966 — Staehelin, E. *Untersuchungen zur ägyptischen Tracht im Alten Reich = MÄS* VIII (1966)

Steindorff 1946 — Steindorff, G. *Catalogue of the Egyptian Sculpture in the Walters Art Gallery* (Baltimore, 1946)

Szafránski 1985 — Szafránski, Z. E. "Buried Statues of Mentuhotep II and Amenophis I at Deir el-Bahari," *MDAIK* 41 (1985), pp. 257–63, pls. 38–39

Thurgau 1985 — *Vom Euphrat zum Nil; Kunst aus dem alten Ägypten und Vorderasien* [exhibition catalog: Thurgau, Switzerland] (Zurich, Berne, 1985)

TR — Temporary Register

TT — Theban Tomb

UCL — University College London

Valbelle 1985 — Valbelle, D. *"Les ouvriers de la tombe," Deir el-Médineh à la période ramesside = BdE* XCVI (1985)

Vandersleyen 1975 — Vandersleyen, C. "Rundplastik der Spätzeit," in *PKG* XV (1975), pp. 255–73 ill.

van de Walle 1967 — van de Walle, B. "L'ostracon E 3209 des Musées Royaux d'Art et d'Histoire mentionnant la déesse scorpion Ta-Bithet," *CdE* 42 (1967), pp. 13–29 ill.

Vandier 1958 — Vandier, J. *Manuel d'archéologie égyptienne* III; *La statuaire* (Paris, 1958)

Vandier 1967 — Vandier, J. "Ouadjet et l'Horus léontocéphale de Bouto; à propos d'un bronze du Musée de Chaalis," *Mon.Piot* 55 (1967), pp. 7–75 ill.

Vandier 1971 — Vandier, J. "Un bronze de la déesse Ouadjet à Bologne," *ZÄS* 97 (1971), pp. 126–29 ill.

Vandier d'Abbadie 1946 — Vandier d'Abbadie, J. "À propos des bustes de laraires," *RdE* 5 (1946), pp. 133–35 ill.

Vandier d'Abbadie 1972 — Vandier d'Abbadie, J. *Catalogue des objets de toilette égyptien* (Paris, 1972)

von Bothmer 1961 — von Bothmer, D. *Ancient Art from New York Private Collections* (New York, 1961)

Wainwright 1925 — Wainwright, G. A. "Antiquities from Middle Egypt and the Fayûm," *ASAE* 25 (1925), pp. 144–48 ill.

Wallert 1967 — Wallert, I. *Der verzierte Löffel = ÄA* XVI (1967)

Wegner 1933 — Wegner, M. "Stilentwicklung der thebanischen Beamtengräber," *MDAIK* 4 (1933), pp. 38–164 ill.

Werner 1979 — Werner, E. K. "Identification of Nefertiti in 'Talatat' Reliefs Previously Published as Akhenaten," *Orientalia* 48 (1979), pp. 324–31 ill.

Wiedemann 1884 — Wiedemann, K. A. *Ägyptische Geschichte* (Gotha, 1884)

Wild 1960 — Wild, H. "Statue d'un noble mendésien du règne de Psamétik Ier au musées de Palerme et du Caire," *BIFAO* 60 (1960), pp. 43–67 ill.

Wildung 1969 — Wildung, D. *Die Rolle ägyptischer Könige im Bewusstsein ihrer Nachwelt* I = *MÄS* XVII (1969)

Wildung 1977a — Wildung, D. *Imhotep und Amenhotep, Gottwerdung im alten Ägypten* = *MÄS* XXXVI (1977)

Wildung 1977b — Wildung, D. *Egyptian Saints; Deification in Pharaonic Egypt* (New York, 1977)

Wildung 1984 — Wildung, D. *Sesostris und Amenemhat* (Fribourg/Switzerland, 1984)

WM — *Wilbour Monographs* (Brooklyn)

Young 1964 — Young, E. "Sculptors Models or Votives? In Defense of a Scholarly Tradition," *BMMA* 22 (1964), pp. 246–56 ill.

Yoyotte 1968 — Yoyotte, J. *Les trésors des Pharaons* (Geneva, 1968)

ZÄS — *Zeitschrift für Ägyptische Sprache und Altertumskunde* (Leipzig)

Ziegler 1987 — Ziegler, C. "Les arts du métal à la Troisième Période Intermédiaire," in *Tanis; l'or des pharaons* (Paris, 1987), pp. 85–101 ill.

PART II

Cycladic Antiquities

by
Pat Getz-Preziosi

ACKNOWLEDGEMENTS

I wish to thank Christos G. Bastis for entrusting me with the entries for the Cycladic objects in his collection and Alexandra Antoniou for her help and patience throughout the project.

43

STANDING FEMALE FIGURE

Neolithic Period, Fourth millennium B.C. or earlier, Aegean area

Shell (Spondylus gaederopus Linne)

The work is made of soft shell, whose layers have been exposed through weathering. In the Cyclades the same or similar material was sometimes used for the carving of figurines in the Early Bronze Age.

Considering the small size of the piece, its forms and details are remarkably well defined. It is in every respect, except perhaps size, a typical example of the standing Neolithic type produced in small numbers over much of Greece.

Characteristic features seen on the work include a marked steatopygy — extreme obesity of the lower torso and legs — contrasting sharply with a narrow waist and a broad-shouldered but essentially thin flat upper body, which is surmounted by a thick neck and a roughly conical head with beaklike nose. The narrow arms are held against the body in symmetrical fashion, an arrangement which, along with the standing posture, persisted among the earliest anthropomorphic Bronze Age Cycladic figures (No. 46). The diminutive figure is intact except for minor abrasions.

MEASUREMENT: Height 5.7 cm.

PROVENANCE: Unknown.

BIBLIOGRAPHY: Thimme 1977, no. 9, ill.

COMMENT: For the basic type in its most fully articulated form, see Thimme 1977, no. 3. Close parallels for the figure are two small works said to be from Aegina: Munich, Antikensammlung 10.060, said to be carved in aragonite but perhaps also of *spondylus gaederopus* shell (Thimme 1977, no. 10), and Aegina, Archaeological Museum (Buchholz and Karageorghis 1973, no. 1181). For further discussion of Neolithic figures, see No. 44. The material has been identified by J. Shackleton.

43 a

43 b

43 c

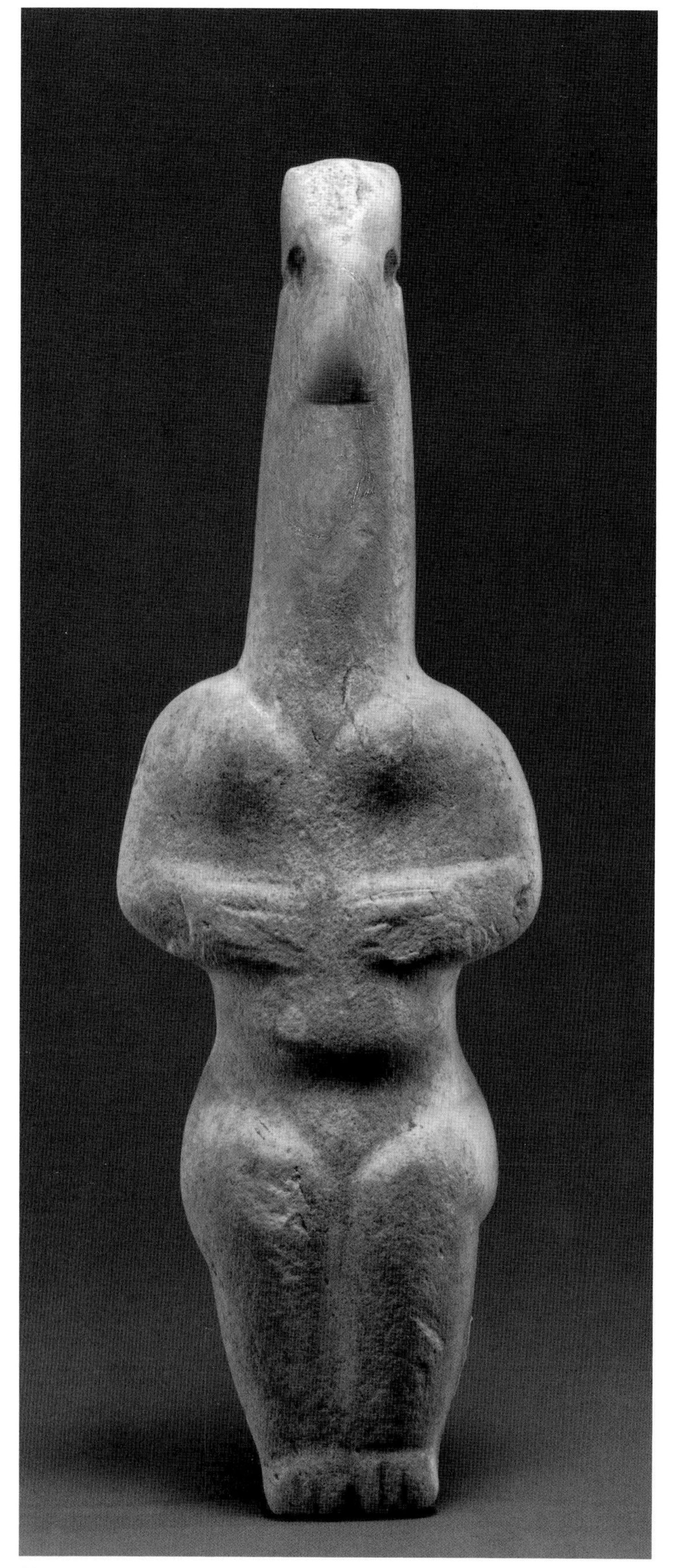
44 a

44 b

44 STANDING FEMALE FIGURE

Neolithic Period, fourth millennium B.C. or earlier, perhaps from the Cyclades

White Marble

The figure is carved in the characteristic standing pose, the legs closely joined, the buttocks accentuated, and the arms placed symmetrically across the body, fingertips nearly touching. Toes and fingers, incorrect in number, are superficially incised, as are other details. There is a distinct contrast between the somewhat amorphous, asymmetrical forms of the body and the severe, precise geometry of the head and neck, which are carved as a single unit, occupying more than a third of the figure's total height, and cut off straight at the top. Moreover, in contrast to the summary incision work on the body, the deeply bored eyes, which may have once received pebble inlays, and which have short incisions at the outside corners, are executed with considerable care.

The relatively slender build, elongated head/neck, bored eye sockets, and small round breasts cause the figure to resemble the Plastiras-type images of the Early Cycladic I Period (Thimme 1977, nos. 65–69) more closely than other, more corpulent Neolithic works. This could be an indication that it was made late in the sequence of Neolithic images. Equally possible however, in the absence of systematically excavated Neolithic examples, the figure may actually be much earlier than the standard standing type (No. 43), from which it differs in head form, lack of separated feet, small raised as opposed to pendent pellet breasts, and lesser steatopygy.

Except for minor surface damage and restoration, in marble, of the nose and a section below the nose, the figure is in fine condition, with much of the original surface polish still visible in places on the back. The front is somewhat worn.

MEASUREMENT: Height 20.9 cm.

PROVENANCE: Unknown.

BIBLIOGRAPHY: Thimme 1977, no. 13, ill.

COMMENT: A similar piece in the Eleusis Archaeological Museum (no. 5161; Zervos 1962, figs. 203–204; Thimme 1977, fig. 31; Kanta 1979, p. 108, fig. 52:1) was in all likelihood carved by the same sculptor. It was apparently found on Amorgos where it was obtained by Christos Tsountas, who gave it to the Museum. A Cycladic origin for the Bastis piece is thus strongly suggested.

To date, standing Neolithic figures have been reported from Naxos (Zervos 1957, fig. 36) and Schinousa (Thimme 1977, no. 19), in addition to Amorgos, but none have been found under controlled conditions (Weinberg 1977, pp. 52–58, especially p. 55). For an early dating of the Eleusis figure, see Gimbutas 1974, p. 133, fig. 112.

45

BEAKER

Early Cycladic I Period
About 3000–2800 B.C.

White marble with some gray inclusions

The vessel is a lovely example of its type and of about average size. The workmanship is very fine, with the translucent walls only .35-.4 cm. thick at the top and the interior hollowed to within .8cm. of the bottom. The exterior was carefully smoothed, while on the inside encircling ridges made by the lathe used in the hollowing process can still be seen.

The beaker, characteristically, has a conical shape and lacks stability when placed on a flat surface. Its rim is very subtly everted where it is still fully preserved, and the short suspension lugs are slender and carefully perforated.

The vase is very well preserved and intact except for slight wear and chipping, chiefly of the rim and one lug. The original epidermis of the marble is still in place over most of the exterior, with smoothing marks clearly visible.

MEASUREMENTS: Height 14.1 cm. Diameter of mouth 9.8 cm., of base 7 cm.

PROVENANCE: Unknown.

BIBLIOGRAPHY: Not previously published.

COMMENT: The beaker is one of very few often repeated vase shapes produced in marble during the Early Cycladic I Period. Some forty-five examples of the type are known at present. Probably a container for liquids, the beaker ranges in size from 8 cm. to 27 cm. or more. Most examples are between 11 and 19 cm. tall. All of them are true to type, and yet each one is quite different from every other. For some of the variation observable within the type, see Thimme 1977, nos. 277–282. The closest published parallel to the Bastis beaker is perhaps an example from Amorgos in Athens (National Archaeological Museum no. 3963; height 15.7 cm. Zervos, fig. 2; *n. b.,* the dimension given in Zervos is apparently the diameter of the mouth, not the height).

46

STANDING FEMALE FIGURE WITH PILOS

Early Cycladic I Period
About 2800 B.C.

White Marble

The figure belongs essentially to the rather rare Plastiras type, the earliest Bronze Age anthropomorphic figure form whose standing posture and arm arrangement were inherited from Neolithic antecedents (Nos. 43 and 44), but whose straight profile no longer shows any inclination toward steatopygy and whose legs are carved separately from the crotch.

Normally the full-blown Plastiras images show, despite rather exaggerated proportions — here, the cap, head and neck comprise close to one-half of the height — a keen interest in anatomy, including well-defined, often bored details, distinctly defined arms with incised fingers, good modeling, and carefully formed feet with arched soles. The figure lacks these features and seems to represent a transition to the simpler Louros-type figurines produced slightly later. These figures may show well-modeled legs, but the faces are normally featureless, and the arms are simple projections at the shoulders.

A small number of the more simplified Plastiras figurines also wear the conical ribbed cap, or *pilos*, which is found as well on one of the seven figurines from the name-grave of the Louros type. The Bastis statuette, which is clearly a female representation, provides evidence that the *pilos* in Early Cycladic art was not a sex-related attribute,

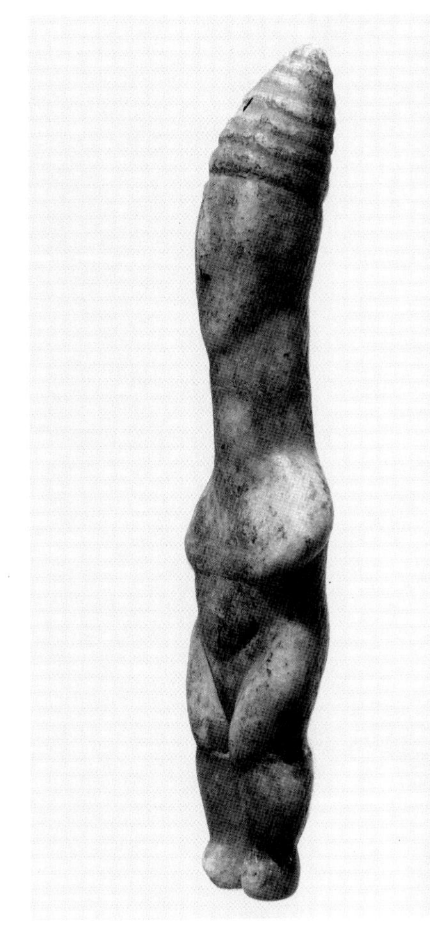

46 a

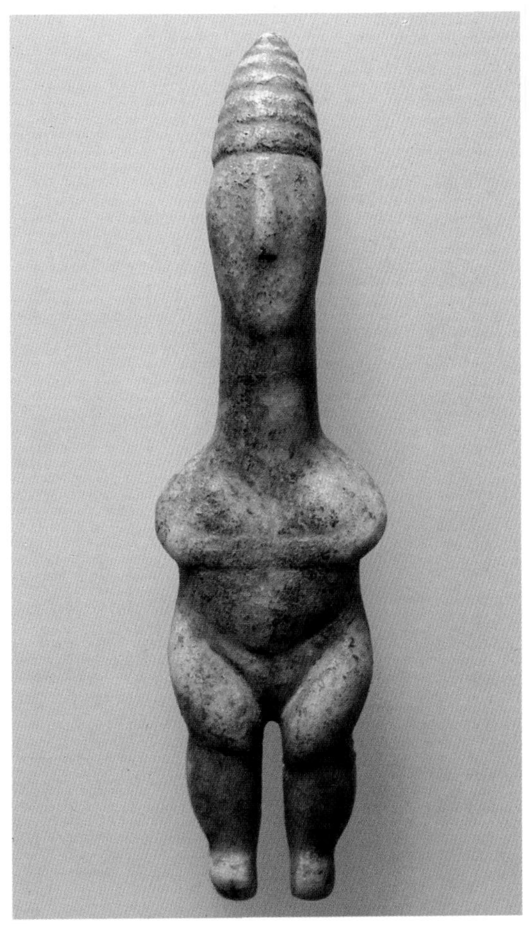

46 b

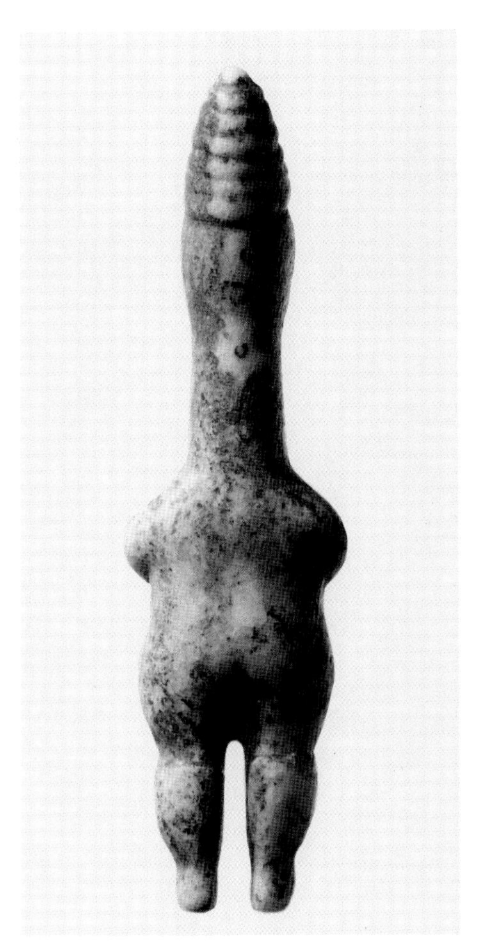

46 c

although it seems to occur more frequently among figures that definitely represent males.

The figure is complete and well preserved. Under previous ownership it was injudiciously cleaned with acid, which has left the surface smooth and mottled with brownish discoloration, although not significantly eroded.

MEASUREMENT: Height 10.2 cm.

PROVENANCE: Unknown.

BIBLIOGRAPHY: A rough sketch is published in Getz-Preziosi 1980, p. 10, fig. 10 c.

COMMENT: The conical ribbed cap is a form of headgear that occurs at various times and in different places, from Neolithic Haçilar (where it appears on female figures) to Geometric Greece (where it appears as a male attribute). It seems unnecessary to look outside the Cyclades for prototypes for the use of the *pilos* on the Bronze Age figures made there. For the basic Plastiras and Louros types, see Thimme 1977, nos. 65–77 (Plastiras), 82–94 (Louros). For other figures combining elements of the two types and/or wearing a *pilos*, see Getz-Preziosi 1980, p. 9, figs. 6–8, p. 10, fig. 10 d.

47

COLLARED/FOOTED JAR (*KANDILA*)

Early Cycladic I/II Period (or end EC I)
About 2800–2700 B.C.

White Marble

This handsome vessel is an atypical and important piece. Basically it belongs to a type known from 200 or more examples. Indeed, the collared/footed jar, or *kandila*, so named for its fortuitous resemblance to a Greek church lamp, was the single marble form, figurative or receptive, most often produced in the Early Cycladic I Period. Carved in a wide range of sizes, from 7 to 37 cm. or more, the standard elements of the form are a roughly hemispherical body, carrying at its widest point four horizontally perforated vertical suspension lugs, a high conical or, less often, a cylindrical collar, and a tall conical or cylindrical foot.

While the beautifully preserved vase exhibits all the basic elements — body, lugs, collar, and foot — and no others, their forms are unusual. In contrast to the hemispherical or ellipsoidal (echinus-shaped) contour, the body has a rounded, globular profile which, with the low collar, is reminiscent of a pomegranate. The lugs are atypically small — two are especially narrow — and project only slightly, their perforations bored more deeply than usual into the body. The cylindrical neck or collar is uncharacteristically low and, finally, the foot, which is also relatively low, instead of having the normal conical profile, flares out towards the base, and there is a curious encircling raised ridge or molding just above the beginning of the flare.

Normally the foot is partly hollowed, as is true here: the underside consists of a rim about 1 cm. wide, within which the base is hollowed to a depth of 1.5 cm. The depth to which the body was carved out and the configuration of the interior of such vessels often bear little relation to their exterior form or potential capacity as containers. In this example, however, the interior has been painstakingly hollowed out, following the exterior contour to a depth of 10 cm. The workmanship is especially fine. Not only was the vase carefully smoothed inside and out — the exterior retains traces of the original polishing — but the marble was reduced to a thickness of only 4 mm. at the mouth, which imbues it with translucency.

Except for a section of the collar that has been imperceptibly restored, the jar is intact.

MEASUREMENTS: Height 13.5 cm., of collar 2 cm., of foot 2.5 cm. Diameter of mouth 7.1 cm., of body (without lugs) 13.1 cm., of base 5.5 cm.

PROVENANCE: Unknown.

BIBLIOGRAPHY: Not previously published.

COMMENT: The unusual features suggest that the vase, rather than being simply the creation of a somewhat idiosyncratic sculptor, was fashioned at the end of the long series of collared jars and that, morphologically at least, it belongs in the transition from Early Cycladic I to II. Whether or not this is correct cannot be determined at present. The shortness of the collar, the small, almost vestigal appearance of the lugs, and the bell shape of the pedestal (see No. 53) all point to a loosening of the old traditional *kandila* form and the emerging of something quite different and simpler, ultimately the spherical pyxis (see No. 51), which typically has a very low collar, two tubular or ledgelike lugs, and is occasionally mounted on bell-shaped foot (Thimme 1977, no. 352).
For the basic form in a variety of manifestations, see *ibid.* nos. 263–276, and p. 95 for a brief discussion of the type. There are, to my knowledge, no published examples that closely parallel this vase with all its unusual aspects, though a number show one or two similarly treated elements (André Emmerich Gallery 1965, no. 40).

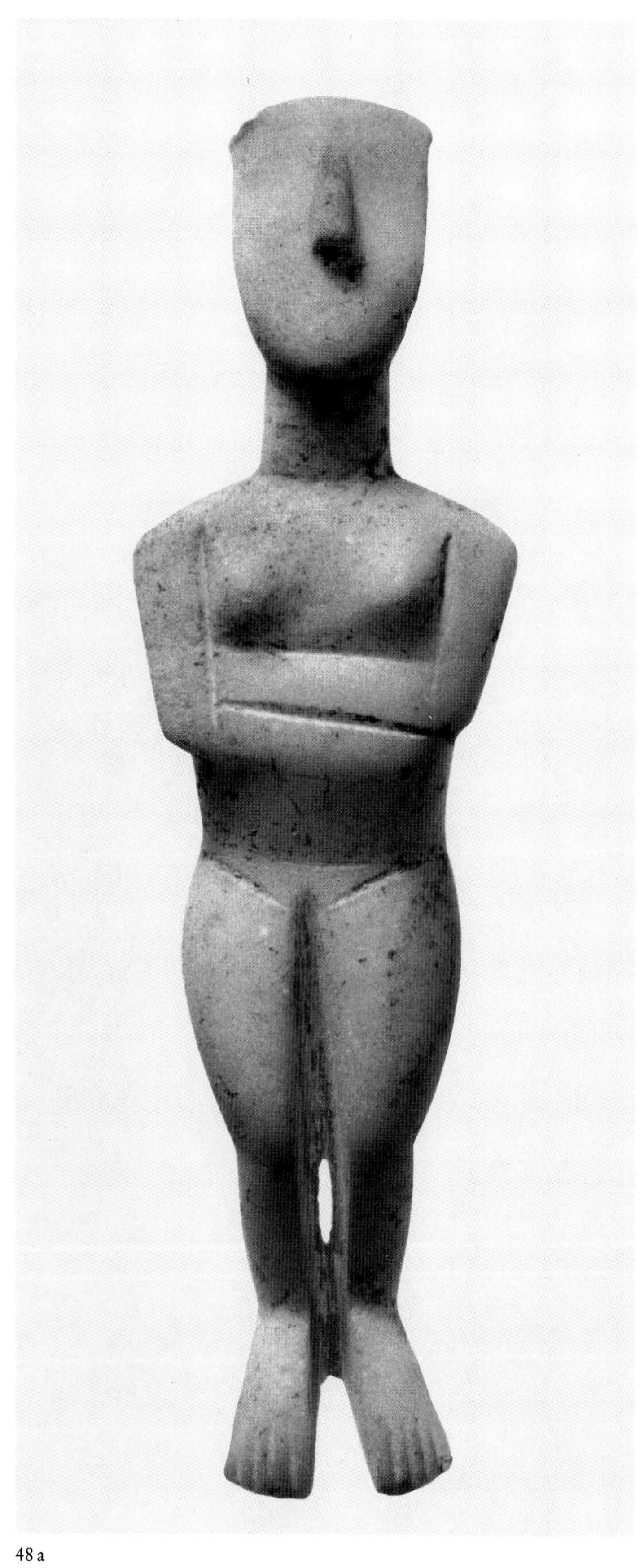

48 a

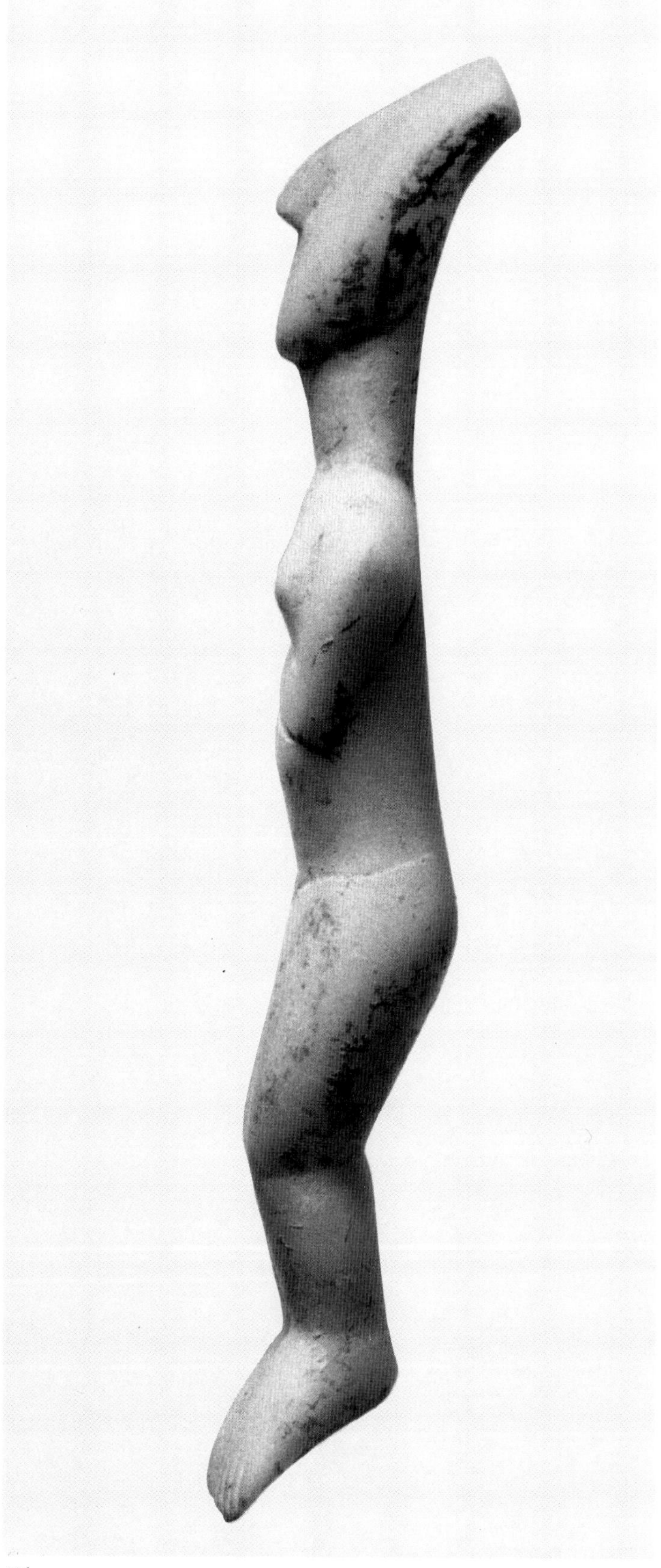

48 b

48

RECLINING FEMALE FIGURE

Early Cycladic II Period
About 2600–2500 B.C.

White Marble

This is a classic example of the Early Spedos variety of the reclining folded-arm figure, made in considerable quantity during the Early Cycladic II Period. The work is of about average size and, characteristically, exhibits a large lyre-shaped head, boldly curving contours, a broken profile, and legs separated for a short distance between the calves. In general, the details are rendered more by incision than by modeling.

The work is attributable to the Fitzwilliam Master, a sculptor from whose hand at least three other figures of similar size can now be identified, including one found in early excavations on Crete. The name-piece, in Cambridge, is said to have been found on Amorgos.

Somewhat unusual characteristics of this sculptor's style, seen on the piece under discussion, are the short calves and correspondingly elongated feet with long finely incised toes. Like many other sculptors of the time, the Fitzwilliam Master tended occasionally to be careless in the engraving of certain details, especially on the arms, allowing the lines to run beyond their proper bounds. On this figure, too, the sculptor failed to align the leg-cleft precisely, with the result that the left thigh in front is wider than the right one, while in back the right thigh is wider than the left. Although probably not deliberate, such minor departures from the overall symmetry of the design add to the interest and animation of the work.

The figure is intact and very well preserved, except for a small piece missing from the top of the head on the right.

Red paint is preserved in the neck grooves as well as on the neck itself, though not in any discernible pattern, and a red line, perhaps composed of dots, marks the hairline on the forehead, extending downward at the temples. Some faint traces are visible on the lower part of the face, too, and a curious small circle is outlined on the back of the head.

MEASUREMENT: Length 20.6 cm.

PROVENANCE: Unknown.

BIBLIOGRAPHY: Getz-Preziosi 1987, Fitzwilliam Master, no. 2.

COMMENT: Unlike the Neolithic sitting and standing types (Nos. 43, 44) and the Early Cycladic I standing type (No. 46), folded-arm figures are, with a few early exceptions, represented in a relaxed reclining position. It is the position in which they were normally placed at the time of burial. The figures show the backward tilt of the head, the slightly bent knees, and the feet held out and down appropriate to a person lying down. Exhibited vertically, as they almost always are, they appear to be standing on their toes (Getz-Preziosi 1981, pp. 25–26).

Besides the name-piece in Cambridge, Fitzwilliam Museum (no. GR. 33.1901), other works attributable to the Fitzwilliam Master are in Stockholm, Medelhavsmuseet (no. 62.10) and in Herakleion, Archaeological Museum (no. 122).

49

UPPER PART OF A RECLINING FEMALE FIGURE

Early Cycladic II Period
About 2600–2500 B.C.

White Marble

Despite its small size, the figure shows careful workmanship, especially in the shaping of the head with a pronounced backward arch, the arms rendered in relief, and the fine incision work. The breasts and pubis are not sculpturally defined, although a pubic triangle may once have been painted. The sex represented in such figures is usually assumed to be female.

The work is unusual for its size, folded-arm figures measuring less than 12 cm. being quite rare. Moreover, on figures that were made quite early in the folded-arm series, it is highly unusual to find the arms folded in the right-above-left position – that is, the opposite of the canonical arrangement adhered to almost without fail for several centuries of intense figure production (see Nos. 48 and 50).

49 a

49 b

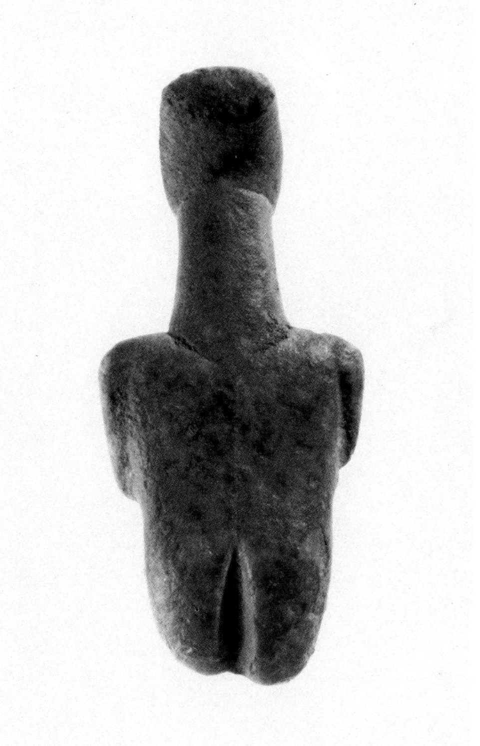

49 c

The diminutive figure, which originally measured no more than about 8.5 cm., is preserved to just above the knees. The break is old, presumably ancient. An abrasion above the chin fortuitously resembles a mouth. Somewhat overcleaned under previous ownership, the surface shows brownish discoloration. Otherwise the work, which belongs to the Early Spedos variety, is well preserved.

MEASUREMENT: Length now 6.6 cm.

PROVENANCE: Unknown.

BIBLIOGRAPHY: Getz-Preziosi 1978, pp. 1–3 (a), fig. 4.

COMMENT: See *ibid.* for other examples of diminutive size and arm reversal. For other Early Spedos examples with unclearly defined sexual characteristics, see Thimme 1977, nos. 130–148.

50

RECLINING FEMALE FIGURE

Early Cycladic II Period
About 2500–2400 B.C.

White Marble

The unusually large figure is a masterful example of the Late Spedos variety of the classical folded-arm type, and one of twelve complete or very nearly complete works attributable to the Goulandris Master, named after the collection that contains two of them. The Goulandris Master was the most prolific and one of the best Cycladic sculptors; his finest work is distinguished by a quiet power and restraint.

Some characteristic features of the master's style as seen in the Bastis figure include the lyre-shaped head, here somewhat larger and broader than usual; noticeably sloping shoulders here are unusually asymmetrical; small,

50 a

50 b

50 d

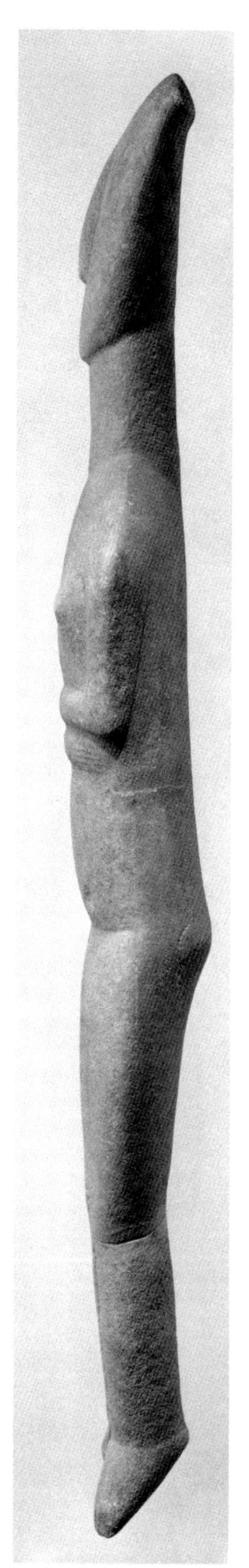

50 c

wide-spaced breasts and narrow arms; a lightly rounded abdomen and gently curved thighs and calves; a pubic triangle marked by a V-shaped incision placed directly beneath a horizontal abdominal groove; and legs divided by deep grooves in front and in back.

Special refinements, found on the Bastis figure and only a few other works of the Goulandris Master, all of them large, are forearms rendered in relief and separated by a space, and long thin fingers marked by incision. The figure in the Bastis Collection is unusual, too, in having a carefully grooved spine, a detail the sculptor indicated on only a small number of works. (Other Late Spedos sculptors indicated the spine on all their figures as a rule.)

The sculpture is of great interest also for its once-painted detail. While no actual pigment remains, some of the parts originally covered by paint are now smoother and slightly raised above the surrounding surface. Almond-shaped eyes with dotted pupils and a solid band across the forehead are still visible. The band continues down the sides of the head to indicate curls and joins a solid area in the shape of a trapezoid at the back of the head. It is likely that all folded-arm figures were painted, but the patterns on them varied, even in the work of one sculptor.

The figure is complete except for superficial chipping and some damage to the end of the nose, to the right upper arm and elbow, and to the feet, particularly the right foot. Breaks at the neck and knees have been mended. Restoration at the joins has necessitated a redrawing of some of the engraved lines. The surface of the figure is worn, especially in front, and the original epidermis is visible only in places, such as at the back of the head, once protected by paint. Because of weathering the incisions are no longer as sharp as they once were. The surface is almost uniformly a rusty beige, indicating long burial in iron-rich soil, and dark oxidation spots are visible, mostly on the back.

MEASUREMENT: Length now 62.15 cm.

PROVENANCE: Said to be from Paros, but more likely from Naxos.

BIBLIOGRAPHY: Getz-Preziosi 1987, Goulandris Master, no. 26 (detail only).

COMMENT: For further literature on the Goulandris Master, see Thimme 1977, pp. 71, 84–88, 269–272, nos. 167–180; Getz-Preziosi 1984, pp. 51–52, figs. 3, 14–16. For the use of paint, see Getz-Preziosi and Weinberg 1970.

51

SPHERICAL PYXIS

Early Cycladic II Period
About 2600–2200 B.C.

White Marble

An unusually lovely example of one of the more common Early Cycladic II marble vase forms, this pyxis is unusual in that it has a rounded shoulder and, instead of the customary low collar or everted rim, it has a simple thickened rim (now partly worn away) created by a depression encircling the top of the vase. The lid fits just inside this rim rather than resting upon it as in most examples.

Whereas most spherical pyxides carry at the widest point on the body a pair of double tubular or semicircular pierced lugs, the Bastis vase is one of the very few that have slender rectangular ledgelike lugs, each with a pair of perforations. It is likely that the lid would have been held in place by thongs or cords threaded through the lugs and crisscrossed over the top.

The vessel is intact except for minor damage.

MEASUREMENTS: Height 8 cm. Diameter of mouth 5.8 cm., of body 12.2 cm.

PROVENANCE: Unknown.

BIBLIOGRAPHY: Not previously published.

COMMENT: For the basic type, see Thimme 1977, nos. 345–349. Other examples with rectangular lugs, each with a pair of perforations, are in Athens, National Museum (no. 6133.5), from Grave 3 at Karvounolakoi, Naxos (Papathanasopoulos 1961/62, pl. 42 b), and a footed example in Karlsruhe, Badisches Landesmuseum (no. 63/50; *ibid.* 1977, no. 352). An unpublished example, similar to the piece in Athens, with a perforated lid projecting well beyond the mouth of the vessel, is in a New York private collection, while another unpublished example in Zürich, Archäologische Sammlung der Universität (no. 2112), like the Bastis vase, has a plain unperforated lid without overhang.

51 a

51 b

52

SPOUTED BOWL WITH LUG

Early Cycladic II Period
About 2600–2200 B.C.

White Marble

The vase is an unusually large and carefully worked example of a common Early Cycladic II form. The type is characterized by a rounded bowl with flared spout on one end and an unperforated ledge lug on the opposite wall slightly below the rim for use as a thumb or finger rest. The Bastis bowl is deeper, its spout more delicate than usual.

It has been suggested that one of the possible symbolic functions of such vases may have been that of a lamp, in which case the spout would have served as a wick support (nozzle).

A large piece as well as smaller pieces are missing from the rim as the result of a recent mishap, and another area with several fractures has been repaired.

MEASUREMENTS: Height 9.15 cm. Diameter 17.24 cm. Length 22.2 cm.

PROVENANCE: Unknown.

BIBLIOGRAPHY: Thimme 1977, no. 324.
For other examples of this basic type, *op. cit.*, 1977, nos. 317–322. For a brief discussion of the type, *ibid.*, pp. 98–99.

53

FOOTED CUP

Early Cycladic II Period
About 2600–2200 B.C.

White Marble

The vessel is a typical example of a type produced in considerable quantity during the Early Cycladic II Period, both in this and on a smaller scale. These vases are virtually all true to type, consisting of a flat-based cup with almost conical or subtly flared sides that become thinner towards the mouth. Most of them, as with this example, have a rounded bowl-like interior and a flaring, bell-shaped pedestal with a slight indentation on the bottom. In this case at least, the depression is bounded by a beveled edge, so that when the vase is placed on a flat surface the outer rim of the base does not touch it.

Except for minor damage to the rim, the cup is intact.

MEASUREMENTS: Height ca. 7.3 cm. (the dimension varies slightly, partly perhaps because of the state of preservation); of foot 3.2 cm. Diameter of mouth 12.6 cm., of base 4.5 cm.

PROVENANCE: Unknown.

BIBLIOGRAPHY: Not previously published.

COMMENT: The conical cup, which occurs also but less frequently without a foot (Zervos 1957, fig. 12), was one of the most common marble forms found in the excavations at Chalandriani on Syros, where it was sometimes carved in dark or banded marble (Zervos 1957, fig. 23). See Tsountas 1899, col. 99. For other examples of the type, see Thimme 1977, nos. 315, 316; Renfrew 1972, pl. 6:1. For a brief discussion of the type, see Thimme 1977, pp. 98–99.

PART III

Stone Sculpture

by
Diana Buitron-Oliver

ACKNOWLEDGEMENTS

We gratefully acknowledge the help of friends and colleagues who kindly offered comments on selected objects in the Bastis Collection: the late Dorothy Kent Hill, David Gordon Mitten and Beryl Barr-Sharrar on bronzes; the late George M. A. Hanfmann, Ariel Herrmann and John Pollini on stone sculptures; Malcolm Bell, III, Ann Brown and Nancy Winter on terracottas; Beth Cohen, Andrew Clark and John Oakley on vases; and Ellen Herscher, Pamela Gaber and H.-G. Buchholz as well as the Department of Antiquities, Cyprus, on Cypriot objects. We are also grateful to Dietrich von Bothmer for reading the entire text and making many helpful suggestions.

Diana Buitron-Oliver
Andrew Oliver, Jr.

54 LIMESTONE HEAD OF A MAN

Cypriot
Sixth Century B.C.

The head is from a small votary, probably originally dedicated in a sanctuary. The man has large eyes, full lips curved in a smile, a long mustache and short beard. His headdress resembles the Egyptian double crown. The hair is rendered in thick locks; the texture of the beard is conveyed by a crisscross pattern of incised lines.

CONDITION: The knob of the helmet was broken off; the nose is broken and worn, the surface abraded.

54 a

54 b

MEASUREMENT: Height 13.2 cm.

PROVENANCE: Acquired in New York in the 1970s.

COMMENT: For a similar treatment of the hair, compare Cypriot terracotta heads from Samos (Schmidt 1968, pl. 69, T663 and pl. 79, T1888+1979). For the eyes, compare a limestone head from Potamia, Cyprus (Karageorghis 1979, pl. XXXVIII:10). For the Egyptian double crown headdress P. Gaber-Saletan compares a head from Kouklia in the Paphos Museum (Maier and Karageorghis 1984, p. 185, fig. 172); D. von Bothmer compares heads in the de Clercq collection (De Ridder 1908, p. 68, no. 23, pl. 8 and pp. 67–68). Compare also a head in Liverpool (Hermary 1985, pp. 689–690, fig. 35).

54 c

55 a

55 b

55

LIMESTONE HEAD OF A YOUTH

Cypriot, Late Archaic
510–490 B.C.

The head comes from a statuette, probably a votive offering in a sanctuary. The youth has large eyes, a round chin, and small mouth, turned up slightly at the corners. The hair is rendered in short curls. The back of the head was broken away and flattened.

CONDITION: The eyes, nose, mouth, and chin are chipped, the hair and ears abraded.

MEASUREMENT: Height 9.8 cm.

PROVENANCE: From Potamia (Nicosia District). Formerly in the Colocassides Collection, no. 188.

BIBLIOGRAPHY: Unpublished.

COMMENT: For the type of head, beardless, youthful, and curly-haired, compare an earlier head in Stockholm (Gaber-Saletan 1980, fig. 9) and a somewhat later head in Nicosia (Karageorghis, 1976, p. 847, fig. 11). On the chronology of Cypriot sculpture, see Gjerstad 1948, pp. 94 ff.; Schmidt 1968, pp. 93–98; Vermeule 1974, pp. 287–290; Maier and Karageorghis 1984, pp. 197–203; and Gaber-Saletan 1986.

56

MARBLE HEAD OF A WOMAN

Greek, Attic
360–340 B.C.

The youthful face has slightly parted lips and downcast eyes. Her hair is parted in the middle and swept up to form a roll on either side of the face. The thick-lidded eyes recall fifth-century B.C. models, but the soft treatment of the lower face indicates a fourth century date. The head was made to be seen in three-quarter view, suggesting that it may have been part of a three-figure composition on a gravestone. The woman would have been in the center background, while two other figures might have stood or sat beside her.

CONDITION: The lower part of the nose was broken off, the lips are somewhat damaged; scratches and root marks are visible on the surface.

MEASUREMENT: Preserved height 22 cm.

PROVENANCE: Said to be from Attica.

BIBLIOGRAPHY: Hanfmann 1954, no. 150, pl. 39; D. von Bothmer review of Hanfmann 1954 in *AJA* 59, 1955, p. 192; F. Eckstein review of Hanfmann 1954 in *Gnomon* 31, 1959, pp. 644–645; D. von Bothmer 1961, no. 111, pls. 32, 35.

COMMENT: For a gravestone with a composition similar to that proposed for this head, compare the stele of Prokleides in Athens (Diepolder 1931, pl. 46). The hairstyle is typical of the period (Diepolder 1931, pls. 42,1, 44, and 45,1).

57 FRAGMENTARY MARBLE GRAVE RELIEF

Greek, Attic
Fourth Century B.C.

The fragment preserves the head of a woman carved in high relief, within a niche framed by a narrow pilaster supporting a projecting cornice with a gable and part of a palmette akroterion. The compositional type is well known in the Kerameikos, the cemetery of Athens. The woman stood facing right, toward one or two other figures, one of whom, probably the deceased, was seated. A name is given: EYK.. IN, perhaps EYKOΛINH, (Eukoline). D. von Bothmer notes that the lettering is later than the carving of the relief and suggests that the relief was reused.

This type of tombstone appeared in Athens towards the end of the fifth century B. C., probably following the repeal of a law controlling funeral expenses that had effectively put a stop to the commissioning of grave reliefs a century before. Another restrictive law in 317 B. C. ended the production of this type of tombstone.

CONDITION: The outer surface is worn; the woman's cheek is chipped.

MEASUREMENTS: Preserved height 25 cm. Preserved length 31.5 cm.

PROVENANCE: Acquired in the late 1970s.

BIBLIOGRAPHY: Fabienne Zanotelli, *Archéologie classique* (undated catalogue, Basel, 1978?), ills. front and back covers.

COMMENT: The name Eukoline occurs on an early fourth-century stele from the Kerameikos, where it refers to a little girl with a dog who forms part of a four-figure composition (Conze 1900, no. 1131, pl. 238).

58

FRAGMENT OF A MARBLE VOTIVE RELIEF

Greek (Attic or Thessalian)
Early Fourth Century B.C.

A nude boy with phiale and fluted oinochoe approaches the head of a banquet couch. Part of the man on the couch is preserved, reclining on his left side, leaning on his left elbow, and wearing a himation around his lower body with his chest bare. There seems to be a headboard without a pillow. A contoured leg of the couch shows behind and to the left of the boy's legs. In front, a table is spread with votive offerings: grapes and two kinds of cakes, a puffed variety, ὀμφαλωτὰ πόπανα, and a pyramidal kind πυραμί-δες. The table, rendered in perspective, is rectangular with three legs and is shown, as is normally the case in other reliefs and vase painting, with the end of the table and two legs at the right, and the third leg, not preserved on the relief, at the left. The horizontal strut or stretcher is visible beneath. A lion's paw usually ornamented the foot of the table legs; here, on the back leg, it is suggested summarily by a molding. Under the table lies a dog, while just visible on the left is the foot and footstool of another figure, perhaps the man's wife, seated at the foot of the bed.

The larger scale and semi-nudity of the reclining man indicates that he is a hero and that this relief belongs to a class of votive reliefs that became immensely popular in the fourth century B.C. They generally show a man or hero on his couch, feasting, his wife sometimes at the couch foot, and a servant of diminutive size approaching with offerings. Such reliefs seem to have been associated with the healing shrines of heroes, which proliferated at this period and which give a good idea of popular beliefs and ideas.

CONDITION: Only the lower right portion of the relief is preserved; it is broken on the left and on top. The right and lower edges are ancient.

MEASUREMENTS: Preserved height 28 cm. Length 24 cm. Thickness 9.5 cm.

PROVENANCE: Unknown.

BIBLIOGRAPHY: Unpublished.

COMMENT: On reliefs of this type, see Svoronos 1908–1937, pls. 82–90, especially pl. 86, no. 1510, dated to the beginning of the fourth century B.C., for a similar perspective rendering of the table; see also Dentzer 1982, p. 578 R 83, pl. 62, fig. 346

59

LIMESTONE RELIEF WITH AMAZONOMACHY

Tarentine
Fourth Century B.C.

On the left, an Amazon mounted on a leaping horse, her shield fallen to the ground beneath the hooves, turns back and seizes the hand of a Greek warrior who has grabbed her by the helmet.

On the right, an Amazon on foot, her chiton girded up at the waist, wearing boots, helmet, and a shield strapped to her left arm, advances on a fallen warrior. Her raised right arm probably held a spear. The warrior, seen in three-quarter view from the back, has fallen on his right leg and protects himself with his shield. A baldric with sword is fastened around his nude body, and a helmet is pushed back on his head. The relief may have come from a small sepulchral building, *naiskos*, or shrine that played a part in the elaborate funerary rituals of the Tarentines, rituals also reflected on their vases where drawings of such shrines commonly occur. The subject, though not directly related to sepulchral matters, is a favorite on these reliefs and continues to appear on grave monuments of other kinds, such as Etruscan urns and Roman sarcophagi.

CONDITION: The relief was broken and mended. The top and bottom edge and the back are worked smooth.

MEASUREMENTS: Height 19 cm. Width 37.7 cm. Depth of relief 2 cm.

PROVENANCE: Unknown.

BIBLIOGRAPHY: D. von Bothmer 1983, p. 39, fig. 29, n. 69.

COMMENT: Greek influence is evident in the composition which reflects the frieze on the Temple of Apollo Epikourios at Phigaleia (Bassae), a frieze that exerted a strong influence on South Italian sepulchral relief carving (D. von Bothmer 1957, pp. 215–216). On the motif of the Greek pulling the Amazon off her horse by the helmet or hair, see D. von Bothmer 1983, p. 39. For a general discussion of Tarentine funerary sculpture, see Klumbach 1937, esp. nos. 4–6, 10, 12. On the type, see Langlotz and Hirmer 1965, pp. 291–292, nos. 136–137, and Carter 1975, pp. 17 ff. Carter suggests that the subject, the heroic combat of Greeks against their barbarian opponents, was popular in Taranto because the city was continually at war with its barbarian neighbors.

60 a

60 b

60 c

60

MARBLE HEAD OF HYPNOS

Roman Copy of a Fourth-century B.C. Greek original
First Century A.D.

The youthful face, with heavy-lidded eyes, soft lips, and cheeks, and the roots of wings jutting out on either side of the head, suggest that this head represents Hypnos, the personification of sleep. A statue of Hypnos of the fourth century B.C. described by the Roman poet Statius, may be reflected in a bronze head in the British Museum, a marble statue in Madrid, and a number of small bronze statuettes. They indicate that the god was shown taking a long gliding step, his winged head down, one arm in front with a jug, the other in back with poppies. Scholars associate several fourth-century B.C. sculptors with the creation of this original and imaginative work.

The hairstyle of the Bastis head does not conform in every detail to other copies of the fourth-century original. The treatment of the eyes, with the sharp outline and heavy lids, along with the hairstyle, suggests that this is an early Imperial version.

CONDITION: The nose is damaged, left eyelid, cheeks, lips, and chin are chipped; the left side of the head is covered with brown incrustation.

MEASUREMENT: Height 19.3 cm.

PROVENANCE: Acquired in 1947.

BIBLIOGRAPHY: D. von Bothmer 1961, p. 29, pls. 37, 39, no. 116; H. A. Cahn, "Antike Kunstwerke aus New-Yorker Privatsammlungen," *Antike Kunst* 3, 1960, p. 90, pl. 16:2.

COMMENT: The identification of the head as Hypnos was first made by Hoffmann (D. von Bothmer 1961, p. 29). For the workmanship of the eyes, John Pollini compares a head of Lucius in the North Carolina Museum of Art, Raleigh (Kiss 1975, p. 64, fig. 125). For the bronze head in the British Museum, see Cook 1976, p. 179, fig. 141; for the statue in Madrid, see Beazley and Ashmole 1932, pp. 56–57, fig. 123. On Hypnos, see Robertson 1975, p. 461. On Hypnos cults and sanctuaries, see Furtwängler 1895, pp. 395–396, and for bronze statuettes, p. 395, n. 8.

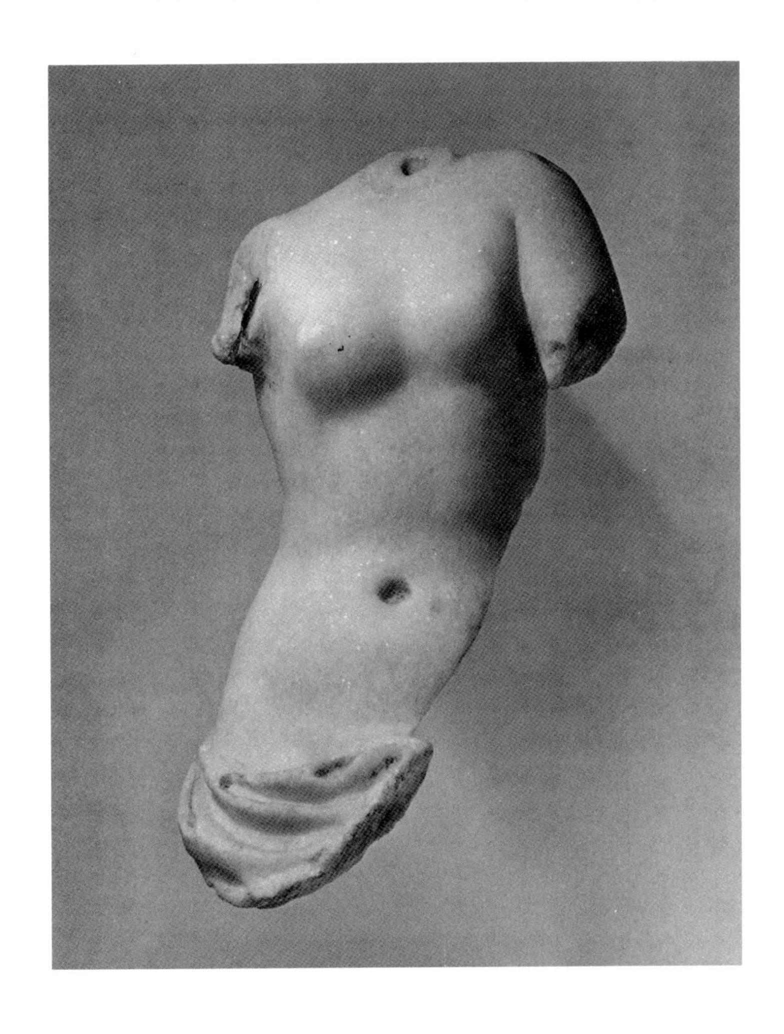

61

MARBLE TORSO OF APHRODITE

First or second century A.D. Reduced Roman copy of a third or second-century B.C. Greek original

The slightly raised left shoulder, twist of the waist, and drapery around the hips suggest that this is an adaptation of the Aphrodite of Capua, a type thought to reflect a fourth-century B.C. original by Scopas or Lysippus. In some copies the figure steadies a shield at her left side in which she admires her reflection. A celebrated version is the Venus de Milo in the Louvre, which may have shown her leaning on a pillar to her left, holding her falling drapery in her right hand. The anatomy of the Bastis marble, especially the breasts, is summarily rendered. An iron dowel in the right shoulder served to attach a separately worked arm; a drill hole in the neck was to attach the head, and another hole was drilled into the top of the left shoulder.

CONDITION: The upper torso and part of the left arm are preserved, as well as the right hip and leg which is partially covered with drapery. The head and all extremities are missing.

MEASUREMENT: Height 20.3 cm.

PROVENANCE: Acquired in 1944.

BIBLIOGRAPHY: Unpublished.

COMMENT: On the Aphrodite of Capua, see Furtwängler 1895, pp. 384–392; Arnold 1969, pp. 236–237; Robertson 1975, pp. 553–554; Bieber 1977, pp. 43 f. and 53, n. 34; and Pasquier 1985.

62 MARBLE TORSO OF APHRODITE

Roman copy of a fourth-century B.C. Greek original.

The lowered right arm and the slight bend forward and to the right of the upper torso indicate that the statue is a reduced copy of the Aphrodite of Knidos by Praxiteles. The original, considered revolutionary because of its nudity and its break from the firm, upright classical stance, is said to have stood in a shrine at Knidos where it could be admired from all sides. The most complete copy of the lost original is in the Vatican. The goddess is shown surprised at her bath. Her left hand lifts her clothing from a *hydria* (water jar) on which it rested. On the Bastis marble two protrusions on the left thigh may be remains of the fingers of the right hand, or struts connecting with the hand. An iron dowel on the side of the left thigh may have joined a *hydria*, now missing which, with the drapery on top of it, would have given the statue additional support.

CONDITION: This figure lacks the head, most of the left arm, the right wrist and hand, and the legs below the knees. Areas of incrustation are visible on the shoulder, arms, breasts, chest, hips and legs.

MEASUREMENT: Preserved height 33.5 cm.

PROVENANCE: Acquired in the early 1940s.

BIBLIOGRAPHY: Unpublished.

COMMENT: Pliny relates that Praxitiles made two statues of Aphrodite, one fully clothed, the other nude. The people of Kos were given first option and chose the clothed version. The Cnidians bought the nude version, which became immeasurably more celebrated (Pliny, *Natural History* XXXVI. 20). Renowned throughout the ancient world, the statue became a model for future artists, inspiring a fashion for naked Aphrodites in the Hellenistic and Roman periods. On the type, see Robertson 1975, pp. 390–394, and pl. 127 b for the copy in the Vatican. Also Vierneisel-Schlorb 1979, pp. 323–352; Pfrommer 1985, pp. 173–180.

62 a

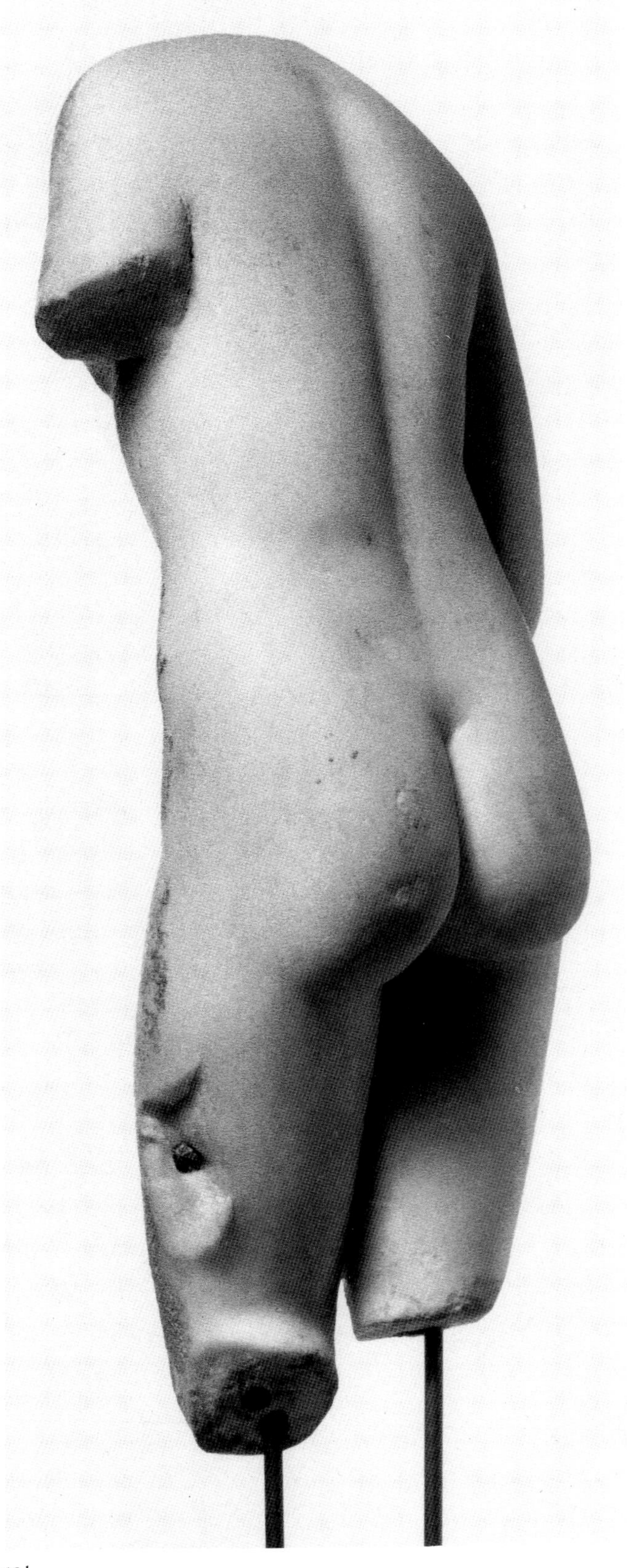
62 b

63 MARBLE HEAD OF A WOMAN

Greek, Hellenistic

The soft, indefinite modeling of face and hair is typical of the so-called Alexandrian style. The unusual hair-do consists of two buns or rolls of hair on the back of the head, bound by a fillet. The head could have come from a small statue of a goddess or nymph. The finished edge at the base of the neck suggests that it was intended to fit into a draped statue.

CONDITION: The nose and upper lip are damaged.

MEASUREMENT: Height 10.2 cm.

PROVENANCE: Acquired in 1943.

COMMENT: Compare several heads in Boston (Comstock and Vermeule 1976, pp. 60–62, nos. 95–97, especially no. 95).

63 b

63 a

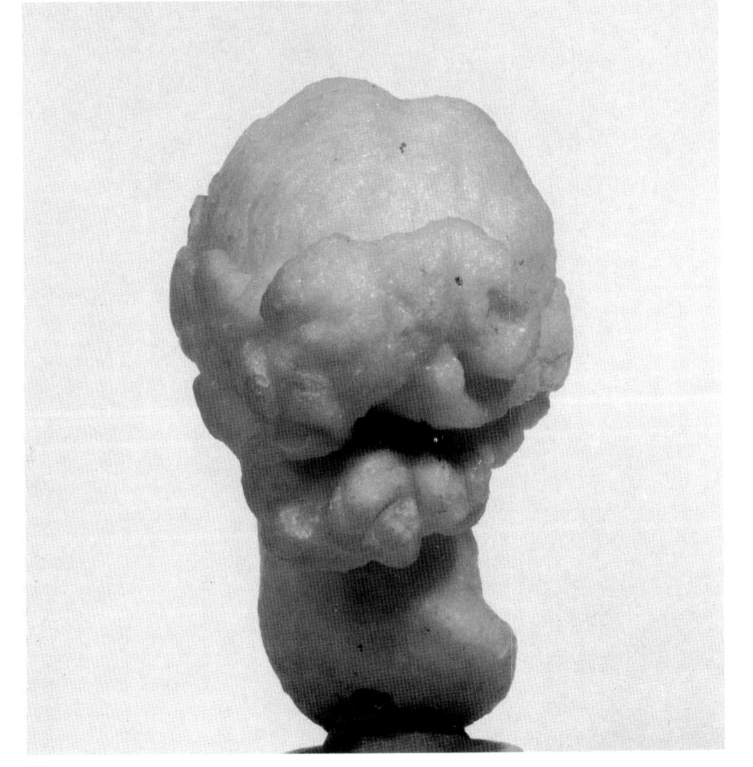

63 c

64 a

64

MARBLE HEAD OF ALEXANDER THE GREAT

Roman
Second or Third Century A.D.

The upward tilted head, with its passionate, deep-set eyes, full lips, and thick, springing hair, generally conforms to the description of Lysippus' famous portrait of Alexander the Great. The rectangular dowel hole on top of the head suggests that it once held an attachment, perhaps the solar rays of the sun disk. Lysippus is also known to have made a statue of the sun god Helios driving his chariot, and it was his pupil, Chares of Lindos, who made a huge

64 b

figure of Helios known as the Colossus of Rhodes. The assimilation of Alexander's features into the Helios type may begin with the Lysippan works, and the type has a long life thereafter. The Bastis head, made in Roman times, may be a late example of the "Alexander Helios" type.

CONDITION: The nose and upper lip are missing; the hair and chin are abraded.

MEASUREMENT: Preserved height 37 cm.

PROVENANCE: Said to come from Egypt.

BIBLIOGRAPHY: *The Search of Alexander, Supplement to the Catalogue,* New York 1982, p. 20, no. S 66.

COMMENT: The association of the head with the Alexander Helios was made by D. von Bothmer. Ariel Herrmann has discussed the evolution of the type (National Gallery of Art 1980, p. 102, no. 8.)

65 RED MARBLE HEAD FROM A MINIATURE HERM

Greek or Roman (archaistic)
Second Century B.C. or later

The broad face has small eyes and ears, a full beard, and long mustache. The thick waves of hair emanating from the top of the head form rows of corkscrew curls over the forehead and wavy locks on the sides and back. Fourteen drill holes encircling the head indicate that a metal fillet was once attached. The individual locks of the beard are carefully rendered. In contrast to the decorative rendition of the hair, the face has realistically modeled forehead and cheeks.

The combination of realistic and decorative elements is typical of the archaistic style. Herms were treated in such fashion to emphasize their traditional character. The Bastis version reflects the herm type generally identified as the Hermes Propylaios, by the fifth-century B.C. sculptor Alkamenes. The miniature size suggests that it might have been used as a votive offering or home cult object.

CONDITION: The tip of the nose is missing; there is considerable abrasion and loss to hair and beard. The head was broken off below the neck.

MEASUREMENT: Preserved height 9.6 cm.

PROVENANCE: Unknown.

BIBLIOGRAPHY: Unpublished.

COMMENT: On Alkamenoid herms, miniature herms and their uses, see Harrison 1965, pp. 131–134. Compare especially pl. 47, no. 169.

66 a

66 b

66

MARBLE HEAD OF A MAN, PERHAPS HERAKLES

Roman
First Century A.D.?

The head is of a man with thick, curly hair and beard, small deep-set eyes, thin nose, fleshy lips, and tiny ears. The headdress consists of a wide, flat band across the top of the head, with three pointed projections (leaves?) descending from it in the middle of the forehead and heavy leaves falling from it on either side of the head. The head is narrow, front to back, with an iron dowel in the center of the back to attach it to another piece of marble, which suggests that the head might have belonged to a double herm.

CONDITION: The surface is very worn, with a slight discoloration; the tip of the nose is broken off, the right eyebrow chipped.

MEASUREMENT: Height 29.2 cm.

PROVENANCE: Acquired in 1944.

BIBLIOGRAPHY: Unpublished.

COMMENT: Compare the double herm with a bearded Herakles in Boston (MFA, 01.8197; Comstock and Vermeule 1976, no. 216). For a wreath with large leaves compare a head of Domitian idealised as Herakles (of the Genzano type) also in Boston (MFA, 1978. 227; Vermeule 1981, no. 257.)

PART IV

Terracottas

by
Diana Buitron-Oliver

67 TERRACOTTA STATUETTE OF A YOKED BULL

Cypriot
Seventh Century B.C.

The animal's head and the front part of its body are preserved. An abraded area on the left side suggests that it might have been one of a pair standing close together. The harness around the neck indicates that it pulled something. The modeling is done by hand; the eyes, nostrils, and mouth formed with a sharp tool. Traces of dark paint remain on the horns and jaw.

CONDITION: Missing, back part of body, legs and tail; horns broken.

MEASUREMENTS: Height 13.2 cm. Length 15.2 cm.

PROVENANCE: Acquired in 1944.

BIBLIOGRAPHY: Unpublished.

COMMENT: Compare a bull from Samos identified as Cypriot in style and dated to the end of the seventh century B.C. (Schmidt 1968, T 1769, pl. 87, p. 84).

Etrusco-Italic
About 525–500 B.C.

A pair of riders, a warrior and his "squire", gallop to left, ready to engage in battle. They are the middle pair in a larger scene that includes three pairs of riders. The entire composition can be reconstructed from fragments formed from the same mold in other collections, most of them in the Ashmolean Museum, Oxford. The warrior wears

greaves and a crested helmet. He carriers a round shield that covers his body and brandishes a double axe with his left arm (not preserved on the Bastis fragment). His squire carries a whip with lashes. A dog runs beneath the horses. The forelegs of the second pair of horses overlap into the scene from behind and the tails of the third pair are visible in front. There is a narrow projecting ledge below the scene.

The warrior is probably a mounted hoplite rather than a cavalryman, who will dismount to fight while his squire holds his horse. The dog beneath the horses is a favorite compositional motif in scenes of hunting from chariots in Syria and the east. Since no evidence exists to suggest that the Greeks trained dogs to fight in battle, it would seem that the dog derives from a Near Eastern compositional type and had no iconographical significance in the Italic terracotta.

The relief, which would have been painted, is from an architectural revetment, probably part of a frieze on the entablature which served to protect the wooden parts of a temple.

CONDITION: Broken and mended, break visible through the horses' hind legs.

MEASUREMENTS: Height 19.8 cm. Length 27.9 cm. Thickness at base 2.5 cm.

PROVENANCE: Acquired in New York in 1970.

BIBLIOGRAPHY: Unpublished.

COMMENT: Fragments from the same or a similar mold come from Rome and Cisterna di Latina. This fragment is almost identical to one in the Ashmolean Museum, Oxford, and is a version of a similar scene of the well-known riders on architectural terracottas from Velletri (Brown 1974, pp. 60–5, with bibliography on cavalry and hoplite battles, and the role of dogs in battle; also Dörig 1975, no. 194). For the provenance, A. Brown cites Melis and Quilici Gigli 1972, pls. 50–51.

69 TERRACOTTA GROUP OF A COW AND A CALF

Boeotian
Sixth Century B.C.

The animals stand on a narrow, ingot-shaped plinth, the calf underneath the cow, as if nursing. The cow's body is decorated with red lines on a white slip. Such primitive figurines are seen in Boeotia long after they had disappeared in the major centers of Athens and Corinth.

CONDITION: The group is intact.

MEASUREMENT: Height 13.3 cm.

PROVENANCE: Acquired in 1944.

BIBLIOGRAPHY: Hanfmann 1954, No. 245, pl. LXXIV; D. von Bothmer 1961, No. 168, pl. 62.

COMMENT: D. von Bothmer compares a pair of horses from Rhitsona in Boeotia (Ure 1934, p. 64, pl. 16).

70 TERRACOTTA SPHINX

Corinthian
525–500 B.C.

The sphinx sits on a short plinth, wings raised, its tail curled up behind its back. The head, turned full face, wears a polos. Similar sphinxes on plinths are known from all over the Greek world. Some have been found in graves suggesting they served as funerary gifts, a role suitable for the sphinx, a creature connected with death; others come from sanctuaries where they served as votive offerings.

The pale, fine clay is typical of Corinth and is covered by a white slip with traces of red paint visible on the polos, chest, and plinth; black paint on the hair and wings.

CONDITION: The sphinx is intact; the surface worn.

MEASUREMENT: Height 8.9 cm.

PROVENANCE: Acquired in the 1940s.

BIBLIOGRAPHY: D. von Bothmer 1961, no. 177, pl. 62.

COMMENT: The sphinx can be dated by comparing its head with the series of molded female heads on Corinthian pottery (Payne 1931, pp. 232–240). For the type see Robinson 1933, nos. 333–4, pl. 41; and Payne 1940, nos. 108, 194–5, pls. 96, 101. Sphinx acroteria in marble are known from Attic grave stelai of the sixth century B.C.

71

TERRACOTTA STATUETTE OF A WOMAN

Greek
Late Fourth-Early Third Century B.C.

The figure stands on a thin plinth, left leg forward bearing the weight, right hip and leg back. Her right arm, enveloped in the folds of her himation, is bent across her chest to rest on her left arm. The himation is worn like a shawl, the two ends meeting on the woman's left side. The head is bent forward to the right; a snood covers the back of her head, and she wears disk earrings.

This statuette and the next are known as Tanagra figurines, so named for the cemetery in Boeotia where the type was first identified. The Tanagra type consists primarily of images of women, although children and Erotes are also known. It has been demonstrated that the type originated in Athens in the fourth century B.C., probably inspired by theatrical performances in which such elegant and graceful women played prominent roles and delighted the public. Tanagras rapidly became extremely popular and were made all over the ancient world.

CONDITION: Cracked on the back, head reattached to body at base of neck. Very fine yellow-pink clay. White slip well preserved, blue band on chiton, traces of red on snood and plinth. Irregular rectangular vent.

MEASUREMENT: Height with plinth 19.5 cm.

PROVENANCE: Acquired from the Joseph Brummer Collection in 1949.

BIBLIOGRAPHY: Sale catalogue, New York, *Parke-Bernet, 8 June 1949,* no. 15, 1; D. von Bothmer 1961, no. 183, pls. 62, 64.

COMMENT: The thin rectangular plinth and rectangular vent are typical of figures found in the cemetery at Tanagra. On the origin of Tanagras see Thompson 1966, pp. 51–63.

72 TERRACOTTA STATUETTE OF A WOMAN

Greek
Third Century B.C.

The woman stands turned slightly to her right, with her weight on the left leg, right arm raised between her breasts, under the mantle. She is enveloped in a thin himation which has been wrapped around her body, one corner thrown over her left shoulder, the other corner pulled around the waist a second time and draped over the lowered left arm, which holds a fan.

CONDITION: Intact; orange-beige clay, blue himation, traces of red on hair. Rectangular vent.

MEASUREMENT: Height 20.3 cm.

PROVENANCE: Acquired in the 1940s.

BIBLIOGRAPHY: Unpublished.

COMMENT: For the drapery compare a figure in Girton College, Cambridge (Burlington Fine Arts Club 1904, no. F85, pl. 83; Birmingham Museum and Art Gallery 1968, p. 30, no. 106, pl. 20 left), and others in the British Museum (Higgins 1986, pp. 130–131, figs. 154–156).

73 a

73 b

73

TERRACOTTA HEAD OF A WOMAN

Tarentine
Late Fourth Century B.C.

The life-size head of a woman, perhaps a goddess, has an oval face with a slightly heavy chin, full lower lip, straight nose and deep-set eyes. The wavy locks of hair rise away from the face and form a nimbus, or roll, around the head. The crown of the head is more summarily treated – the waves of hair are linear, incised, and not given body or relief. There are traces of red paint on the hair.

Taranto was a Greek colony in South Italy where, due to a scarcity of marble and other hard stone, a flourishing coroplastic center developed from the seventh century B.C. on, culminating in elegant creations such as this.

CONDITION: Intact. Reddish-orange clay, cream slip; round vent hole on upper back of head.

MEASUREMENT: Height 30.5 cm.

PROVENANCE: Unknown.

BIBLIOGRAPHY: Unpublished.

COMMENT: Compare three heads in Taranto of the fourth century B.C.: Langlotz and Hirmer 1965, pl. XII and fig. 132; and Zanotti-Bianco 1962, p. 210.

73c

74 a

74 TERRACOTTA GROUP: WOMEN SEATED AROUND A WELL HEAD

Tarentine
Second half of the fourth century B.C.

The five seated women support small shallow bowls on their heads in which to burn incense or for other offerings. All five are made from the same mold, arms and feet made separately, the back finished by hand. Variety is achieved through the use of different colors of paint, and the different objects held in the hands.

One of them sits on a red chair. She wears a yellow chiton and red himation, has black hair, eyes and shoes, and holds a red unguent vase and a small jar. The other four sit on the edge of a round well head. Clockwise from the figure on the chair, the first woman wears a red chiton and yellow himation and holds a red pomegranate and yel-

74b

low *phiale* (libation bowl); the second is in a red chiton and black himation and holds a yellow phiale and a jug; the third has a yellow chiton and red himation and holds a yellow fan or mirror; and the fourth has a red chiton and black himation, and holds a red, black and yellow dove and a yellow fruit. All have brown hair, black eyes, brows, and shoes.

The well head is wheel-made, has a molding at the top, and six triangular cut-outs; it is painted red outside, yellow inside.

The objects held by the women can be associated with the cult of Demeter and/or Persephone. The dove, a marriage symbol, may refer to Persephone's union with Hades, and the pomegranate is a frequent offering at sanctuaries to both goddesses. The saucershaped headpieces suggest that this group might have been a votive offering, the scene a reflection of some aspect of the cult ritual.

CONDITION: The head of the third figure has been reattached at the neck. Parts of the chair have been restored in plaster. Pale buff clay, paint very well preserved.

MEASUREMENTS: Diameter of well head 19.1 cm. Height of women seated on well head 20–21 cm. Height of woman on chair 20.9 cm.

PROVENANCE: Unknown.

BIBLIOGRAPHY: Unpublished.

COMMENT: On seated figures in a votive context see Bell 1981, p. 94.

75 TERRACOTTA STATUETTE OF A DANCING WOMAN

Sicilian
Third Century B.C.

The coroplast shows us the dancer as she performs a leaping turn to the right, her voluminous skirts swirling behind her. Both arms are swathed in her cloak; the right arm held against her torso because that is the direction of the turn, the left arm and shoulder slightly forward giving momentum to her rightward leap. Her head, thrust back and to the right, is balanced by her kicked-out left leg. There is a strong feeling of motion in the figure achieved through the twists of the pose and the flying drapery. This dancer's head is bare but she is related to the so-called 'mantle dancers' whose heads are enveloped in mantles. Mantle dancers have been found in sanctuaries, suggesting their connection with cult rituals.

CONDITION: Broken and mended, hair reattached; orange-beige clay, traces of white slip on face, red hair. No vent.

MEASUREMENTS: Height 26.5 cm. Length 18.8 cm.

PROVENANCE: Unknown.

BIBLIOGRAPHY: Unpublished.

COMMENT: The dancer bears some resemblance to a group of mantle dancers from Morgantina and to a group of dancers with wildly swirling drapery from Syracuse, Centuripe and Taranto (Bell 1981, nos. 454–5, pp. 64–65, 186).

76

TERRACOTTA STATUETTE OF A WOMAN

Sicilian, perhaps Centuripe
Late Third-Early Second Century B.C.

Standing with her weight on her right leg, the woman reaches across her body with her right hand to adjust the sandal on her raised left foot. Her left arm is extended for balance. Her short himation is worn over the left shoulder. The type may be inspired by representations of nude Aphrodite removing her sandal before a bath.

CONDITION: Broken and mended, head and arms reattached; fine pale beige clay; blue bands and black lines on himation and chiton, red hair and sandle. Irregular round vent.

MEASUREMENT: Height 29.2 cm.

PROVENANCE: Unknown.

BIBLIOGRAPHY: Unpublished.

COMMENT: There are two variations on the sandal-binder type, the earlier with the right foot raised. The type with the left foot raised is especially popular in Centuripe where it has been found in tombs of the late third and early second centuries B.C. (Bell 1981, pp. 63–64, where additions are made to Winter 1903, 207:4). Close in pose to this example is a nude Aphrodite from Centuripe (Langlotz and Hirmer 1965, fig. 160.)

77

TERRACOTTA STATUETTE OF A NUDE FEMALE, PERHAPS A DOLL

Greek
Third Century B.C.

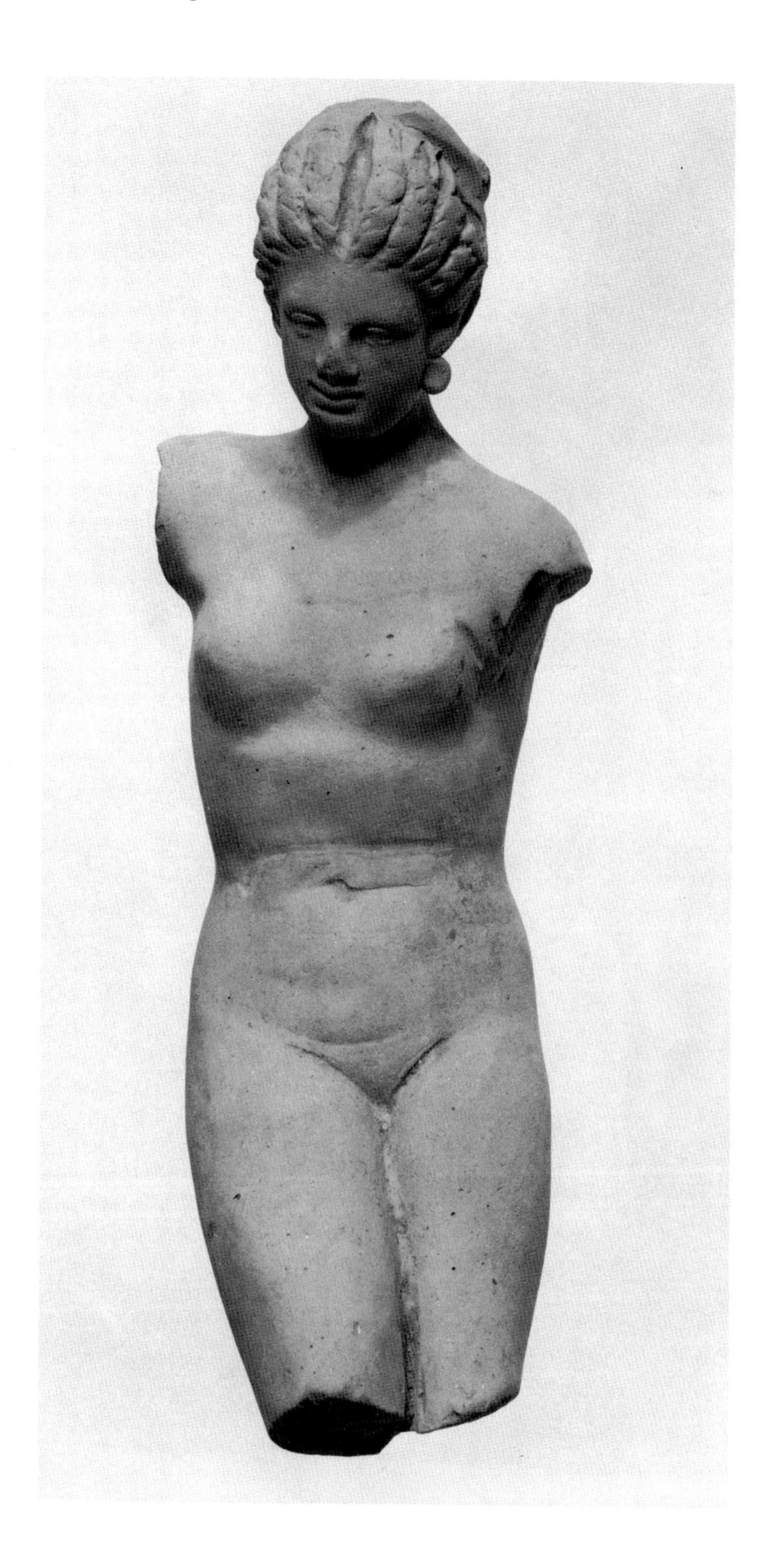

The nude figure is bent slightly at the waist, hips turned a little to the left; perhaps she is seated. The arms and lower legs are missing. The head, bent forward, is delicately modeled; the hair in the "melon coiffure", is held by an ornament on the top of the head, and there is a large disk earring on the left ear (the right ear is missing).

CONDITION: The right side and back of the head are abraded, the tip of the nose is missing; there are gashes on the left breast; the back is discolored. The figure is solid cast, probably in several molds, and finished by hand. The clay is pale yellowish, pinkish beige. The body was once covered by a flesh colored slip, traces of which remain on the lower face and around the waist.

MEASUREMENTS: Height 15.0 cm. Width 5.1 cm.

PROVENANCE: Unknown.

BIBLIOGRAPHY: Unpublished.

COMMENT: D. von Bothmer observed that the figure might be a doll, a type especially popular during the Hellenistic period. Dolls were usually nude and were intended to be provided with real clothes. The melon hair-do with a bun at the top of the head and the seated pose are characteristic of the type.

The antecedents of these nude figures were often connected with fertility cults, and dolls must retain this association in the Hellenistic period. They may be votive gifts dedicated by young girls upon their marriage. On dolls see Thompson 1963, pp. 87–94; and Bell 1981, pp. 94–7.

78

TERRACOTTA MASK

Greek, Third Century B.C. or later

The mask represents an old man with knitted brows, a grimacing mouth, receding hairline, long beard and mustache. The eyes and mouth are pierced, and there are two holes for suspension on top of the head. Masks were used in Greek theater production from archaic times on; those used in New Comedy of the last part of the 4th century B.C. are listed by Pollux in a thesaurus written in the 2nd century A.D. which included a section on theaters (*Onomasticon*, IV, 143 f.). This mask seems closest to the description of the *pornoboskos*, the procuror, the title of a play by the Middle Comedy playwrite Euboulos, and a character in comedy, Greek and Latin, thereafter. The small size of this mask and the two holes for suspension suggest that it served a votive or decorative function.

CONDITION: Intact.

MEASUREMENT: Height 14.4 cm.

PROVENANCE: Acquired in New York 1943.

BIBLIOGRAPHY: None.

COMMENT: For the masks representing old men see Webster 1969, pp. 14–7.

Also compare the masks illustrated in Bernabó Brea 1981, p. 149; and Bieber 1961 a, pp. 94, 189, fig. 268.

PART V

Bronzes

by
Andrew Oliver, Jr.

79

BRONZE AND SILVER SCEPTER HEAD

Eastern Mediterranean
Second Millennium B.C.

The scepter head is pierced by a large hole and must once have fit onto a shaft. Two pairs of connected spirals are formed with inlaid strips of silver worked flush with the surface of the bronze.

CONDITION: The piece is intact.

MEASUREMENTS: Height, top to bottom 3.4 cm. Maximum diameter 4.4 cm. Diameter of hole 2.2 cm.

PROVENANCE: Unknown.

BIBLIOGRAPHY: Unpublished.

COMMENT: There is no close parallel to the object.

79 a

79 b

80

BRONZE ORNAMENT

Greek (Macedonian)
Eighth Century B.C.

A variety of beads, bells, and ornaments in the form of birds, animals, miniature vases, and other objects have been found in Macedonian tombs of the Geometric Period. How they were used is not always known, and objects of the type illustrated are something of a puzzle. Four sets of knobs, sixteen in all, project from the shaft and are bordered above and below by reel moldings. The shaft ends in a molded knob at the bottom. Above, on a plinth, is a seated figure, elbows on knees, hands to face, very possibly a man drinking. The edge of the plinth shows cross-hatching.

CONDITION: The ornament is intact.

MEASUREMENT: Height 9.5 cm.

PROVENANCE: Unknown.

BIBLIOGRAPHY: Unpublished.

COMMENT: Ulf Jantzen suggested that objects like this served as bottle stoppers and that flax or old rope wrapped around the shaft and catching in the knobs made it into a cork (Jantzen 1953, pp. 56–57). This view, however, has been challenged. Examples in the Stathatos Collection in the National Museum, Athens were said to have been found on the deceased as if they had been worn as ornaments (Amandry 1963, p. 242). Furthermore, the existence of a double ornament in a Swiss private collection, with connecting struts and a suspension loop, also suggest some other use (Rolley 1983, p. 66, fig. 45). Known provenances of comparable ornaments include Thessaly and Macedonia (Bouzek 1974, pp. 76–85).

80 a

80 b

80 c

81 BRONZE STATUETTE OF A HORSE

Greek (Laconian?)
Eighth Century B.C.

The horse, cast solid, stands on a rectangular base with an open-work lattice; the tail, as with most bronze horses, is connected to an extension of the base. The tail is lozenge-shaped in section with an engraved line running the length of each side. The fetlocks are shown, but additional spurs appear on the fore- and hindlegs. The ears are tall and furrowed; the eyes are indicated; the nose is done with moldings at the end of the head.

CONDITION: A greenish-brown patina covers the statuette, with traces on it of red cuprite corrosion.

MEASUREMENTS: Height 7.2 cm. Base 5.2 × 3.2 cm.

PROVENANCE: Unknown.

BIBLIOGRAPHY: Unpublished.

COMMENT: The horse is stylistically close to one in London, said to come from Phigaleia (British Museum 1905.10–24.5; Cook 1976, p. 36, fig. 24), to another from Olympia without a base, now in Berlin (Br. 8091; Herrmann 1964, p. 23, fig. 4), and to a third, said to be from Tegea, in Oxford (Ashmolean Museum G. 396).

81 b

81 a

82

Greek
Eighth Century B.C.

The horse, cast solid, stands on a rectangular base with an open-work lattice. The tail, round in section, is connected to an extension of the base. The neck is short; mouth, tail, and ears are indicated. The fetlocks are correctly shown.

CONDITION: The horse has a mottled, blue and green patina.

MEASUREMENTS: Height 6.2 cm. Base, excluding extension, 3.6 × 2.3 cm.

PROVENANCE: From Olympia.

BIBLIOGRAPHY: Hanfmann 1954, p. 30. no. 189, pl. 57 (before cleaning); D. von Bothmer 1961, p. 33, no. 127, pl. 43; Herrmann 1964, p. 24 and n. 26.

COMMENT: A horse found at Sparta is closely related (Dawkins ed. 1929, pl. 77 b).

82 b

82 a

83 BRONZE STATUETTE OF A HORSE

Greek (Corinthian?)
Eighth Century B.C.

The horse, cast solid, stands on a rectangular base with an open-work lattice pattern. The tail, round in section, is connected directly to the base and not to an extending spur. The body is slender, the head small; mane and ears prominent. The fetlocks are incorrectly shown on the fore-legs.

CONDITION: The statuette was broken and repaired in many places. The back of the left hoof is missing. Mottled, gray-green patina covers the surface.

MEASUREMENTS: Height 7.0 cm. Base 5.7 × 2.2 cm.

PROVENANCE: Unknown.

BIBLIOGRAPHY: Unpublished.

COMMENT: The horse belongs to a group first put together by H.-V. Herrmann (Herrmann 1964, pp. 28–32) and exemplified by two large horses, one in New York (Metropolitan Museum of Art 21.88.24; Richter 1953, p. 23, pl. 13:e), the other in Berlin (West) (31317; Rolley 1983, p. 56, fig. 33). A horse closely related both in scale and size is in Lamia, Greece, from the region of Kammena Vourla (Touchais 1977, pp. 588–589, fig. 176).

83 a

83 b

84 a

84

BRONZE STATUETTE OF A HORSE

Greek
Eighth Century B.C.

84 b

The horse, cast solid, stands on a rectangular base, the underside of which shows chevron patterns in intaglio. It probably served as a stamp seal. The tail, round in section, is connected to an extension of the base. The legs are without fetlocks, the neck is long, the head swells at the center and the end. The ears are not represented.

CONDITION: A rough, green patina covers the surface.

MEASUREMENTS: Height 10.1 cm. Base overall 7.1 × 3.0 cm.

PROVENANCE: Unknown

BIBLIOGRAPHY: Unpublished.

85

BRONZE STATUETTE OF A HORSE

Greek
Eighth Century B.C.

The horse, cast solid, stands on an unperforated rectangular base. The head flares at the end; the ears are prominent; the neck is flat and set off from the body. Three sets of dotted, concentric circles are engraved on the neck; horizontal lines mark the legs.

CONDITION: A green patina appears on the surface. The base is damaged, and the lower half of the tail is missing.

MEASUREMENTS: Height 4.4 cm. Length of base 3.7 cm.

PROVENANCE: Unknown.

BIBLIOGRAPHY: Unpublished.

COMMENT: Several bronze horses are related stylistically to this one: a horse from Leukas (Dörpfeld 1927, p. 169, pl. 79 a, l, whence Heilmeyer 1979, p. 89, ill.), another in Tübingen (Archäologisches Institut 150; Herrmann 1964, p. 31, fig. 13), and a third in Houston (De Menil Collection; Hoffmann 1970, pp. 126–127, no. 44, ill.).

85 a

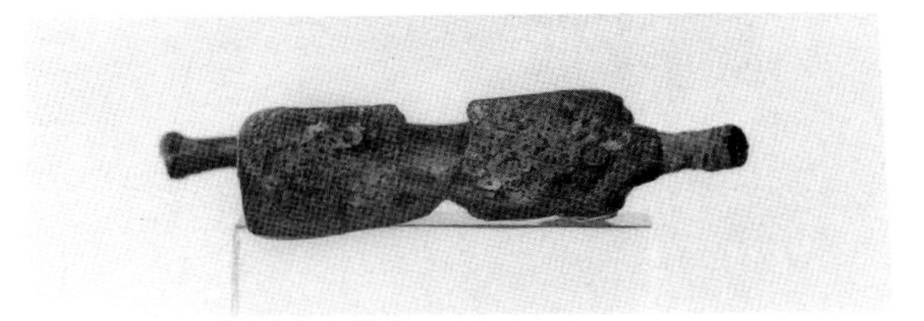

85 b

86

BRONZE STATUETTE OF A BULL

Greek
Eighth Century B.C.

The bull was probably a votive offering in a sanctuary, and resembles those found all over the Greek world. Although the anatomy is only roughly modeled, the pizzle and dewlap are clearly indicated.

MEASUREMENTS: Height 3.6 cm. Length 4.7 cm. Width 3.0 cm.

PROVENANCE: Unknown.

BIBLIOGRAPHY: Unpublished.

COMMENT: Several bronze bulls from Olympia, though longer in the leg, are comparable (Heilmeyer 1979, pp. 206–207, nos. 106, 124, pls. 16, 18).

87

BRONZE STATUETTE OF A BULL

Greek
Seventh or Sixth Century B.C.

The bull belongs to a stylistic tradition different from that of the "geometric" horses. The legs are blocky and irregular, the feet flattened to provide stability in the absence of a base. The hindquarters are set off from the torso. The genitals are shown. Nostrils and mouth are delineated on the nose, and the eyes are indicated. Neck and face are lined to show the shagginess of the beast.

CONDITION: A greenish-brown patina covers the surface.

MEASUREMENTS: Length 6.5 cm. Height 5.5 cm.

PROVENANCE: Unknown.

BIBLIOGRAPHY: Unpublished.

COMMENT: Compare a bull in Baltimore (Walters Art Gallery 54.2379; Hill 1955, p. 41, pl. 30:10).

88 BRONZE TRIPOD LEG WITH FOREPARTS OF A HORSE

Greek
Sixth Century B.C.?

The complete tripod would have had three arched supports alternating with three upright rods fixed to a horizontal ring. Originally there were three horses. There is a hole in the top of the horse's head behind the top knot, about 0.45 cm. in diameter.

CONDITION: On the inner face of the ring, at the junction of the horse's legs, a casting fault has been repaired. The bronze has a greenish-yellow patina, which is ancient, according to Larry Majewski of the Conservation Center of the Institute of Fine Arts, New York University. The surface of the metal is pitted in places.

MEASUREMENTS: Height 19.0 cm. Width 13.9 cm.

PROVENANCE: Acquired in New York in 1965.

BIBLIOGRAPHY: Unpublished.

COMMENT: The bronze is related in format and size to a tripod fragment from Samos in Berlin (East) (Staatliche Museen Sa 69) on which, however, the horse protome faces to the right (Kyrieleis 1986, p. 197). The Berlin horse is bridled and the bronze is worked with substantially more detail in the features and hair. The Bastis bronze is in fact unusual, if not unique, among Greek and Etruscan horse heads on tripods by facing to the left. Horse heads, but without forelegs, also appear on the ring of the complete Greek bronze tripod from Metaponto in Berlin (West) (Staatliche Museen Fr. 768; Lamb 1929, p. 132, pl. XLV a).

89 a

89

BRONZE PHIALE OR LIBATION BOWL

East Greek
Sixth Century B.C.

The bowl was used to pour liquid offerings to a deity and was easily held with a finger on the hollow of the omphalos on the underside. It was cast, not hammered, and is relatively thick-walled. The moldings on the interior around the omphalos are not present on the exterior. Engraved within the rim is a Carian inscription of thirty characters separated by six vertical strokes to indicate seven words. Roberto Gusmani has provided a full commentary (see bibliography), but Carian, a language of southwest Asia Minor, is not well understood, and the inscription cannot be translated.

CONDITION: The phiale is intact.

MEASUREMENTS: Height 4.6 cm. Diameter 11.5 cm.

PROVENANCE: Unknown.

BIBLIOGRAPHY: Gusmani 1978, pp. 67–75, pls. I–II.

COMMENT: Michael Pfrommer has drawn our attention to a nearly identical bronze bowl (Height 4.4 cm. Diameter 10.6 cm), brought to the museum of Miletus by local people and thought to have been found in the vicinity (*Istanbuler Mitteilungen* 36, 1986, pp. 34–36, pl. 6).

89 b

89 c

90 a Bronze Statuette of a Hoplite

90 b

90 c

90 d

90

BRONZE STATUETTE OF A HOPLITE

Greek (Laconian?)
Sixth Century B.C.

The figure, cast solid, stands on a rectangular base, left leg forward. The base is pierced by two holes, on the front right and back left corners, the former still retaining a pin by which it was secured to a more solid support. The warrior wears a Corinthian helmet with a crest, a cuirass, and greaves. Beneath the cuirass he wears a short skirt, broadly scalloped, that covers his buttocks behind, but is short enough in front to leave his genitals exposed. His left arm once supported a shield, his right a spear, the clenched fists pierced to retain shield and weapon. A palmette and two volutes are engraved on the cuirass; the edge of the skirt has a lined and dotted border. The upper edges of the greaves are dotted and are modeled to indicate kneecaps. Only the right side of the crest is decorated; it features moldings, engraved triangles, and hatching for the horsehair crest. The left side is plain and even lacks the curved moldings. Horizontal lines, depicting hair, also appear only on the right side.

CONDITION: Casting flaws are visible on the back of the cuirass, buttocks, and left thigh. The figure has a green and tan patina.

MEASUREMENT: Height 21.7 cm.

PROVENANCE: Unknown.

BIBLIOGRAPHY: Unpublished.

COMMENT: Madeleine Jost and Marlene Herfort-Koch have provided recent discussions of bronze statuettes of striding hoplites (Jost 1975, pp. 355–363; Herfort-Koch 1986). Only two other statuettes wear a skirt like this one: a statuette in the Worcester Art Museum (Jost no. 6; Mitten and Doeringer 1967, p. 56, no. 39), and one lent to the Antikenmuseum in Basel in 1978 (Berger 1979, p. 46, pl. 17:3–4; not known to Jost). In neither of these, however, do the genitals show. Two other statuettes, both in Ioannina, wear protective lappets below the cuirass (1411, 4913; Jost nos. 16–17; note that nos. 17 and 18 in her list are identical). With the exception of a third statuette in Ioannina (4914; Jost no. 12) and one formerly in the de Kolb Collection (Jost no. 4; André Emmerich Gallery 1977, no. 63 and cover ill.), all other hoplites are shown naked below the cuirass.

The absence of engraving and other details on the left side of the Bastis figure suggests that it was once mounted on a large vase or utensil and was meant to be seen only from the right, more finished side. In this respect it matches a bronze figure of a striding warrior in Berlin (West) said to come from Dodona and likewise once attached to a larger object (10560; Jost no. 9; Walter-Karydi 1981, pp. 20, 26, no. 32, fig. 20).

91

BRONZE FIGURE OF A SPHINX

Greek (Laconian?)
Late Sixth Century B.C.

The sphinx is rampant, head turned sharply to the right. The wings are folded back against the torso, the tail lies along the hind legs. The hair is done to form six braids in back, two pairs in front. The polos is set off with a fillet or molding. A rectangular tang projects from the forelegs; remains of a circular pin are visible at the hind legs.

CONDITION: The surface of the sphinx is cracked in places. The body, face, and legs show red cuprite; the high relief has a green patina.

MEASUREMENT: Length, feet to feet 6.3 cm.

PROVENANCE: Acquired in 1981.

BIBLIOGRAPHY: Unpublished.

COMMENT: The sphinx probably comes from a mirror, helping to secure the disk to the handle, much as the eagle griffins do on a mirror in New York (MMA 38.11.3; Congdon 1981, p. 137, no. 15, pls. 12–13). A reclining sphinx from Olympia, evidently once part of a utensil, is related in style (B 5300; Mallwitz and Herrmann 1980, p. 132, pl. 92).

91 a (enlarged)

91 b (enlarged)

92 a

92 b

92 BRONZE PATERA HANDLE: STATUETTE OF A BOY

Greek
About 500 B.C.

The boy served as the handle of the patera and is cast solid. The figure is carefully modeled, perhaps better than its present condition suggests. The features are well shown, especially the eyes. Nipples are indicated. The hair in back is marked with vertical lines and subsidiary cross strokes. The legs are separated at the level of knees and shins, joined at calves and feet. The feet rest on a volute-and-palmette ornament. The head and raised hands joined an attachment which was once secured to the rim of the bowl. The attachment is engraved with volutes and flanking palmettes, the volutes separated by pointed leaves and connected with a hatched ribbon. A second attachment to which the bottom of the bowl was once soldered is decorated with volutes and palmettes, the former engraved, the latter modeled in the round.

CONDITION: The bowl is missing. Mottled green patina with spots of red cuprite corrosion appear on the lower palmette. Areas of the surface are pitted.

MEASUREMENTS: Length 23.0 cm. Original diameter of bowl about 24.0 cm.

PROVENANCE: Acquired in New York in the 1950s.

BIBLIOGRAPHY: Unpublished.

COMMENT: Pateras were made in Greece and Magna Graecia and were widely exported in the Mediterranean world. The Bastis handle is similar to several found on the Acropolis and is probably Attic (Gjødesen 1944, p. 112). Pierre Amandry and Ulf Jantzen have provided more recent discussions of patera handles (Amandry 1953, pp. 45–70, and Jantzen 1958, pp. 5–29).

93 BRONZE MIRROR HANDLE IN THE FORM OF A GIRL

Greek (Thessalian?)
Fifth Century B.C.

The girl wears a Doric peplos and pointed slippers. She carries a phiale in the left hand and once held another object in the right. Her hair is brushed up on the sides, done up in a roll behind, and secured by a fillet. The support of the mirror disk is engraved above with palmettes and a lotus flower.

CONDITION: The peplos and the disk support have been roughly scraped. The patina is dark green with brown areas.

MEASUREMENT: Height 10.9 cm.

PROVENANCE: Acquired in New York in the 1960s.

BIBLIOGRAPHY: Sale catalogue, Basel, *Münzen und Medaillen, Auktion XVIII, Kunstwerke der Antike,* 29. Nov. 1958, p. 12, no. 27, pl. 8; Congdon 1981, pp. 218–219, no. 128, not ill.

COMMENT: The workmanship is summary, and the proportions, especially the head and neck, are unusual, but the style is matched by other bronzes, among them a caryatid figure known since the turn of the century in Belgium (Musée de Mariemont G 95, Congdon 1981, p. 174, no. 63, pl. 59). A bronze statuette of a girl, in the Kestner Museum, Hanover, is also related (Liepmann 1975, p. 110, B 14, ill.). Another stylistically related bronze statuette of a girl, said to be from Pelion, is in a private collection in Volos, thus suggesting a Thessalian origin for the whole group (Biesantz 1965, pp. 35, 100, pl. 62).

94

BRONZE STATUETTE OF A MAN

Greek
Mid-fifth Century B.C.

The man, cast solid, stands with his weight on the left leg, right knee slightly flexed. The right arm is forward, the left is behind his back, concealed in a himation with a V-shaped overfold in front. The finely engraved hair radiates from the center of the crown of the head. Beard and mustache, shown in exquisite detail, are neatly clipped. Since the right hand is making the gesture of offering a sacrifice, the statuette was probably a votive gift at a sanctuary.

CONDITION: The left foot and right hand are broken off. The statuette is covered with a dark, gray-brown patina.

MEASUREMENT: Height 8.0 cm.

PROVENANCE: Acquired in New York in the 1940s.

BIBLIOGRAPHY: Unpublished.

COMMENT: The bronze figure of a man offering a sacrifice in Munich is larger but related in pose, dress, and hairstyle (3698, Sieveking 1913, p. 434, no. 3, ill.). In size, style, and degree of detail the Bastis figure is matched by a bronze statuette of a girl with a dove in Boston (01.7497; Comstock and Vermeule 1971, p. 53, no. 54, ill.). The gesture of the left arm is repeated in another bronze statuette of a girl in the Fogg Art Museum in Cambridge, and the folds of the himation across the man's back are similar to the folds of the himation on the Fogg bronze (1960.666; Fogg Art Museum 1973, pp. 24–25, no. 6, ill.).

95

BRONZE HANDLE OF A HYDRIA

Greek
Mid-fifth Century B.C.

The handle, of cast bronze, was attached to the shoulder and rim of a *hydria* or water jar. The horizontal side handles are missing, as are the separately made foot and the hammered body of the hydria itself. A siren, standing on an orb within an elaborate volute and palmette complex, serves as the shoulder attachment. Traces of solder remain on the back. The siren wears a stephane; her hair is indicated by cross-hatching and hangs down below the ears. A curved rod, open on the inner face and terminating in gorgon masks was secured to the rim of the vessel. A lion's face overlooks the rim of the jar, as if it were a lion-head spout at a fountain, an effect emphasized by the throat which is open to the cavity within the rim attachment. The lion's mane forms the relief decoration on top of the

95 a

95 b

95 c

95 d

95 e

95 f

handle. The ears are recessed in the bronze. A serpent's head with beaded body runs along the spine of the handle shaft.

CONDITION: On the lower exterior of the shaft and in spots on the siren is a mottled gray-green patina with extensive traces of red cuprite corrosion. Golden bronze shows on the upper inside of the shaft and on the left rim attachment. The center of the shaft is splitting on the sides. Extensive, bubbly corrosion is present on the lower inside of the shaft, below the level of the rim, probably caused by contact with remains of the missing neck of the hydria.

MEASUREMENTS: Height 28.5 cm. Width, from gorgon to gorgon, 18.9 cm.

PROVENANCE: Unknown.

BIBLIOGRAPHY: Unpublished.

COMMENT: The earliest bronze hydriai were made in the first half of the sixth century B.C. in Greece proper and in Magna Graecia. They were widely exported, many to Etruria, and owe their survival to being placed in tombs where they were often used as cinerary urns. They were also won as prizes, dedicated in sanctuaries, and even used as ballot boxes. This hydria handle is related stylistically to several assembled by Erika Diehl and by Dietrich von Bothmer in his review of Diehl's book (Diehl 1964, pp. 216–217; D. von Bothmer 1965, pp. 601–602). The handle is closest to those in Sofia (Seure 1925, p. 435 fig. 13), in Ancona (Diehl 1964, p. 216, B 91, pl. 7:2), and to one in Berlin (8006; Diehl 1964, p. 216, B 92; Neugebauer 1923–24, pp. 373–374, figs. 11–12).

96 Bronze *Kerykeion* (Herald's Staff)

96

BRONZE *KERYKEION* (HERALD'S STAFF)

Greek (South Italy or Sicily)
Fifth Century B.C.

Two intertwined serpents, joined at the body, rest upon an Ionic capital. The hollow stem projecting downward is broken and must originally have been longer or have fitted into a wood shaft.

CONDITION: It has a green patina with brown patches.

MEASUREMENTS: Height 18.5 cm. Width 11.6 cm.

PROVENANCE: Unknown.

BIBLIOGRAPHY: Unpublished.

COMMENT: As an attribute of Hermes, the *kerykeion* was a herald's staff: it was the symbol of office of an ambassador or a public messenger. Some twenty such objects are known, most of them of bronze. Two come from sanctuaries at Olympia and Samos, one from the Athenian acropolis, one from Crete bearing a dedication to Hera of Argos, and the rest, where the provenance is known, from South Italy and Sicily. Some are inscribed to indicate that they were the property of a city, such as Thurioi or Syracuse. At least two come from tombs, suggesting that they were the personal property of the herald. They could also have served as attributes for statues of Hermes or Iris. (*Kerykeia* are discussed by Crome 1938–39, pp. 117–126, and Hornbostel 1979, pp. 33–62).

97

BRONZE FITTING IN THE FORM OF A SERPENT

Greek
Fifth Century B.C.

The fitting is cast solid. It has a serpent's head at one end and a knobbed molding at the other. The serpent's features are carefully done, with the ears engraved on both sides. Directly behind the head the object is pierced vertically by a large hole, graduated in diameter, from .95 cm. above to 1.1 cm. below. This enabled it to be fitted snugly onto an upright rod.

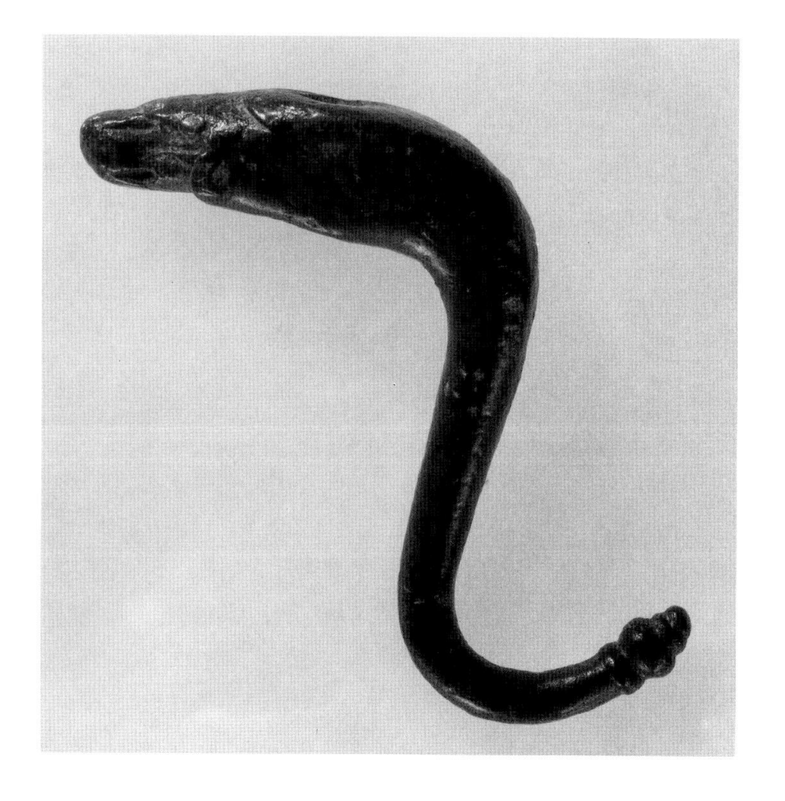

CONDITION: The patina is brown with green patches.

MEASUREMENT: Length 10.5 cm.

PROVENANCE: Unknown.

BIBLIOGRAPHY: Unpublished.

COMMENT: The protome of a serpent from Delphi, possibly from a candelabrum, is related in function to this one (Delphi Museum 9420; Rolley and Rougemont 1973, pp. 520–521, figs. 27–28; Rolley 1983, p. 146, fig. 138). Rolley drew attention to a complete candelabrum from Locri in Reggio Calabria which includes serpent attachments related to the Bastis and Delphi fittings (Foti 1972, pp. 57–58, color pl. III).

98 BRONZE ATTACHMENT WITH TWO HEADS

Greek
Fourth Century B.C.

The attachment shows in relief two heads of Pan, face to face, recognizable by the snub noses, goats' ears, and horns. An inverted leaf fills the space between forehead and nose. The back is roughly hollowed; the contoured edge projects towards the back and is in one plane, not curved. The original method of joining may have been solder, since no sign of mechanical attachment to a larger object is apparent.

CONDITION: The attachment bears a uniform green patina.

MEASUREMENTS: Height 4.4 cm. Width 6.7 cm.

PROVENANCE: Said to be from Greece.

BIBLIOGRAPHY: Unpublished.

COMMENT: We know of no close parallel to this piece.

99 BRONZE STATUETTE OF PAN

Greek
Fourth Century B.C.

Horns, long ears, hairy legs, and cloven hooves identify the figure as Pan. He is shown dancing, with arms extended. Roughened palms indicate that he once held something, perhaps torches, in his hands. A Y-shaped incision runs down the shoulders and back. The bottom of the lentoid plinth is flat; the right hoof is connected to it by a strut.

CONDITION: The statuette has a green patina.

MEASUREMENT: Height 12.6 cm.

PROVENANCE: Unknown.

BIBLIOGRAPHY: Unpublished.

COMMENT: Other bronze statuettes of Pan are related in pose, style, and, we must suppose, function, among them one in the Schimmel Collection (Muscarella ed. 1974, no. 25), and another in Lyon (Musée des Beaux-Arts L 74; Boucher 1970, pp. 22–23, no. 6); the latter is closest in style. They both once held objects in their hands and, on both, a strut connects the right leg to the base.

100

101

Greek
Late Fourth Century B.C.

The objects catalogued here were said to have been found together at Amphipolis in northern Greece; they comprise a pair of drinking cups (kylikes), a ladle, a combination funnel-strainer and a bottle; also a bronze bracelet and two rings, and five silver drachms. Joan Mertens has elsewhere provided a full discussion of these objects which makes only a summary description with selected comments necessary here (Mertens 1976, pp. 71–84).

THE VESSELS

Two cups: The cups were cast in two parts, bowl and stem, which were soldered together and turned on a lathe; the handles with leaf shaped attachment plates were cast separately and joined by soldering.

The top of one handle is mended. Both cups have a brown patina with patches of red and green corrosion.

The ladle: The ladle, also cast, has a shallow bowl and a long handle ending in a hook with a duck's head finial. Ladles of this general design are relatively common in bronze and in silver not only in the fourth century but also as late as the early Roman Imperial period.

The end of the handle is repaired. It has a brown patina with patches of red and green corrosion.

The Funnel-Strainer: This object, presumably used to remove coarse impurities from wine, has a sieve inserted into the top of the funnel. The sieve element is a hammered dish perforated with holes forming a pinwheel design. Otherwise the funnel was cast and the bowl turned on a lathe. Two loop handles, one partially broken, terminate in duck heads. Curlicues, shaped as if formed by a penknife peeling a strip of wood, mark the flat parts of the handle joining the bowl. A bead molding circles the rim.

The funnel-strainer has a heavy green patina.

The bottle: The bottle, lacking subsidiary decoration, and raised, not cast like the other bronzes, has a protruding foot and a flat lip. Joan Mertens has associated the object with related vases found in South Russia, concluding that it is a local version of a non-Greek shape (see bibliography).

It has a brown patina with patches of red and green corrosion.

102

103 a

MEASUREMENTS: Kylix A: Height 8.3 cm. Width 24.0 cm. Kylix B: Height 8.4 cm. Width 23.8 cm. Ladle: Height 26.7 cm. Funnel-strainer: Diameter 10.8 cm. Length, as preserved, 20.8 cm. Bottle: Height 7.3 cm.

PROVENANCE: Unknown.

BIBLIOGRAPHY: Sale catalogue, Paris, *Hôtel Drouot, 14 November 1973*, lot 138, ill.; Mertens 1976, pp. 71–84, figs. 1–6; *The Search for Alexander, Supplement to the Catalogue*, New York, 1982, pp. 10–11, nos. S. 29–33.

COMMENT: Where were such objects as the cups, ladle and strainer likely to have been made? Corinth has been suggested as one of the principal centers of manufacture, partially on the strength of statements in Strabo and Pliny (see Payne 1931, pp. 348–351) and because of the discovery at Galaxidhi near Delphi of a large group of such bronzes now in the British Museum. Related bronzes have been found in Macedonia: a pair of cups identical to the ones here was found in grave B at Derveni (Thessaloniki Museum; Makaronas 1963, pl. 228 b, illustrating one). Two funnel-strainers in the Thessaloniki Museum were found in graves A and B at Derveni (Thessalonike 1978, pp. 61, 66, nos. 170, 210); another in the Kavalla Museum was found at Nikesiani (Thessalonike 1978, p. 97, no. 404). Joan Mertens cites five more in European museums. Other bronzes of these types have been found at Ithaka (Waterhouse 1952, p. 233, pl. 47 a–b), at Votonisi (Vocotopoulou 1975, pp. 729–788) and at a site in Jugoslavia (Popovic et al. 1969, p. 77, no. 55 ill.). A collection reported to be from a tomb at Corinth was once in the Hoffmann collection *(Catalogue des Objects d'art antiques*, Vente Drouot, Paris 28–29 May, 1888, lots 419–446: lots 424, 432 and 433 are now in the Allard Pierson Museum, Amsterdam nos. 3379, 3378 and 3367 respectively, having been acquired in 1923; lot 427 is in New York, MMA 21.88.68). A group of bronzes from Vitsa Zagoriou in Epirus contained a skyphos bearing a dotted inscription KOP meaning perhaps "Corinthian" or "of Corinthian manufacture" (Vocotopoulou 1975, p. 770; Catling 1974, p. 24, fig. 43; Michaud 1974, p. 631, fig. 137). The same letters are scratched on the bottom of a silver cup from Derveni. A complete survey of bronze and silver vases of this design has yet to be undertaken.

103 b

104

105

106

107

THE JEWELRY

The bracelet: The hoop is circular in section and terminates in flattened snakes' heads. The bracelet is intact.

The rings: The hoops of the rings are elliptical in section; the bezels feature subjects done in intaglio relief: one shows an Eros playing *auloi* (a double flute), the other, more circular, shows a pacing lion. The rings are intact.

MEASUREMENTS: The bracelet: Diameter 4.6 cm. Ring with Eros: Diameter 2.5 cm. Ring with lion: Diameter 2.15 cm.

BIBLIOGRAPHY: Sale catalogue, Paris, *Hôtel Drouot, 14 November 1973,* lot 138; Mertens 1976, pp. 71–84, figs. 9–11; *The Search for Alexander, Supplement to the Catalogue*, New York, 1982, pp. 10–11, nos. S 34–36.

THE COINS

Five silver drachms: Acquired with the bronzes and jewelry and reported to have been found with them, were five silver drachms of Alexander the Great showing the head of Herakles wearing his lion's head on the obverse and an image of Zeus enthroned with eagle and scepter on the reverse. They were minted in Asia Minor between 327 and 304 B.C. In her publication Joan Mertens included a table which, with her permission, we repeat here:

Mint	*Date*	*Weight in grams*	*Reference*
Sardis	327 B.C.	4.15	Thompson-Bellinger 5
Abydos	324 B.C.	4.0	Thompson-Bellinger 2
Lampsakos	322 B.C.	3.5	Thompson-Bellinger 8
Kolophon	316 B.C.	4.2	Thompson-Bellinger 10
Kolophon	305/04 B.C.	3.85	Thompson-Bellinger 21/22

The reference is to M. Thompson and A. R. Bellinger, "A Hoard of Alexander Drachms," *Yale Classical Studies* 14, 1955, pp. 3–45. The arabic numbers cited above refer to the authors' list of issues in each mint.

All five coins show signs of wear.

BIBLIOGRAPHY: Sale catalogue, Paris, *Hôtel Drouot, 14 November 1973,* lot 138; Mertens 1976, pp. 71–84, figs. 12–13; *The Search for Alexander, Supplement to the Catalogue,* New York 1982, pp. 10–11, nos. S 37–41.

COMMENT: For further reading on coins of this type see Thompson and Bellinger, *loc. cit.,* and Bellinger 1963, esp. pp. 21–23, 44. Other tombs with bronzes of the type in the Bastis collection have contained coins, e. g. one at Nikesiani (Lazarides 1959, pp. 45–6, pl. 54; Daux 1960, p. 800).

108 a

108 b

109

BRONZE MIRROR

Greek
Late Fourth Century B.C.

Greek compact mirrors had two disks hinged together: one, the mirror proper, had a reflecting surface on the inside, concentric moldings on the outside; the other, the cover, was frequently decorated with a relief made separately. On this mirror the reflecting disk is missing, but the disk of the cover with hinge, handle, and relief decoration, is preserved. Three rivets secure the front part of the hinge to the disk. The lower edge of the hinge is serrated; the "omega"-shaped handle is lozenge in section. The bold repoussé relief shows Herakles in a drunken state, reclining on his lion skin, about to seduce Auge, the daughter of King Aleus of Tegea. His club lies nearby on the rocky ground.

CONDITION: The relief is positioned incorrectly on the disk; it should be lower and turned slightly counter-clockwise. The mirror disk, as already mentioned, is missing.

MEASUREMENT: Diameter of disk 15.2 cm.

COMMENT: Auge's son by Herakles was Telephos, who later became King of Mysia. The story formed the subject of lost tragedies by Sophocles and Euripides (Page 1941, pp. 13–21, 131–133; Frazer, ed. 1921, vol. I, pp. 252–255, n. 2; Anderson 1982, pp. 165–177). Other bronze mirrors with nearly identical reliefs are in the National Museum, Athens (Amandry 1963, pp. 73–77, no. 19, pl. X; Charbonneaux 1973, p. 225, fig. 237) and in Munich (Antikensammlung SL 45; Sieveking 1930, pp. 5–6, pl. 6). The same subject appears in relief in the tondo of a silver phiale from Rogozen, Bulgaria (Fol, Nikolov, Hoddinott 1986, p. 34, no. 4, ill.). Andrew Stewart has provided a summary of how bronze mirrors were made (Stewart 1980, pp. 24–34).

110a

110b

110c

110

BRONZE STATUETTE OF A SATYR

Greek
Third or Second Century B.C.

The satyr stands with his weight on the right foot, the left knee flexed, the left foot back. He looks down to the left. The figure lacks a tail, but exhibits a horse's ears, a flowing beard, and rude features, all proof of his identity. He wears an ivy wreath with berries.

CONDITION: Both arms are missing; no trace of an attachment remains for the left arm, suggesting that it was cast separately and soldered to the body. Separately cast left arms for bronze statuettes have been discussed by Dorothy Hill, who notes that the practice began in the Hellenistic Period (Hill 1982, pp. 277–283).

MEASUREMENT: Height 21.0 cm.

PROVENANCE: Acquired in New York.

BIBLIOGRAPHY: Unpublished.

COMMENT: Two bronze statuettes are related in size, pose, and style: one is a figure of the youthful Dionysos from Egypt, now in the Museum of Fine Arts, Boston (03.987; Comstock and Vermeule 1971, pp. 66–67, no. 67, ill.): note the buttocks, the position of the legs, the swing of the torso, the eyes, and the large vine wreath; the other is a figure of Herakles in Jerusalem, excavated at Samaria and dated before the destruction of the city in 107 B.C. (Crowfoot 1957, pp. 71–72, pl. VI.1–4). A bronze statuette of a satyr with torch and wineskin in New York is also related (41.11.6; Bieber 1961b, p. 112, fig. 447). The Bastis satyr may also have once held attributes of Dionysiac revelry.

110d

111

BRONZE STATUETTE OF POSEIDON

Greek
Third or Second Century B.C.

The god steps forward, right arm raised; the extended left hand supports a hippocamp, an attribute identifying the figure as Poseidon. He wears boots with the laces indicated and the lining folded over. The pubic hair and the hair of the head and beard are sharply delineated in a distinctive style. The eyes, nipples, and navel are also well defined.

CONDITION: The right hand and foot are missing. The left leg was fractured at the ankle and repaired. A casting flaw in the form of a small hole exists under the left thigh. The statuette has a greenish-gray patina.

MEASUREMENT: Height 14.7 cm.

PROVENANCE: Acquired in New York in 1980.

BIBLIOGRAPHY: Unpublished.

COMMENT: The pose, suitable for Zeus or Poseidon, goes back to the fifth century B.C.; see, for example, the bronze statuette found at Olympia in 1976 (Touchais 1977, p. 566, fig. 110). The hair of the Bastis bronze is rendered in a manner comparable to that on the Hellenistic bronze of Poseidon from Pella (Pella Museum M 383; M. Siganidov in National Gallery of Art 1980, p. 179, no. 154, ill.). Despite differences in pose and scale this comparison suggests a Hellenistic date for the Bastis bronze.

112a

112b

112

BRONZE STATUETTE OF A YOUTH

Greek
Second or First Century B.C.

The boy's body is twisted and bent back, the knees are slightly flexed, with the weight on the toes. His head is flung back, with the left arm up, the fingers curled. The hair is indicated in broad locks radiating from the crown of his head; long in back, it is parted over the forehead. The eyes were originally inlaid, probably with silver; the nipples were also once inlaid with another material, probably copper. The figure is cast solid.

CONDITION: Mechanical cleaning has smoothed a corroded surface. The right arm is missing.

MEASUREMENT: Height 20.5 cm.

PROVENANCE: Unknown.

BIBLIOGRAPHY: Unpublished.

COMMENT: The torsion of the body suggests a date not earlier than the late Hellenistic Period. A bronze boy in a comparable pose but twice the size and of Roman date is in Epinal, France (Musée départemental des Vosges; Braemer 1963, p. 99, no. 434, pl. XXXII).

113 BRONZE FLASK IN THE FORM OF A PIGSKIN

Greek
Second or First Century B.C.

The legs and tail of the pigskin are suggested by the protruding knobs. The tenon and grooves at the neck helped to secure a cord by which the flask could be hung up; it could also sit, as shown in the photograph. There must once have been a stopper.

MEASUREMENTS: Height 10.7 cm. Width 6.1 cm.

PROVENANCE: Acquired in 1982.

COMMENT: A similar flask, complete with leaf-shaped lid, is in the collection of Norbert Schimmel (Muscarella, ed. 1974, no. 38, where other flasks are cited).

114 BRONZE FURNITURE ATTACHMENT WITH A HORSE'S HEAD

Greek
First Century B.C.

The attachment fitted over the right end of a *fulcrum*, the head- and arm-rest of a dining couch. Head-rests were decorated in this manner in the late Hellenistic and Roman periods with the ornament usually taking the form of a horse or mule head, less commonly that of a dog or duck. The horse's head is turned sharply to the right, the torsion emphasized by wrinkles rendered at the neck. Locks of hair fall over the forehead but, apart from a ridge with four lines engraved on it, the mane is not really shown. Eyes, nostrils, and open mouth with teeth are realistically modeled; the pupils and irises of the eyes are dotted and circled.

Crossing the horse's neck is a *nebris* or fawn skin, a Dionysiac attribute, and an appropriate adjunct to the attachment of a banquet couch.

The bronze flange of the socket in back of the horse's head is cut away in places, but the original edge is partially preserved, as is a nail hole. The lower edge displays a set of crescent moldings. Here, too, the edge is not original, for the bronze once extended in a curved bar to a lower ornament, perhaps in the form of a head of Dionysos or Eros. The back part of the head is hollow.

CONDITION: The attachment has a green patina with spots of red cuprite corrosion on it and small areas of shiny bronze.

MEASUREMENT: Greatest dimension 9.8 cm.

PROVENANCE: Acquired in New York in the 1960s.

BIBLIOGRAPHY: Unpublished.

COMMENT: The soft rendering of the features and the absence of bold corkscrew curls on the mane, so often found on Roman horse- and mule-head attachments, suggest that this is a late Hellenistic bronze. The fawn skin is also modeled without elaboration and without the silver inlay often occurring on Roman pieces.

Fulcra are discussed in the following publications: Greifenhagen 1930, pp. 137–165; Boube-Piccot 1960, pp. 189–286; Richter 1966, pp. 57–58, 105–109; Mitten 1975, pp. 176–179; and Bonci 1977, pp. 183–200. The Antikenmuseum in Basel recently acquired the bronze fittings of a couch, including legs, frame and *fulcra* with horse heads (Seiterle and Mutz 1982, pp. 62–70, pls. 11–13).

115

BRONZE STATUETTE OF A FEMALE DEITY

Hellenistic or Roman
First Century B.C. or A.D.

The goddess is represented wearing a chiton belted high under the breasts, with a himation covering the lower body and rolled around the hips. The chiton is pinned at the shoulders, but has slipped off the right shoulder, revealing the breast. She also wears a diadem set with five inlays of other materials (perhaps copper and silver), three square ones alternating with two rectangular ones. She does not wear earrings. Her feet are without sandals.

The features are fleshy and soft; the pupils are indicated. Her hair, parted in the middle, is tied in a bun in back and falls in two ringlets on either side. The drapery clings to the body, especially around the lower legs and ankles; the modeling of the folds is mannered, noticeably so below the left arm, under the left breast, and on the chiton, as it bunches against the top edge of the himation.

The torso was cast hollow in two halves, the upper half in one piece with the head. The join is concealed under the lower edge of the roll of the himation. The arms were cast separately and fitted into sockets that have finished, cylindrical edges. The upper left arm was inclined downward at a 45° angle. The bottom of the statuette is open.

CONDITION: Both arms are missing. The cylindrical ends of the upper arms are partially broken. There is a crack on the left side of the hip. In places the statuette has been cleaned to the metal. A brownish-gray crust spotted with red cuprite and green corrosion forms a skin over part of the reddish-brown, smooth surface. The interior has a light gray, gritty surface.

MEASUREMENT: Height 53.0 cm.

PROVENANCE: Formerly in the collection of Claude Annet; said to have been acquired at Persepolis in 1910.

BIBLIOGRAPHY: Unpublished.

COMMENT: Large scale statuettes of this sort were fashionable in the late Hellenistic and early Roman periods, especially in artistic centers of the eastern Mediterranean. A bronze statuette in the art market of similar size and dress, but more classicizing in style, is related to this figure (Sale catalogue, New York, *Sotheby's, June 10–11, 1983,* lot 120; The Barakat Gallery 1985, p. 43, ill.). The smaller bronze figure of Tyche in the collection of William Herbert Hunt is also more classicizing in style than the Bastis bronze (Kimbell Art Museum 1983, pp. 120–121, ill.).

115a

115b

115c

115d

117a

116 FIBULA OR SAFETY PIN

Etruscan
Seventh Century B.C.

The body of the pin is in the form of a dog, the tail describing two loops. A collar is indicated by incision. The raised forelegs grasp the pin.

CONDITION: The catch-plate which secured the pin is missing.

MEASUREMENTS: Height 2.1 cm. Length 5.0 cm. Length of dog alone 3.3 cm.

PROVENANCE: Unknown.

BIBLIOGRAPHY: Unpublished.

COMMENT: Animal pins are known in Greece and Etruria. Those from the Boeotian Ptöon and the sanctuary of Apollo Tyritios, near Tyros on the Gulf of Nauplia, differ in style and design (Cahn 1950, pp. 185–199, esp. p. 190, fig. 2; reprinted in Cahn 1975, pp. 17–32, esp. p. 22, fig. 2). The Bastis pin resembles those from Etruria, such as one from Tarquinia, Poggio Gallinoro (Hencken 1958, p. 269, pl. 69, fig. 32:f).

117 BRONZE LION HEAD

Etruscan
Eighth or Seventh Century B.C.

The head is powerfully modeled in repoussé with details done by chasing. The mouth is open with the teeth showing. Chased, wavy lines simulate the fur bordering the mouth and the raised ruff. The ruff comes to a point over the forehead and is angled back on the sides. Semicircular, raised areas in the angles of the ruff probably represent the lion's cheek bones. The ears are folded back behind the ruff; the fur of the inner surface is shown with chased lines. Lines are deeply chased on the nose, the nostrils are dotted, and fur on top of the nose is done in parallel lines. The eyes are semicircular with extended inner corners. The eyebrows are dotted. The head was nailed to a larger object through holes visible in the partially preserved flange.

117b

CONDITION: Much of the lion's right side behind the ruff is missing. The head has a pale green patina.

MEASUREMENTS: Height 9.5 cm. Depth, nose to back 8.5 cm.

PROVENANCE: Unknown.

BIBLIOGRAPHY: Unpublished.

COMMENT: The head is comparable to a much larger one in the same technique excavated at Olympia in 1960 (B 4999; Herrmann 1981, pp. 72–82, pls. 4–7). The Olympia piece is considered to be an eighth-century, late Hittite centerpiece of a votive shield. Although differing in scale and in the placement of ears, shape of eyes, and contour of ruff, it is related in style to the Bastis bronze. Nevertheless, despite these similarities, the Bastis bronze is probably a forerunner of a group of sixth-century Etruscan lion heads of hammered bronze of similar function (W. Ll. Brown 1960, pp. 98–101).

118a

118b

118

BRONZE STATUETTE OF A LION

Etruscan
Late Sixth Century B.C.

Sets of bronze lions, reclining or seated on their haunches, ornamented a wide variety of Etruscan vessels and utensils, including cauldrons, braziers, and incense burners. Remains of solder on the feet of this beast indicate that he too was once attached to a larger object, perhaps a portable brazier. The lion looks straight ahead, mouth open, tongue hanging out, paws individually modeled with claws incised. The tail lies along the right hindquarters and is not separated from the body, as it usually is with Etruscan lions of this function. The head is blocky and the chin does not protrude significantly from the neck. The rounded forms of head, neck, and back meet at an angle along the top side. The ears and the front of the mane are modeled, but engraving is limited to defining whiskers, ruff, eyes, and cheek. The mane seems not to have been incised at all.

CONDITION: A dark green patina covers the figure, with abundant traces of red cuprite, especially on the neck.

MEASUREMENTS: Height 5.9 cm. Length 8.4 cm.

PROVENANCE: Acquired in New York before 1970.

BIBLIOGRAPHY: Unpublished.

COMMENT: Is this an Etruscan or Greek lion? It is not unlike a bronze lion in Boston, whose origin is disputed between Etruria and Asia Minor (66.9, Comstock and Vermeule 1971, pp. 307–308, no. 433, ill.). Though broader in the head and with a more pointed and closed mouth, the profile of the Boston lion is not dissimilar, especially in the paws, haunches, and tail. Nevertheless, despite differences in the tail and other individual features from lions that are surely Etruscan, the Bastis lion probably goes with lions from Etruscan braziers and other objects assembled by Llewellen Brown and not with Greek lions (W. Ll. Brown 1960, p. 91, pls. XXXVI–XXXVII). It differs in style, for instance, from two lions found at Perachora, from the shoulder of a dinos (Payne 1940, pp. 136–137, pl. 43:8–9).

119

BRONZE HIPPOCAMP FROM A TRIPOD

Etruscan
550–500 B.C.

The marine horse is perched on top of a set of rod supports, one of the forelegs touching the rod. The mane and details of the face are incised. The piscine hindquarters are marked with scales, while fins and tail are incised. Part of the hammered bowl of the missing cauldron, once supported by the tripod stand, adheres to the back of the hippocamp.

MEASUREMENTS: Height 16.5 cm. Length of hippocamp 13.5 cm.

PROVENANCE: Unknown.

BIBLIOGRAPHY: Unpublished.

COMMENT: Tripod stands supporting cauldrons were a specialty of Etruscan bronze workers; many are thought to have been made at Vulci (Neugebauer 1943, pp. 206–278). The upright frame was formed by three curved rods, as here, alternating with three straight ones, the lower ends connected by struts and fitted into three lion-paw feet. The rods were decorated with animals, monsters, and human figures. The major part of the tripod to which the hippocamp belongs is in Oxford (Ashmolean Museum 1971.912; Haynes 1966, pp. 101–102, pl. 24:1–4). A second hippocamp, formerly in the Currier estate and now in another American private collection, belongs to the same tripod (Mitten and Doeringer 1967, p. 190, no. 196).

120 a

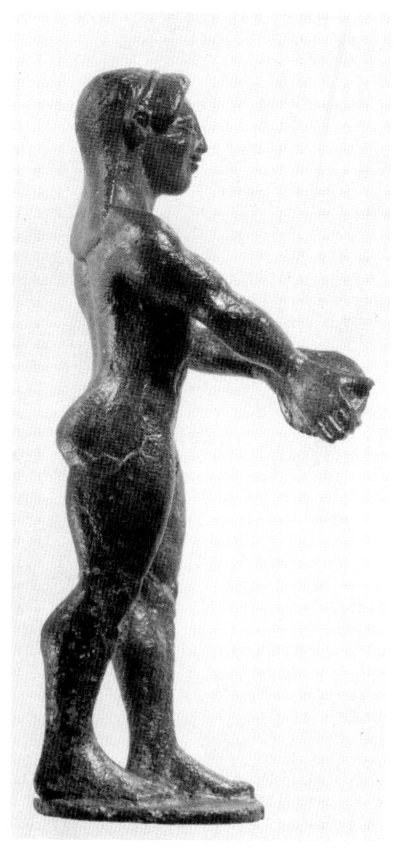
120 b

120 c

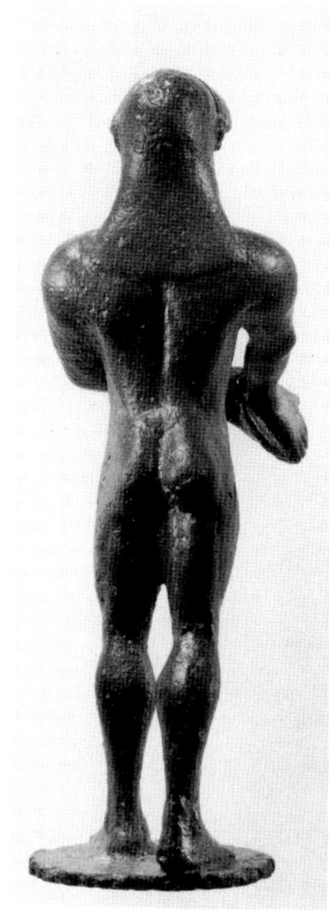
120 d

120

BRONZE STATUETTE OF A DISCUS THROWER

Etruscan
Late Sixth Century B.C.

The youth stands erect, left leg forward, both hands outstretched, the left hand grasping the discus, the right steadying it. The muscles are well developed. He wears a fillet behind the hair over the forehead. The statuette is probably the finial from the top of a candelabrum or the lid of a cauldron.

CONDITION: Rust-colored corrosion shows through the green patina of the surface. A line running zig-zag across the buttocks and across the genitals probably has to do with the casting.

MEASUREMENT: Height 9.8 cm.

COMMENT: Discus throwers were often used as finials on Etruscan candelabra and cauldron lids, but they usually hold the discus in only one hand. Compare, for example, a finial formerly in the Swiss art market (Sale catalogue, Lucerne, *Ars Antiqua, Auktion V, 7 Nov. 1964*, p. 11, no. 30, pl. X) and the bronzes listed in Richardson 1983, p. 207, n. 13.

121 a

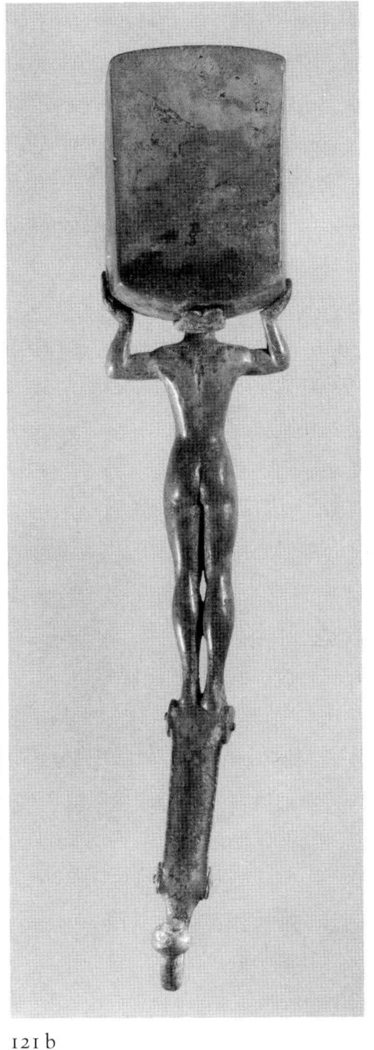

121 b

121 c

121

BRONZE SHOVEL WITH A GIRL AS THE HANDLE

Etruscan
Early Fifth Century B.C.

The girl is represented holding the shovel in her hands; it is riveted to the palms and her swept-up hair. She stands on an elaborate finial which incorporates spool-shaped elements, ending in a hook to hang up the shovel. An Etruscan inscription is engraved along the girl's left side. The shovel was probably used for incense. A full discussion is given by Dietrich von Bothmer in the article cited below.

CONDITION: The shovel has a green patina. Three fingers of the right hand and the rivet through the hair are missing.

MEASUREMENT: Length 32.7 cm.

PROVENANCE: Unknown.

BIBLIOGRAPHY: D. von Bothmer and J. Heurgon "An Etruscan Bronze in New York," *Monuments et Mémoires. Fondation E. Piot,* 61, 1977, pp. 45–59, figs. 1–3, 11; Haynes 1985, pp. 283–289, no. 104, ill. p. 183.

COMMENT: The inscription reads:
MI SELVANSEL ⁝ S MUCINΘIUNAI TULA which freely rendered means: "I belong to Selvans. S(ethra) Mucinthiuna dedicated me." Selvans is equated with the Latin Silvanus, the Roman deity of wilderness beyond cultivated land; it is to his Etruscan counterpart that a woman has offered the incense shovel. Jacques Heurgon provides a full commentary on the inscription in the article cited above.

122 a

122

BRONZE *THYMIATERION* (INCENSE-BURNER)

Etruscan (Vulci?)
500–475 B.C.

To the city of Vulci are attributed some of the finest Etruscan bronzes, among them tripod-stands, candelabra, and incense burners. Most of them embody sculptural elements of human figures and animals, the more striking being figures of Herakles, satyrs, and dancers, both male and female. On the Bastis incense-burner a girl dancing with castanets is twirling, as the flare of the skirt suggests. She is barefoot, but wears ribbons on her ankle and instep. Her hair is bunched, folded, and tied in back in a bun or *krobylos*, and braids encircle her head. She wears disk earrings. On her head she balances the support of the incense bowl: a short molded shaft ending in leaves and knobbed stems. The legs of the tripod base, six-sided in section, terminate in lion paws resting on disks. Inverted palmettes project from the junction of the legs.

CONDITION: The bronze has been mechanically cleaned, leaving a mottled, dark red and green patina. A gritty surface, unfinished even in antiquity, is visible on the resting surfaces of the disks and the backs of the palmettes. The tripod base is attached to the dancer's base with a modern screw. Originally, a bronze pin would have secured the two parts. The incense bowl that appears in old photographs is now missing.

MEASUREMENTS: Height 33.3 cm. Height of dancer 16.8 cm.

PROVENANCE: Acquired in New York in the 1970s.

BIBLIOGRAPHY: Unpublished.

COMMENT: The incense burner is related stylistically to one in the collection of William Herbert Hunt in which a satyr is the sculptural element (Kimbell Art Museum 1983, pp. 106–107, no. 32, ill.), to another in the Bibliothèque Nationale, featuring a kouros (Adam 1984, pp. 43–44, no. 45, ill.), and to a third in the Louvre in which a female dancer with castanets is figured (Giglioli 1935, pl. 211:2; Banti 1973, pl. 44 a center). The arrangement of moldings and leafy stems above the figures in the Hunt collection and the Bibliothèque Nationale matches that above the Bastis figure. Compare also an incense burner in the Ny Carlsberg Glyptotek, Copenhagen (H. I. N. 477, Haynes 1985, p. 266, no. 57, ill.). On the Bastis bronze the manner in which the braids come forward around the head and are tied in front recalls the braids on the bronze statue of Zeus or Poseidon from the sea off Artemision and on the replicas of the so-called Omphalos Boy, works dated in the decades around 475 B.C. Other incense burners and the Vulcian school of bronzes are discussed by Neugebauer 1943, pp. 206–278, and by Zandrino 1952, pp. 329–339, ill. Dancers appear in Etruscan tomb paintings. Among the painted figures in the late sixth-century Tomb of the Jugglers at Tarquinia is a girl balancing an incense burner on her head, wearing crossed bands on her body, and a skirt that flares like that of the Bastis bronze (Sprenger and Bartoloni 1983, p. 105, no. 92, ill.). A poorly preserved painting from the Tomb of the Colle Casuccini at Chiusi shows a girl with crotala wearing ribbons on her feet like those of the Bastis piece (Stenico 1963, p. 22, pl. 39).

122 b

122 c

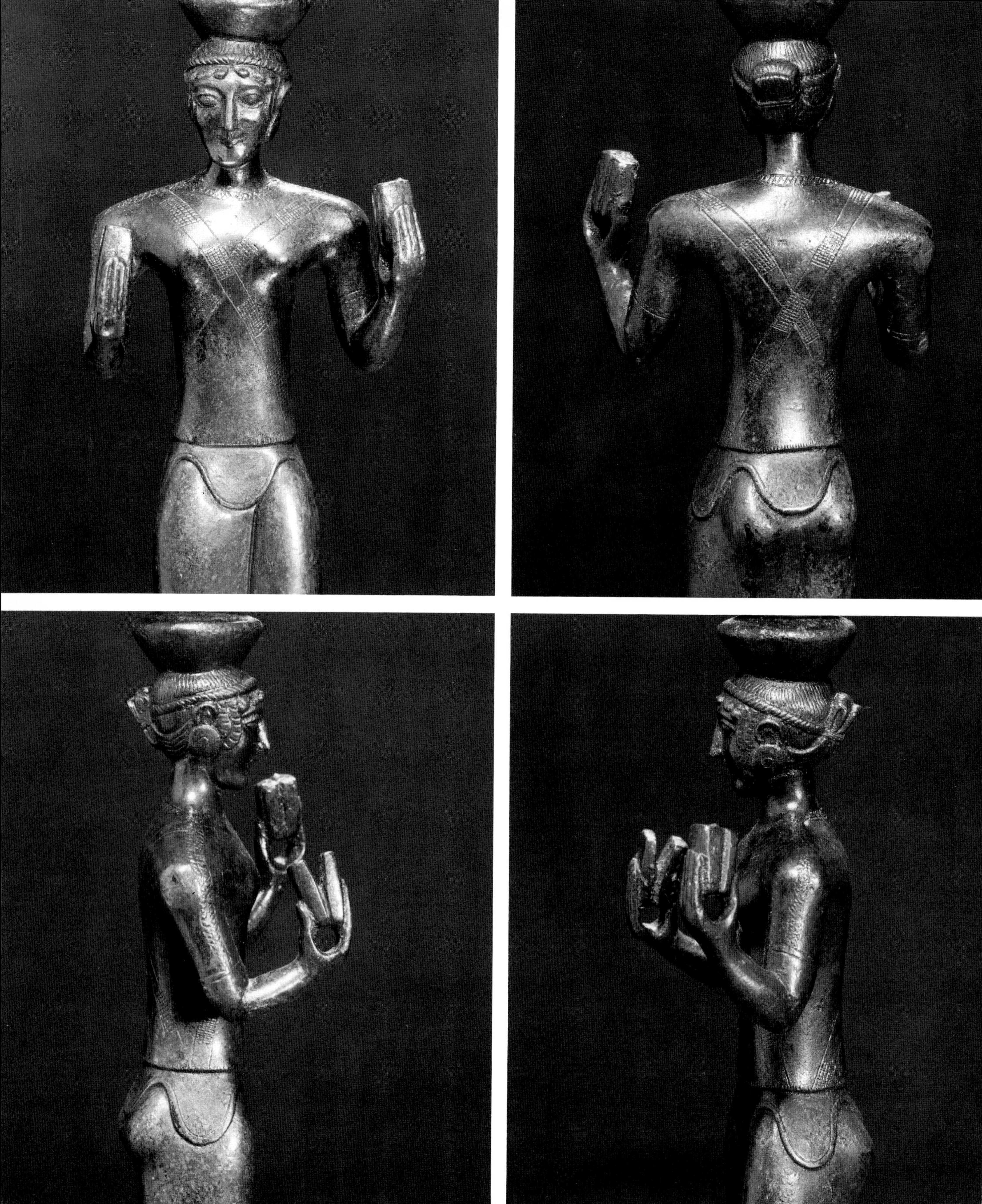

123

BRONZE BOWL OF A *THYMIATERION* (INCENSE-BURNER)

Etruscan
Fifth Century B.C.

Only the crowning members of the *thymiaterion* are preserved: a finial of three leaves and three-knobbed stems, and the incense bowl itself; the tripod base and shaft are missing. Four animals, cast in one piece with the bowl, sit on the rim, two felines and two mules, the latter identifiable by the hooves and long ears. They turn their heads outward.

CONDITION: The bowl has a mottled green-brown patina. The tip of one leaf is broken off. The lower element is riveted to the bowl.

MEASUREMENTS: Height 10.5 cm. Diameter 10.5 cm.

PROVENANCE: Unknown.

BIBLIOGRAPHY: Unpublished.

COMMENT: We know of no close parallel to the piece.

124 a

124 b

124

TWO BRONZE LEGS OF AN INCENSE-BURNER

Etruscan
Mid-fifth Century B.C.

Originally there were three legs; one is lost. A kneeling youth, hands on hips, is shown riding a winged lion's paw. The paw rests on a molded disk riveted to its underside. Rivets also secured the ends of the wings. Despite minor differences, the two legs must have come from the same burner.

CONDITION: Most of the left wing of the larger leg is missing; the top of the right wing of the smaller leg is also missing. A brown patina on both legs shows traces of green and red corrosion.

MEASUREMENTS: Height of one 7.8 cm. Height of the other 7.7 cm.

PROVENANCE: Unknown.

BIBLIOGRAPHY: Sale catalogue, New York, *Sotheby Parke Bernet Nov. 22, 1974*, lot 193, ill.

COMMENT: Fifth-century B.C. Greek writers, quoted by an author of the Roman period (Athenaeus I 28 bc; XV 700 c), state how valued Etruscan bronzes were in Athens. Tangible evidence of this is provided by Etruscan bronzes actually excavated in Greece, among them two legs of this very type, one from Olympia (B 1001; Mallwitz and Herrmann 1980, pp. 120–121, pl. 82; Gauer 1984, p. 52, pl. 12:4), another from Lindos (Blinkenberg 1931, p. 746, no. 3217, pl. 151), both from incense-burners probably deposited as votive offerings in the sanctuaries where they were found.

A complete stand of this type is in the Vatican Museum (Giglioli 1935, p. 59, no. 4, pl. 315:4; Cain 1985, p. 24, pl. 3:1–2). Almost a meter tall, it has a pyramidal base made of sheet bronze and an elaborate stemmed support with disk moldings. Three feet from such a stand, similar to the Bastis pair, are in New York (20.37.1 a–c; Metropolitan Museum 1940, p. 30, fig. 88; formerly in the Borelli Bey Collection [Sale catalogue, Paris, *Hotel Drouot, 11–13 juin 1913*, no. 250, pl. XXXI], and the Canessa Collection [Canessa 1919, no. 24, ill.]). Singletons are in the Archaeological Museum, Florence (no. 678), in the Bibliothèque Nationale, Paris (Adam 1984, p. 94, no. 106, ill.), in the Staatliche Museen, Berlin (Neugebauer 1924, pl. 30), in the Ny Carlsberg Glyptotek, Copenhagen (Poulsen 1927, pl. 95), and in the New York art market (Sale catalogue, New York, *Sotheby's May 22, 1981*, lot 109; Sale catalogue, Basel, *Münzen and Medaillen, Auktion XVIII, Kunstwerke der Antike, 29. November 1958*, p. 14, no. 35, pl. 11). Although the group has been described in part (Kunze 1951, pp. 736 ff.), no up-to-date study of such incense stands exists.

125 a

125 b

125

BRONZE STATUETTE OF A GODDESS OR WOMAN

Etruscan (Umbrian)
475–450 B.C.

She wears an ankle-length garment with sleeves to the elbow. The garment is decorated with dotted spirals and with rows of circles down the middle both in front and in back and along the sleeves. She wears a necklace with triangular pendants and a feathered crown. The bronze was a dedication at a sanctuary.

CONDITION: The feet and hands are broken off; the feathered crown is bashed on top.

MEASUREMENT: Height 21.7 cm.

PROVENANCE: Acquired in New York in the 1940s.

BIBLIOGRAPHY: D. von Bothmer 1961, p. 41, no. 156, pl. 54; Richardson 1983, p. 320, no. 19.

COMMENT: In his publication of the piece D. von Bothmer drew attention to a figure of this type in Berlin (West), excavated at Ancarano near Norcia (7913; *Notizie degli Scavi* 1878, pp. 13 f., pl. 2:2). Similar statuettes of girls with feathered crowns are in the Bibliothèque Nationale, Paris (Adam 1984, pp. 169–170, no. 250, ill.), in the Museo Archeologico, Verona (Franzoni 1980, p. 43, no. 25, ill.), in the collection of Hans Cohn, Los Angeles (unpublished), and in the estate of Frederick Stafford (Isaac Delgado Museum of Art 1966, pp. 17, 143, no. 40, ill.). A sixth statuette in Rio de Janeiro (Museu Nacional 2026) is known through photographs by the late H. R. W. Smith brought to our attention by D. von Bothmer. The piece in the Cohn Collection preserves feet and tangs below the feet, indicating that it once fitted into a base, as must also have been the case with the other bronzes.

129 a

129 b

126

BRONZE STATUETTE OF A WARRIOR

Etruscan (Umbrian)
Fifth Century B.C.

The figure, cast solid, is dressed as a Greek hoplite. He wears a helmet with hinged cheek pieces raised, a leather cuirass (breastplate) with belt and shoulder straps, and under it a cloth garment that is visible below the cuirass and at the neck. Of his greaves (shin guards), only the top of the one at the left is preserved. The cuirass is decorated with engraved designs: circles, quatrefoils, and dotted lines.

CONDITION: The lower legs, the right arm, and the crest of the helmet are missing. The left arm would have held a shield, the right hand a spear. The chin and tips of the cheek pieces are corroded. The mottled green patina forms a skin.

MEASUREMENT: Height 15.5 cm.

PROVENANCE: Acquired in New York in the 1940s.

BIBLIOGRAPHY: Unpublished.

COMMENT: Bronze statuettes of warriors of this size and style have been found in central Italy, especially around Todi, Foligno, Calvi, and Ancarano. Emeline Richardson has devoted several studies to the type (Richardson 1971, pp. 161–168 and Richardson 1983, pp. 172–195).

127

BRONZE MIRROR

Etruscan
Late Fourth Century

The tang, cast in one piece with the disk, once fitted into a wood or bone handle. The edge of the convex reflecting surface is marked with a hatched line and is turned towards the back or engraved side to form a flange. A palmette is engraved in the space above the tang. The engraving on the back shows a boy restraining a rampant horse. The horse is bridled and wears a collar. The boy, who wears a cloak, has the horse by a lead and holds an extra coiled length of rope in his left hand. An acanthus plant suggests an open field where the action takes place. Lyre volutes and a palmette fill the space above the tang. The scene is framed by an ivy wreath without berries knotted at the top.

CONDITION: A triangular section of the disk, including the boy's head, was broken and repaired.

MEASUREMENTS: Length 19.2 cm. Diameter 13.4 cm.

PROVENANCE: Unknown.

BIBLIOGRAPHY: Unpublished.

COMMENT: A similar composition, in reverse, appears on a mirror in Boston (99.495, Comstock and Vermeule 1971, p. 265, no. 282; Fischer-Graf 1980, pp. 91–92, V 55, pl. 23:3).

128

BRONZE MIRROR

Etruscan
Third or Early Second Century B.C.

The disk, cast in one piece with the handle, has a convex reflecting surface to allow a whole face to be seen. The edge of the mirror is turned towards the back or engraved side to form a flange, and the flange is milled and bordered with two engraved lines. The handle ends in an animal head, which may be that of a hind, and is ornamented with florals. Engraved on the back is a scene depicting the Judgment of Paris. The hero, nude except for cloak and boots, mingles with the three goddesses, Hera, Athena, and Aphrodite, who, without attributes, are not readily distinguishable. One wears a long chiton; the other two, leaning on columns, wear each a short tunic and boots. They all wear a snood.

CONDITION: The mirror bears a shiny, light green patina, peeling on the handle.

MEASUREMENTS: Length 22.8 cm. Diameter 11.7 cm.

PROVENANCE: Acquired in New York in the 1970s.

BIBLIOGRAPHY: Unpublished.

COMMENT: H. S. Roberts discusses mirrors of this type (Roberts 1983, pp. 31–54).

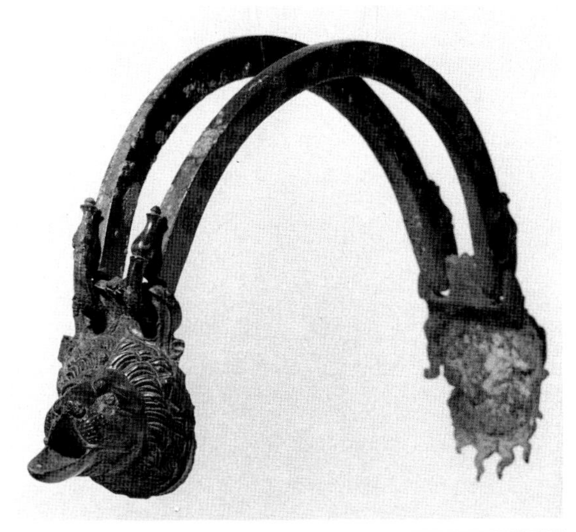

129 a

129 b

129

BRONZE HANDLES OF A SITULA

Etruscan or Greek
Fourth or Third Century B.C.

The handles are formed by two curved bars, rectangular in section, the extremities looped through two attachments. One attachment, which also serves as the spout, is in the shape of a lion's head, the other in the form of a satyr's mask. Both are finely modeled, with subsidiary detail incised.

CONDITION: A rich, green-blue patina with gray-brown protuberances of corrosion lies over the smooth patina. The inner faces of the swinging handles are beveled at the top of the rise, as if they were worn by being clapped together. The satyr's mask is backed by a crossbar with holes for the handles, either an ancient repair or the original two-piece construction. Solder remains in the cavity of the mask.

MEASUREMENTS: Height of satyr's head 8.5 cm. Length of handles 18.0 cm.

PROVENANCE: Unknown.

BIBLIOGRAPHY: Unpublished.

COMMENT: Numerous buckets of the type from which These handles come are known, many from firm contexts, yet their origin is debated. Stéphanie Boucher has suggested that they were made in Etruria and exported to western Europe, northern Greece, Thrace, and South Russia, where they have been found (Boucher 1973, pp. 79–96). Beryl Barr-Sharrar, on the other hand, has argued for a Macedonian origin (Barr-Sharrar 1982, pp. 123–139), but her argument does not take into account the Italian and western European provenances or the renown of Etruscan bronze-workers. Michael Pfrommer has demonstrated the complexity of the interdependence of late Classical and early Hellenistic metalwork (Pfrommer 1983, pp. 235–285).

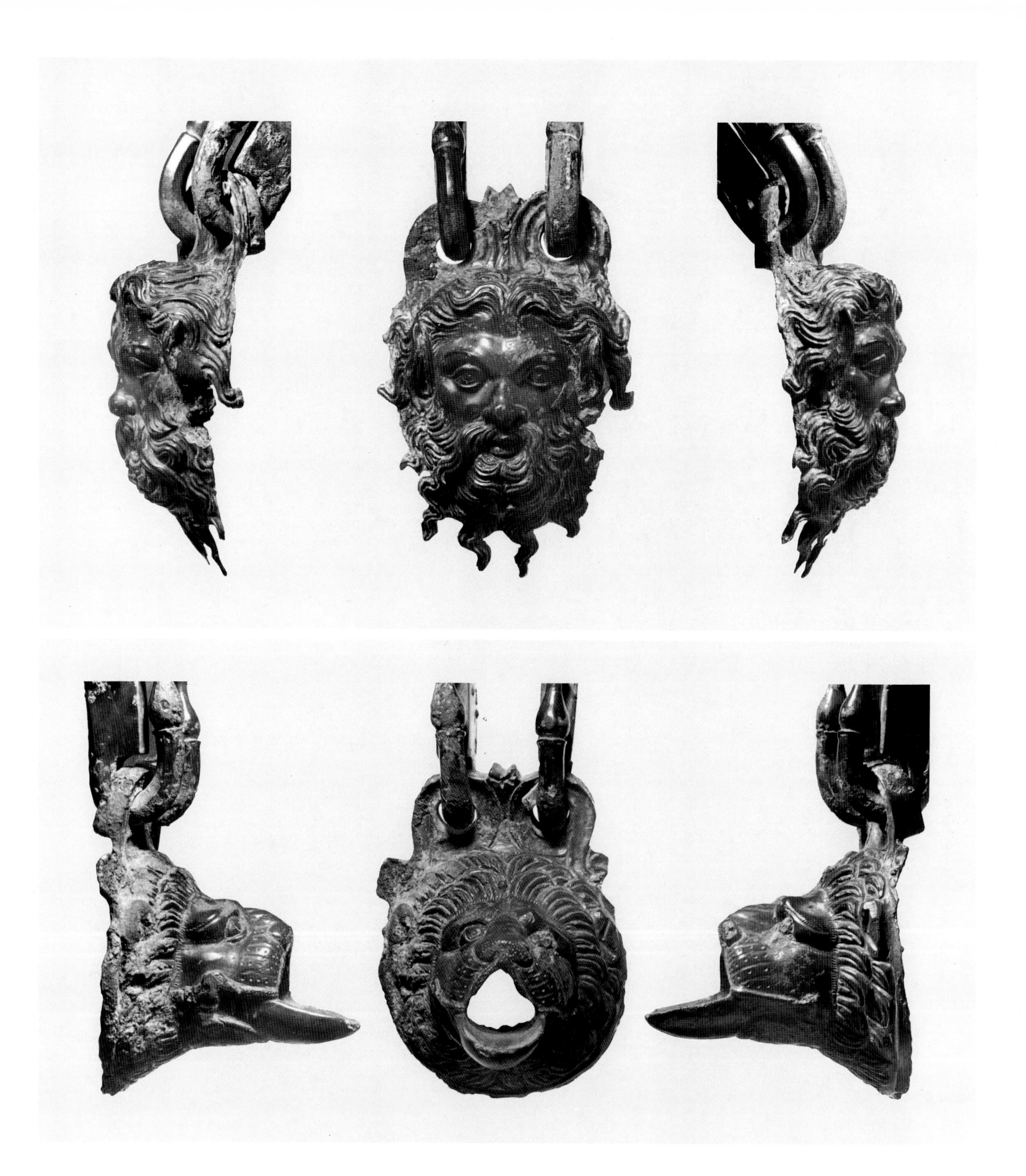

130 SATYR HEAD ATTACHMENT FROM A BRONZE BUCKET

Etruscan or Greek
Fourth or Third Century B.C.

The bronze attachment, which once held one end of a pair of swinging handles, is a variant of the satyr's mask on No. 129. This satyr is balding, has a snub nose, and generally a wilder appearance. He wears an ivy wreath.

CONDITION: The attachment is intact.

MEASUREMENTS: Height 7.5 cm. Width 4.5 cm.

PROVENANCE: Unknown.

BIBLIOGRAPHY: Sale catalogue, New York, *Sotheby's, June 10–11, 1983,* lot 82.

COMMENT: See No. 129.

131 a

131

BRONZE HEAD OF ALEXANDER THE GREAT

Greek or Roman
First Century B.C. or A.D.

The face shows the full features, bold brow and upswept hair normally associated with images of Alexander. The lips are inlaid with copper, the eyes with silver.

CONDITION: The head is broken from a statuette. Most of the surface has been cleaned to the bare metal, but a greenish-brown corrosion remains in the hollows of the modeling. A casting flaw in front of the right ear has been plugged.

MEASUREMENTS: Height 5.8 cm. Width 4.0 cm.

PROVENANCE: Unknown.

BIBLIOGRAPHY: *The Search for Alexander. Supplement to The Catalogue,* New York 1982, p. 20, no. S 65; R. W. Hartle, "The Search for Alexander's Portrait," *Philip II, Alexander The Great, and The Macedonian Heritage,* eds. W. L. Adams and E. N. Borza, Lanham, Maryland 1982, p. 164, figs. 6–7.

COMMENT: Although cast hollow, the head is not necessarily from a statuette; it could also have come from a bust or the emblematic centerpiece of a bowl. Inlays of silver and copper, here used respectively for the eyes and lips, are common on late Hellenistic and early Roman bronzes.

131 b

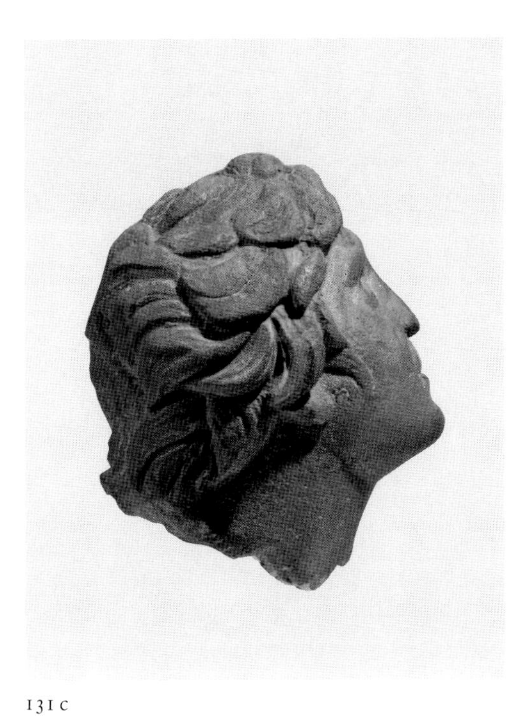
131 c

131 d

132 a

132 b

132

BRONZE STATUETTE OF APHRODITE

Roman
First or Second Century A.D.

She is represented leaning over to remove the sandal from her left foot. The left arm was extended for balance. The hair is secured in a bun behind the head and falls over her shoulders.

CONDITION: Both arms and the right leg below the knee are missing. The missing parts of the arms were made separately and attached.

MEASUREMENT: Height 10.0 cm.

PROVENANCE: Acquired in New York in the 1940s.

BIBLIOGRAPHY: Sale catalogue, New York, *American Art Association, Anderson Galleries, (P. Jackson Higgs Collection) December 7–9, 1932*, p. 61, no. 133, ill. (Information by the kindness of D. von Bothmer).

COMMENT: Aphrodite removing her sandal was one of the more frequently repeated themes in antiquity. Reproductions in bronze, marble, and terracotta, a few of them Hellenistic in date, but most of them Roman, have been found at many sites of the ancient world. Ernst Künzl has suggested that the original was a half life-size bronze created in Asia Minor in the decades around 200 B.C. (Künzl 1970, pp. 102–162).

133

BRONZE LAMP HANDLE

Roman
First Century A.D.

The curved shaft, square in section, terminates in a floral from which a leopard's head emerges. Oval- and almond-shaped inlays of copper and silver, fourteen in all, spot the leopard's face. The eyes are also inlaid. A shallow groove runs along the outer side of the handle.

CONDITION: Some of the inlays are missing. Traces of silvery-colored solder adhere to the end that was once attached to a lamp. The upper and lower teeth are missing from the right side of the leopard's mouth.

MEASUREMENT: Height 8.7 cm.

PROVENANCE: Unknown.

BIBLIOGRAPHY: Unpublished.

COMMENT: Bronze lamps with handles of this design have been found at Pompeii and in the Sudan, indicating a wide distribution and suggesting a date in the first century A.D. Most of the handles terminate in heads or foreparts of horses or big cats. On a lamp from Pompeii in Naples (Museo Archeologico 72225; Petit Palais 1973, no. 46; Valenza Mele 1981, p. 123, no. 295), with a horse-head finial, the lid to the lamp is chained to the horse's mouth. The same may have been true of the lamp from which the Bastis handle came. Loss of the chain could be the cause of the damaged teeth. A lamp from Meroë, in the Sudan, is in Boston (24.976, Comstock and Vermeule 1971, pp. 348–349, no. 489). A lamp in the Basel art market has a feline head emerging from a comparable floral (Sale catalogue, Basel, *Münzen and Medaillen, Auktion 60, Kunstwerke der Antike, 21. September 1982,* p. 64, no. 128, pl. 41).

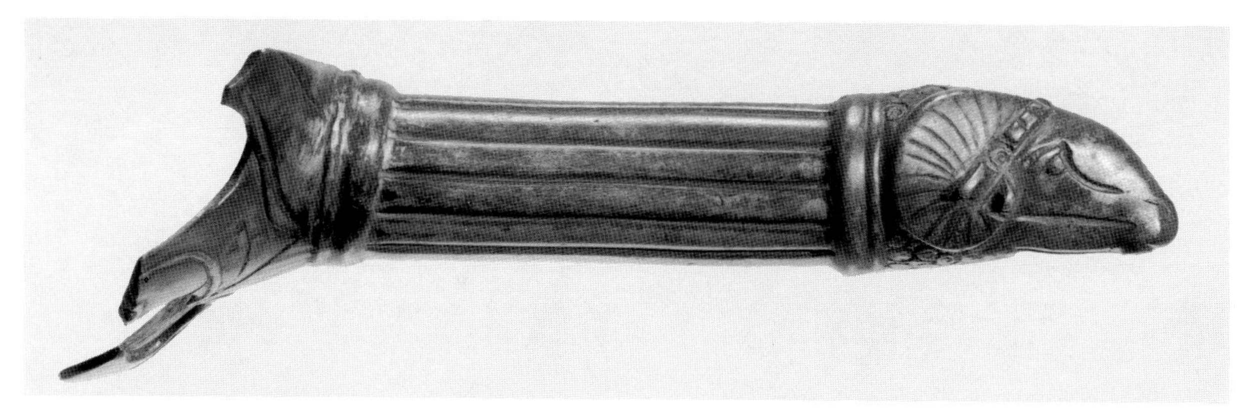

134a

134b

134

BRONZE HANDLE OF A PATERA

Roman (Italian?)
First Century A.D.

The handle is hollow and was cast. It has a fluted stem with a ram's head finial and a contoured attachment plate once soldered to the bowl of the patera. The features of the ram's head are starkly yet effectively modeled. Small circles render the hair in front of the horns and under the head. Florals and volutes are done in relief on the attachment plate.

CONDITION: The end of one of the volutes is broken. In most areas the handle has been cleaned to the metal, leaving the surface bronze-colored with black patches.

MEASUREMENT: Length 15.8 cm.

PROVENANCE: Unknown.

BIBLIOGRAPHY: Unpublished.

COMMENT: H. V. Nuber has provided a full discussion of Greek and Roman paterae of this design (Nuber 1972). The type is known in Greece in the fourth century B.C., but was reintroduced and became widespread in the first century A.D. all over the Roman Empire. In Roman burials paterae are usually found with pitchers, with which they were used in religious rites. A rich series from Belgium, for example, has recently been published (Faider-Feytmans 1979). Often only the handles remain; as the bowls were hammered and are thinner, they tend to disintegrate more easily.

135a

135b

135

BRONZE FITTING IN THE FORM OF A FELINE HEAD

Roman
First or Second Century A.D.

The boldly modeled head is cast, with details incised and inlaid. Teeth and the fur around nose, mouth, chin and ears are incised. A teardrop-shaped inlay of another metal appears on top of the head, while square inlays, also of another metal, perhaps copper, spot the cheeks. The latter are too regularly placed to be plugs for casting flaws.

The open mouth holds a cylinder. Two holes, piercing the sides of the cylinder, once held a transverse pin. At the open neck, or back of the head, a vertical pin remains in place, the lower end fastened against the outside of the head, the upper end connected to a horizontal strip. The hollow interior of the head is partially filled with lead.

MEASUREMENT: Length 5.2 cm.

PROVENANCE: Unknown.

BIBLIOGRAPHY: Unpublished.

COMMENT: The head must have been an intervening part of a utensil, pinned and leaded to other parts, now missing, in front and in back. It is difficult to say what the utensil was. Inlays and construction suggest a date in the early Roman period.

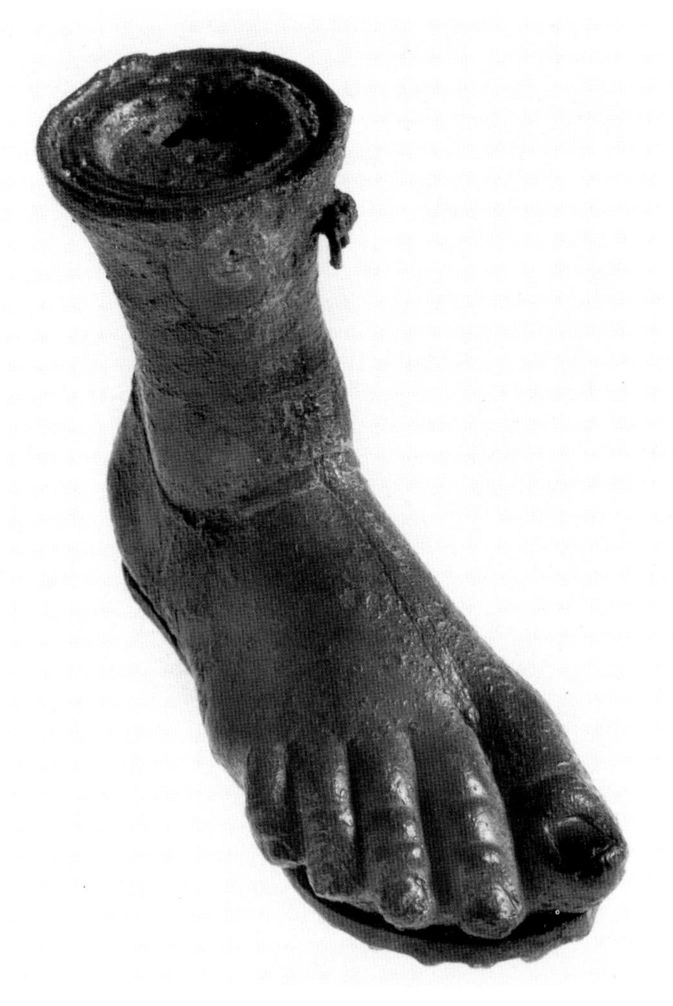

136a

136b

136 BRONZE CONTAINER IN THE FORM OF A SANDALED FOOT

Roman
First or Second Century A.D.

The container, cast hollow, is in the form of a sandaled right foot, realistically modeled. The sole of the sandal was made separately and joined. The lid at the top of the ankle is now corroded fast and cannot be removed. It has an opening in the shape of a *pelta* (Amazon-shield) large enough to let a spatula reach the contents, which was probably oil or perfume. A stud and a ring on the side of the ankle are all that remain of an attachment for a chain or loop handle, originally secured on the opposite side of the ankle, where now there is only a hole.

CONDITION: The sole of the sandle has separated from the foot, and both exhibit bubbly corrosion. The chain or handle is missing, as is much of the sandal strap, which had been applied separately to the surface of the foot.

MEASUREMENTS: Height, including sandal 10.5 cm. Length 13.7 cm.

PROVENANCE: Acquired in New York in the 1940s.

BIBLIOGRAPHY: Unpublished.

COMMENT: A related object in Berlin (West) takes the form not of a sandal but of a laced boot; an indentical *pelta*-shaped opening appears in the lid (30095; Berlin 1978, p. 181, fig. 238). Another booted-foot container found in Belgium is now in Brussels (Musées Royaux d'Art et d'Histoire inv. B 454; Faider-Feytmans 1979, p.126, no. 219, pl. 88).

137

BRONZE ATTACHMENT WITH THE HEAD OF PAN

Roman
First Century A.D.

The attachment, perhaps from the lower part of a *fulcrum* or headrest of a couch, is in the form of the head and shoulders of the youthful Pan, recognizable by budding horns on his head. A goatskin is knotted in front and, at his side, he holds pipes. The piece is cast hollow, and there are traces of solder in the cavity behind the right shoulder. The relief is deeply indented above the pipes and behind the left ear. The back surface is in one plane.

CONDITION: A dark greenish-black patina covers the attachment. A piece below the pipes is broken off. Small holes, evidently casting flaws, appear in the hair, behind the right ear and below the left ear.

MEASUREMENTS: Height 7.2 cm. Width 7.1 cm.

PROVENANCE: Unknown.

BIBLIOGRAPHY: Unpublished.

COMMENT: Busts of those associated with Dionysos are standard features of *fulcrum* attachments. Heads of Pan are not common, however, and no parallel incorporating pan-pipes comes to mind. For ornaments of this kind, see Barr-Sharrar 1987.

138 BRONZE MALE BUST

Roman
First or Second Century A.D.

The figure wears a conical hat or *pilos* and a cloak, part of which falls over his left shoulder. He stares upward and sharply to the right, so that the face is nearly in profile when viewed straight on. The features, strongly influenced by those associated with Alexander the Great, are full, and the hair is swept up in front, while curling in thick locks on the side, again recalling the image of Alexander. The object probably came from a piece of furniture to which it was secured by a tang projecting 3.0 cm. from the back. The bronze was cast hollow and was once gilded.

If an incised mark, part of the original casting, on the back of the *pilos*, represents the letter "D" written retrograde, it might indicate that the object was part of a set of at least four attachments, lettered serially.

CONDITION: Gilding is well preserved on the chest.

MEASUREMENTS: Height 14.0 cm. Width of shoulders 11.1 cm.

PROVENANCE: Unknown.

BIBLIOGRAPHY: Unpublished.

COMMENT: Despite the influence of the image of Alexander the Great, the head is more likely to represent one of the Dioscuri, Castor or Pollux, who are often shown wearing a *pilos*. Compare, for instance, a statuette considered to be one of the Dioscuri, in Boston (60.137; Comstock and Vermeule 1971, pp. 69–70, no. 71, ill.), and another, from Paramythia, Greece, in London (Swaddling 1978, pp. 103–105, pl. 50:3).

139 a

139 b

139

BRONZE HEAD OF SERAPIS

Roman
Second Century A.D.

The bronze shows a male head with long hair, full beard, and a mustache curled up at the ends. His hair is parted over his forehead; the beard hangs in curls. The pupils of the eyes were once inlaid, probably with silver and the irises are incised. The forehead is furrowed. The hair style identifies the head as that of Serapis, a Graeco-Egyptian god associated with Zeus and Hades, whose cult was established in Egypt in the Hellenistic Period. The Greek sculptor Bryaxis made a colossal seated statue of Serapis for the Serapeion in Alexandria. With the spread of the cult during the Roman Period, small reproductions or abbreviated versions were produced for portable shrines. The Bastis head probably came from a small seated image of the god.

CONDITION: The head is cast hollow. Some of the hair on the right side is broken off; the rest seems to end in a finished edge, making it unclear how the head was attached to the shoulders.

MEASUREMENT: Height 6.0 cm.

PROVENANCE: Unknown.

BIBLIOGRAPHY: Unpublished.

COMMENT: The hair style compares favorably with that of a stone sculpture of Serapis in Stockholm (National Museum Sk 40; Hornbostel 1973, p. 189, pl. LXX, fig. 127), and that of a silver statuette of Serapis in a New York private collection (Hornbostel 1973, pl. LXXIII, fig. 131).

140 BRONZE STATUETTE OF A BULL

Roman
First or Second Century A.D.

The statuette represents the Egyptian god Apis, identifiable by the crescent moon between the horns. The bull is realistically modeled, the head turned slightly to the right, curly hair on the forehead done in relief.

CONDITION: The lower legs and the end of the tail were probably broken when the bull was wrenched from its base. A chocolate-brown patina was originally covered with a mottled green crust which still adheres to the crescent, genitals, legs, and areas under the body and tail.

MEASUREMENTS: Height 8.9 cm. Length 10.5 cm.

PROVENANCE: Unknown.

BIBLIOGRAPHY: R. S. Bianchi, "Egyptian Art from The Bastis Collection," *Apollo* 108, September 1978, p. 155, figs. 8–9.

COMMENT: The cult of the deity Apis was popular among the Romans, and images like the Bastis bull served in small shrines. An Apis bull in Detroit, from a villa near Pompeii, stands on its own bronze base (Institute of Arts 45.120; Sogliano 1899, pp. 394–395, figs. 5–6; see also Mitten and Doeringer 1967, p. 289, no. 283). Like the Bastis bull it once wore a crescent, but of silver not bronze. Now missing, it was illustrated in the original excavation report.

141

BRONZE STATUETTE OF A BULL

Roman
First or Second Century A.D.

This bronze bull may also have represented the Egyptian god Apis. The figure, cast hollow, is chunkier and less well modeled than No. 140. The head is turned to the right, the folds of the dewlap indicated; the swirl of the hair on the forehead is engraved, not done in relief. The legs are planted apart, hooves seemingly too large. The purpose of the hole under the right ear is not clear, but could have served to secure the Apis crescent moon or a garland.

CONDITION: The statuette is intact, but may be missing a headdress of some kind. It has a uniform gray-green patina.

MEASUREMENTS: Height 5.8 cm. Length 7.2 cm.

PROVENANCE: Acquired in New York in the 1940s.

BIBLIOGRAPHY: Unpublished.

COMMENT: The hair on a bull formerly in the Currier estate is rendered in the same manner (Mitten and Doeringer 1967, p. 140, no. 143, ill.; Sale catalogue, New York, *Sotheby's, November 21–22, 1985*, lot 63).

142 a

142 b

142 BRONZE STATUETTE OF A BOAR

Roman
First or Second Century A.D.

The statuette, once a votive figure in a sanctuary, was mounted on a base by tangs on the left hind leg and the right foreleg, the latter tang broken off. Ears, eyes, and tusks are prominent. The nostrils are drawn on the front of the snout. The animal's tail is switched over the right haunch, revealing genitals and anus. The rough skin of the back and flanks is indicated by lines scored in the bronze.

CONDITION: The left foreleg appears to be wrenched back. The boar has a green patina with a whitish cast.

MEASUREMENTS: Height 6.7 cm. Length 10.5 cm.

PROVENANCE: Unknown.

BIBLIOGRAPHY: Unpublished.

COMMENT: This Roman boar is readily distinguishable from a Greek one in a Swiss private collection (Schefold 1960, p. 180, no. 185) and a late Etruscan one from Ghiaccio Forte, Italy (Del Chiaro and Talocchini 1973, p. 330, pl. 60:7). The Greek boar is more organically modeled, the bone structure of the legs shown, the hair of the chest carefully delineated. Both Greek and Etruscan boars have relatively small eyes compared with those of the Bastis bronze. For other bronze boars see Gschwantler 1984, pp. 71–77.

143

BRONZE STATUETTE OF AN EAGLE

Roman
First or Second Century A.D.

The eagle is shown alighting or about to fly. The claws were made separately and pinned to the legs; the right foot is missing. The right wing, also cast separately, was soldered to the body.

MEASUREMENTS: Length, beak to tail 15.5 cm. Wingspread 19.0 cm.

PROVENANCE: Unknown.

BIBLIOGRAPHY: Unpublished.

COMMENT: The bird may have perched on an orb in the hand of a statue of an emperor or a god, perhaps of Jupiter or Victory. A right wing in bronze, from Augst, also made from a separate casting, was once soldered to a now missing bird (Kaufmann-Heinimann 1977, p. 97, no. 122, pl. 99). A bronze eagle of this size from Silchester, now in Reading, exhibits similar techniques of manufacture, with separately made feet and wings; the wings are missing (Toynbee 1962, p. 150, no. 60, pl. 61; National Art-Collections Fund 1980, pp. 98–99).

PART VI

Vases

by
Diana Buitron-Oliver

144

ASKOS IN THE FORM OF A MOUFFLON SHEEP

Middle Cypriot III
About 1650 B.C.
White-painted V Stringhole Style

The handmade askos is a ceramic container in the form of a moufflon sheep, recognizable by the curving horns. The cross-hatch decoration is done in reddish paint on a brownish clay ground. The vase has a sack-shaped body with four short legs and a high loop handle. The head has punctures for eyes and a slit for the mouth. The pinched spout for pouring at the other end stands in place of a tail. The stringhole lugs on either side of head and spout characterize the style. Although the lugs at the head are not pierced, those at the spout are, and could have been used to suspend the vessel. In later examples of the stringhole style, the lugs are not pierced and are purely decorative. The idea of covering vases with stringhole projections may have had its origin in the center of the island. Most theriomorphic vessels of this type come from sites there. The small size and elaborate shape suggest that the vessel might have contained perfumed oil which, in suspension, would have perfumed the air.

CONDITION: The askos is intact. Parts of the surface are covered with a white incrustation.

MEASUREMENTS: Maximum height, at spout 11.5 cm. Height at handle 10.5 cm. Length 15.3 cm.

PROVENANCE: Acquired in the 1940s.

BIBLIOGRAPHY: Unpublished.

COMMENT: For white-painted V Stringhole style see Åstrom 1972, p. 34, n. 1; compare especially fig. 18:2 from Dali Potamia. For the type compare an askos in Nicosia in the collection of Andreas Photiades (Karageorghis 1981, pp. 977–978, fig. 35, from Ayia Paraskevi); another in Sarasota, Florida, The John and Mable Ringling Museum of Art (*Ancient Art from Cyprus* 1983, no. 176); and two in Oxford (Ashmolean Museum; Frankel 1983, pl. 16, no. 208, and pl. 35, no. 1274, the latter from Ayia Paraskevi).

145

STIRRUP JAR

Mycenaean
Fourteenth Century B.C.

The globular, squat body is decorated with broad black bands framing sets of lines. The handles connect with a central stem or dummy spout; the true spout sits off center. Irregular black patterns mark handles and spout.

CONDITION: The stirrup jar is intact except for a spall in the body and a small piece missing on the underside. The surface is worn and abraded.

MEASUREMENTS: Height 10.3 cm. Diameter 11.8 cm.

PROVENANCE: Acquired in 1957.

BIBLIOGRAPHY: Unpublished.

COMMENT: The squat shape of the body places the vase in the Mycenaean III A 2 Period (Furumark 1941, figs. 5–6; Vermeule 1964, pl. XLV:A).

146 a

146 b

146

SKYPHOS WITH LID

Attic, Late Geometric I b
750–735 B.C.

The main zone on both sides of the body is divided into five panels, or metopes, separated from one another by three vertical lines. The centermost panel, with octofoil, is flanked by two others showing marsh birds with swastikas; the outer panels feature circles surrounded by dots. The rim has a row of lozenges with dots while the handles, which have projections at the roots, show a connected row of buds. The lid is decorated with concentric bands and lines; the knob has a rosette with 16 petals.

CONDITION: The bowl is intact, but the surface is worn; the lid was broken and mended.

MEASUREMENTS: Height with lid 10.7 cm.; without lid 7.4 cm. Diameter 14.7 cm. Width across handles 19.3 cm.

PROVENANCE: Acquired in New York after 1948.

BIBLIOGRAPHY: D. von Bothmer 1961, p. 49, no. 186, pl. 65.

COMMENT: The shape, with flat bottom and tall vertical lip, is a variant of the standard skyphos, which is taller. A similar example was found in the Athenian Kerameikos (Kerameikos 342, Grave 71; Coldstream 1968, pl. 10:f).

147

BLACK FIGURED ALABASTRON

Middle Corinthian
600–575 B.C.

A marsh bird stands between two heraldic lions; the space around them is filled with incised blobrosettes. The scene is framed by two lines above and below. Tongue patterns decorate the bottom, neck, and mouth; dots circle the rim.

CONDITION: The alabastron was broken and repaired.

MEASUREMENT: Height 16.3 cm.

PROVENANCE: Formerly in the collection of Alphonse Kann. Acquired in New York before 1948.

BIBLIOGRAPHY: Sale catalogue, New York, *American Art Galleries, 6–8 January 1927*, no. 6; D. von Bothmer 1961, pp. 49–50, no. 190, pl. 65.

COMMENT: The alabastron is a perfume vase, the Corinthian version taking its shape from Asiatic not Egyptian, alabastra. But the basic shape goes back to an early period in Egypt. It is debated whether the name is derived from that of the stone, alabaster, out of which many Egyptian vases were made, or from the vase itself. Amyx compares two other Middle Corinthian alabastra, one in Paris (Musée Rodin TC 144; *CVA Musée Rodin* pls. 3,1–3, 4,7) another in Berkeley (8/3304; *CVA University of California* pl. 9,1).

148 a

148 b

148

BLACK FIGURED ALABASTRON

Middle Corinthian
600–575 B.C.

A bearded deity with wings is pictured, dressed in a short chiton, his legs in the *knielauf* or running pose, thought to imply rapid movement or flight. On the back is a marsh bird. The space around the figures is filled with incised blob rosettes. The scene is framed by two lines above and below; tongue patterns decorate the bottom, neck, and mouth; those on the mouth are alternately red and black. Dots circle the rim.

CONDITION: The alabastron is intact.

MEASUREMENT: Height 17.5 cm.

PROVENANCE: Acquired in New York in 1983.

BIBLIOGRAPHY: Unpublished.

COMMENT: M. von Heland has discussed the identification of the winged deity who appears on many Corinthian vases (von Heland 1970, pp. 19–32).

149 a

149 b

149

BLACK FIGURED OINOCHOE

Chalcidian
About 520 B.C.

Attributed to the Phineus Painter (Rumpf).

On the body, deer, panther and siren; on the shoulder, ivy with its fruit, korymboi; at the base, rays.

CONDITION: The oinochoe is intact except for a break on the edge of the foot.

MEASUREMENT: Height 26.3 cm.

PROVENANCE: Formerly in the collection of William Rome. Acquired in New York in the 1940s.

BIBLIOGRAPHY: Sale catalogue, London, *Christie's 18 December 1907*, no. 65:2; A. Rumpf, *Chalkidische Vasen*, Berlin/Leipzig 1927, pp. 32, 104, 109–111, 125, 146, no. 179, pls. 160–162; D. von Bothmer 1961, no. 193, pls. 65, 71; A. H. Ashmead and K. M. Phillips, Jr., *Catalogue of the Classical Collection, Museum of Art, The Rhode Island School of Design, Classical Vases,* Providence 1976, p. 48, no. 56.

COMMENT: The disposition of the panels with the division between shoulder and body is characteristic of the Chalcidian style; so also is the ornament, the ivy and korymboi on the shoulder and the assymetrical palmette emerging from the right border. Chalcidian vases were first thought to have been made in Chalkis on the basis of the alphabet used in the inscriptions, but most scholars now believe them to have a western origin, perhaps Reggio, which was a Chalcidian colony (Boardman and Schweizer 1973, pp. 207–283.
A tiny modern graffito is inscribed on the underside of the foot which suggests that the vase is from the Torlonia excavations at Vulci (D. von Bothmer, quoted in Ashmead and Phillips *op. cit.,* p. 48).

150 a

150

BLACK FIGURED AMPHORA WITH LID

Attic
About 540 B.C.

Signed by Andokides as potter.

Side A: A chariot is driven by a bearded charioteer wearing a long belted chiton, a hat, and a Boeotian shield strapped to his back.

Inscribed above: ΑΝΔΟΚΙΔΕΣ and below: ΕΠΟΙΣΕ "Andokides made it." On the left and right are meaningless inscriptions: ΗΟΙΛΟΕΣ and ΠΙΟΤΣΙΝΣ.

The right pole horse is white; it and the right trace horse have red manes and tails; the right trace horse has a red breastband decorated with white dots on the edges; the charioteer's chiton is red, white dots appear on his belt and on the carrying strap of the shield.

Side B: A victorious chariot, as indicated by the eagle with a snake in its beak flying above the horses, is driven by a charioteer, clad like the one on Side A, but without the shield. He is accompanied by a small man preceding the chariot who carries a wreath and sprig, other indications of victory. The right pole horse is white, as is the charioteer's hat; the mane and tail of the right trace horse are red; the tail of the right pole horse is also red.

The ornament consists of rays at the base, palmette-lotus crosses under the handles, a double row of ivy and dots above the picture, and a row of rosettes with white centers on the reserved rim of the vase. The lid has myrtle leaves and dots on the rim, three dot bands separated by circles, and a leaf pattern.

CONDITION: The amphora is unbroken. The modern knob on the lid has been removed.

MEASUREMENTS: Height with lid (modern knob removed) 26.2 cm.; without lid 24.7 cm. Diameter of mouth 11.3 cm.; of vase 18.5 cm.; of foot 9.3 cm.

PROVENANCE: Formerly in the collections of the Earl Fitzwilliam and W. R. Hearst, Acquired in New York in 1951.

BIBLIOGRAPHY: Sale catalogue, London, *Christie's 15 July 1948*, no. 12, ill.; Sale Catalogue, New York, *Parke Bernet, 7 December 1951*, no. 8, ill.; Hanfmann 1954, no. 254, pl. 76; *ABV* 253, 715; C. Vermeule and D. von Bothmer, "Notes on a new edition of Michaelis, Ancient Marbles in Great Britain. Part Two," *AJA* 60, 1956, p. 346, pl. 112 figs. 34–5 D. von Bothmer 1961, no. 198, p. 51, pl. 73; D. von Bothmer, "Andokides the Potter and the Andokides Painter," *Bulletin of the Metropolitan Museum of Art* 24 February 1966, p. 207, fig. 8; E. Paribeni, "Attici Vasi," *Enciclopedia Arte Antica*, suppl.1970, p. 100, fig. 103; *Paralipomena* 113; B. Cohen, *Attic Bilingual Vases and their Painters,* New York 1978, p. 3, pl. 1:2; *Beazley Addenda* 1982, p. 32.

COMMENT: The vase, signed by the potter Andokides, is his earliest known work; it antedates the potter's red-figured vases several of which are painted by an anonymous painter called the Andokides Painter. The painting on the Bastis amphora, however, is not by the Andokides Painter. Beazley notes a kinship with amphorae of Group E, and Bothmer relates the palmette-lotus crosses to the earliest Nicosthenic neck-amphorae.

150 b

150 c

151

BLACK FIGURED NECK AMPHORA WITH LID

Attic
About 540 B.C.

Attributed to a painter in Group E (Bothmer).

Side A: Herakles, naked, stabs the Nemean Lion with his sword; Athena, dressed in a peplos, stands behind him, holding a spear; Iolaos, carrying the club, is on the right. White is used for Athena's flesh, details of her dress, and the handle of Herakles' sword; Iolaos' hair and beard are red, as are Herakles' fillet and beard, the edge of the lion's mane, and Athena's fillet and dress.

Side B: Theseus, wearing a loincloth, thrusts his sword through the head of the Minotaur, who is shown with a stippled, hairy body. On either side are a youth and a maiden holding a wreath, representing the seven youths and seven maidens sent each year by the Athenians as tribute to Minos, King of Crete. The tribute ended with the slaying of Pasiphae's offspring, the Minotaur. White is used for the maidens' flesh and the hilt of Theseus' sword; red for the Minotaur's rock and blood, Theseus' fillet and loincloth, the fillets of the youths and maidens, and portions of the maidens' dresses.

The shoulder scene on both sides of the amphora shows four horsemen. One rider on each side wears a white tunic; topknots, manes, and tails of the horses are usually red, as is the riders' hair.

The ornament consists of rays at the base, a chain of upright lotus buds with two rows of dots below the picture, lotus-palmette swags with swastikas under the handles, tongues below the neck, and a lotus-palmette chain on the neck. The lid has rays around the knob.

Dipinto: ΓΟ (perhaps an abbreviation for ποικίλος "decorated").

CONDITION: The amphora was broken and repaired; the lid is cracked. The drill holes of ancient repairs indicate that the vase was broken and repaired in antiquity.

MEASUREMENTS: Height with lid 46.3 cm.; without lid 37.1 cm.

PROVENANCE: Found in Tarquinia, August 1862. Acquired in New York in 1981.

BIBLIOGRAPHY: Sale catalogue, Angers, *12 décembre 1979*, pp. 40–41, no. 142, ills. on cover and pp. 60–61.

COMMENT: For the dipinto see Johnston 1979, Type 8F, pp. 155–156, 225, fig. 12 t. For the unusual shape, a special type, see *ABV* 137. For the handle ornament, compare a neck-amphora in Berlin (*ABV* 137, 62), and one in New York (*ABV* 137, 61; *CVA* New York 4, pls. 14–15). The two rows of dots in the lotus bud chain are unusual.
The subjects, the pan-Hellenic hero Herakles and the Athenian hero Theseus, each killing a dangerous monster that threatened civilized life, were popular during the middle and third quarter of the sixth century B.C. They appear together on other vases of Group E and near Exekias (*ABV* 134, 18–20; 148, bottom).

151 a

151 b

151 c

151 d

151 e

151 f

152

BLACK FIGURED AMPHORA

Attic
525–500 B.C.

Side A: Herakles fights the Amazons. Herakles, wearing the lion skin and brandishing his club, advances against two Amazons, one of whom has fallen on her right knee, holding up her shield in defense. The second Amazon still stands, confronting him. The Amazons wear short chitons, the fallen one has an animal skin draped over her shoulder and hips, the other a *chlamys* (cloak). They wear crested Attic helmets and carry spears. Behind Herakles a warrior, armed with shield, spears, a Corinthian helmet, and greaves (shin guards), departs to the left. The shield devices are: tripod, bull's head, and snake; white is used for the Amazons flesh, the shield devices, and two of the helmet crests.'

Side B: In an assembly of standing gods, Apollo, in the center, holds a kithara and plectrum attached with a string. He faces a goddess, probably Leto, his mother. Behind Apollo is his sister, Artemis, with bow and arrows. The three form the Delian triad: Apollo and Artemis were the twins born to Leto on the island of Delos. On the left stands Hermes, with caduceus, *petasos* (traveling hat) and boots; on the right, Dionysos, with grapevine, accompanied by a satyr carrying a drinking horn. White is used for the goddesses' flesh, the ivory parts of the kithara, and Hermes' hat; red is used for details of the garments, Dionysos' wreath, and the satyr's hair, tail and beard.

The ornament, standard for neck amphorae, consists of rays at the base, lotus buds below the scene, framed tongues above the scene, lotus-palmette tendrils at the handles, and a lotus-palmette chain on the neck.

CONDITION: The amphora was broken and repaired, one of the handles reattached.

MEASUREMENT: Height 38.2 cm.

PROVENANCE: Acquired in New York in the 1940s.

BIBLIOGRAPHY: D. von Bothmer 1957, p. 36, n. 22, p. 39, pl. XXXI:2.

COMMENT: Herakles' ninth labor was to obtain the girdle of the Amazon queen. The theme was popular on Attic vases from the second quarter of the sixth century to the mid-fifth century B.C., perhaps symbolizing the conflict of Greeks vs. barbarians. A number of different compositional types developed. This one Bothmer places in his Type B, showing less than three complete groups of combatants. Here an Amazon and a Greek are without opponents. See Devambez 1981, pp. 586–597.

152a

152 b

153 a

153

BLACK FIGURED NECK AMPHORA

Attic
520–500 B.C.

Side A: A maenad, wearing a short dress and holding leafless vines, rides a mule between two cavorting satyrs. White is used for the maenad's flesh and the underbelly and muzzle of the mule; red for the satyrs' hair, beards and tails, the mule's mane, and the maenad's dress and fillet.

Side B: Hermes, carrying the caduceus and wearing a *petasos* (traveling hat), boots, and cloak, leads two pairs of women to the right. The profiles and necks of the near women, as well as their right arms, are outlined in glaze. White is used for the females' flesh and embroidered details of their garments, Hermes' tunic and hat; red is used for Hermes' hair and beard, the women's fillets and parts of their garments.

The ornament, standard for neck amphorae, consists of rays at the base, lotus buds below the scene, lotus-palmette tendrils at the handles, tongues above the scene (on side A only), and a lotus-palmette chain on the neck.

Graffito under the foot:

CONDITION: The amphora is unbroken.

MEASUREMENT: Height 27.2 cm.

PROVENANCE: Unknown.

BIBLIOGRAPHY: Unpublished.

COMMENT: The subject of side B is unusual. Hermes leading pairs of women variously identified as goddesses, muses, or nymphs, occurs on a series of vases of the last quarter of the sixth century B.C. The compositional type may derive from scenes of the Judgment of Paris in which Hermes leads the three contending goddesses before Paris. See *ABV* 726, under Hermes and Nymphs, Zanker 1965, p. 56, and *CVA* British Museum 4, pl. 56:4. For the graffito see Johnston 1979, Type 27A, pp. 84, 191.

153 b

153 c

153 d

154 a

154

Attic
515–500 B.C.

BLACK FIGURED HYDRIA

Attributed to the Leagros Group.

On the body of the hydria Herakles fights Kyknos. Herakles, wearing the lion skin around his shoulders and over his left arm, armed with bow and sword, leaps upon Kyknos who falls on one knee. Athena, Herakles' patron, in Attic helmet and aegis, stands behind him, and Ares, Kyknos' father, in Corinthian helmet and short chiton, supports his son. Inscribed in front of Herakles: HEPAKVES.

White is used for Athena's flesh, the teeth of the lion skin, details of the helmets, swords and scabbards, and the shield devices which are three rings (Athena), a bull's head (Kyknos), and two dolphins (Ares). Red is used for details of dress and armor and for Athena's flower.

The shoulder scene shows the departure of a warrior. A youth mounts a chariot, his mother stands behind the horses, his father sits on a camp-stool on the right. Armed warriors accompanied by two dogs stand at the sides, and a third dog stands behind the horses.

White is used for the mother's flesh, the father's hair, and the shield devices: a snake and three balls; red for details of dress, armor, and the horses' manes and tails.

The hydria is a favorite shape of the Leagros Group. The ornamental scheme on the Bastis hydria, showing rays at the base, palmettes below the scene, rows of ivy on either side, tongues, alternately black and red at the neck, conforms to the Leagros Group's tradition. Less usual are the reserved handles and rim with a narrow black line running lengthwise along them.

CONDITION: The hydria is intact, with some areas of pitting and abrasion; the edge of the rim is chipped.

MEASUREMENTS: Height 39.3 cm.; height with handle 44.8 cm.

PROVENANCE: Unknown.

BIBLIOGRAPHY: Sale catalogue, London, *Sotheby's 11–12 July 1983*, lot 352 (ill.).

COMMENT: The story of Herakles' battle with Kyknos is first told in the epic poem, *The Shield of Herakles*, generally linked to Hesiod and dated no later than the early sixth century B.C. For the relationship of the representations on vases to literary sources, see Boardman 1974, p. 8, and Shapiro 1984, pp. 523–529; for the development of the representation, see Vian 1945, pp. 5–32.

For the clay-ground lateral handles decorated with a black glaze line, D. von Bothmer compares the trefoil olpai by the Amasis Painter (*ABV* 152–153, nos. 29–31; *Paralipomena* 66; D. von Bothmer 1985, nos. 26–30) and the trefoil olpe by the Gela Painter in the Louvre (*ABL* p. 214, no. 197).

For the graffiti, see Johnston 1979, p. 46.

154 b

155 a

155 b

155

BLACK FIGURED CYPRO-JUG

Attic
About 530 B.C.

Herakles fights the Nemean Lion which holds him in a death hug; its right foreleg crosses Herakles' back, three claws visible behind his shoulder. Iolaos, on the left, carries Herakles' club, for at least one literary tradition holds that, since the beast was invulnerable, weapons were useless against it and Herakles, as shown here, had to choke it to death with his bare hands (Apollodorus II.V.). Athena, wearing an Attic helmet, the aegis, and carrying a spear, stands on the right. The unusual shape, which Beazley named a Cypro-jug, is known from four complete examples (*ABV* 441; Beazley 1947 b p. 33). The vase is similar to jugs of Type V in the Cypriot series (for example, Gjerstad 1948, fig. LIV,1). The five known Cypro-jugs of Attic origin, including this one, were made in imitation of the

155 c

155 d

Cypriot shape, perhaps to please a Cypriot client. The parallels to this vase were all found in Cyprus.

The ornament consists of ivy at the sides, tongues above the scene, black dots connected by lines on the offset collar at the junction of body and neck, and rays on the neck itself. The neck and thickened rim are black. The double handle terminates in a reel molding below which is a black palmette in relief.

CONDITION: The Cypro-jug is intact. The handle is cracked, the surface of the lower body pitted. Where pitted, the legs of all the figures, except Iolaos, have been repainted.

MEASUREMENT: Height 27.7 cm.

PROVENANCE: Unknown.

BIBLIOGRAPHY: Unpublished.

COMMENT: The Bastis Cypro-jug is closest to the jug now in Nicosia (Cyprus Museum C 433; *ABV* 441, 2, and more recently Buchholz 1984, pp. 555–564), which Beazley attributed to the Euphiletos Painter. The proportions are similar and the jugs share the same offset collar at the junction of body and neck, and the double handle with reel molding at the lower end, with a black palmette below that. The conception of the scene and the style of drawing are very like that of other vases by this painter, for example, the scene on the shoulder of a hydria in Paris (Cabinet des Médailles 254; *ABV* 324, 38), where Herakles struggles barehanded with the Nemean Lion whose claws are visible behind Herakles' shoulder.
Recent excavations at Amathus, Cyprus, brought to light fragments of a fifth Cypro-jug, now in the Limassol Museum (no. 698; Robertson 1987, pp. 33–34, no. 4, pl. XIX).

156

BLACK FIGURED OINOCHOE OF SHAPE I

Attic
530–520 B.C.

Attributed to the Painter of Munich 1760; Altenburg Class (Clark).

The scene represents the introduction of Herakles to Olympus. Herakles and Athena have stepped into a four-horse chariot. Athena holds the reins; Herakles leans on the railing with his right hand and shoulders his club with his left. They are accompanied by Apollo playing the kithara, Dionysos with drinking horn and vines in the background, and Hermes in short chiton, chlamys, *petasos* (traveling hat) and boots, carrying the caduceus. The near trace horse, shown as usual slightly in advance of the two pole horses, has a brand on the rump in the form of a caduceus.

The introduction of Herakles to Olympus was very popular in the second half of the sixth century B.C. and may have had contemporary political significance. John Boardman suggests that Peisistratos, ruler of Athens in the mid-sixth century, identified himself with Herakles. The scene may reflect the exiled leader's triumphant return to Athens and to power, as Herodotus relates (Book I, 60; Boardman 1972, pp. 60–66).

White is used for Athena's flesh, the teeth of Herakles' lion skin, the ivory parts of Apollo's kithara, Hermes' hat, and dots on the garments. Red is used for details of garments, armor, chariot, and horses, as well as for hair and beards.

Ornament consists of ivy branches on the sides, black tongues above the scene, and a ribbon decoration on the collar, around the neck of the vase.

The shape, with raised fillets between the broad echinus foot and body, and between the body and neck, the tall neck with trefoil mouth and high-ridged handle with rotelle at the rim, recalls metal vases of the period.

CONDITION: The oinochoe is broken and repaired, the missing sections filled and painted; it is dented on the right front of picture panel.

MEASUREMENTS: Height (to top of mouth) 25.2 cm.; (to top of handle) 29.4 cm.

PROVENANCE: Unknown.

BIBLIOGRAPHY: *Architectural Digest* 36, 1979, p. 90, ill.

COMMENT: A brand on a horse may indicate its value or the stable the horse came out of. The caduceus is the brand most frequent on horses on vases (Braun 1970, pp. 129–269; *CVA* New York 4 (USA 16), pl. 16, and Moore 1978, n. 40, pp. 378–381).

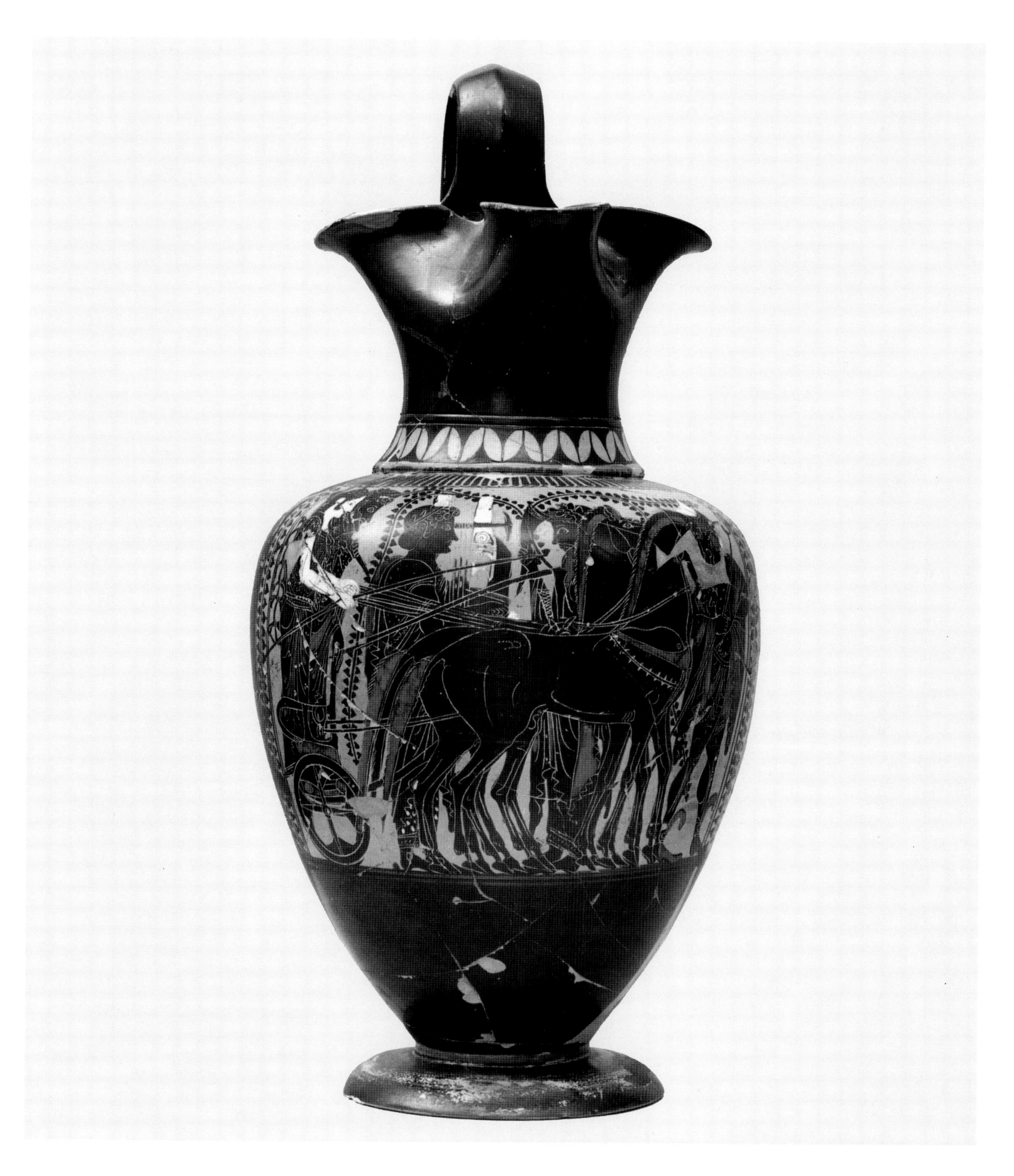

157

BLACK FIGURED ALABASTRON (WHITE GROUND)

Attic
About 490–480 B.C.

Attributed to the Diosphos Painter (Bothmer).

Side A: Poseidon, holding a fish and the trident, faces his wife, Amphitrite, daughter of Nereus, who sits on a camp stool. The inscriptions in the field are meaningless.

Side B: Herakles, wearing his lion skin and carrying his club, sits on a block seat. Beside him Athena, wearing the aegis, with a spear in her left hand, holds out her Attic helmet in her right hand. The two groups are separated by a lion on each side; below the lug A/B, a flying eagle carries off a snake.

The subjects depicted are rare in Attic vase painting. Amphitrite and Poseidon as a wedded couple are first mentioned by Hesiod (*Theogony*, 930–933) and already appear in art on a series of Corinthian pinakes of the late seventh to mid-sixth century B.C., and slightly later on the François vase in Florence and on the Sophilos dinos in London, at the wedding of Peleus and Thetis in the company of other immortals. The combination of a *seated* Amphitrite with a *standing* Poseidon is unique in Attic art and perhaps occurs here so as to balance the scene on the other side of the alabastron. Herakles *seated* with Athena *standing* is not a common subject either, and the representation on the Bastis alabastron differs from other known examples which generally show Athena serving wine to the resting hero.

The ornament consists of reserved lines below the scene; and above, a battlement meander, four rows of dots and tongues.

CONDITION: The alabastron was broken and repaired.

MEASUREMENT: Height 18.9 cm.

PROVENANCE: Unknown.

BIBLIOGRAPHY: *ABV* 510, 21; D. von Bothmer 1961, no. 217, pls. 76, 79; *Paralipomena* 249; *Beazley Addenda* 1982, 61; N. Kunisch, "Zur helmhaltenden Athena," *Mitteilungen des Deutschen Archäologischen Instituts, Athenische Abteilung* 89, 1974, p. 91, no. 74; S. Kaempf-Dimitriadou, "Amphitrite," *Lexicon Iconographicum Mythologiae Classicae* I, Zurich/Munich 1981, pp. 724–735, pl. 578.

COMMENT: For the compositional type of Side B, see Beazley 1961, pp. 49–67. On Athena's gesture, see Kunisch *loc. cit.* pp. 85–104.

157a

157b

158 a

158

BLACK FIGURED CUP OF SHAPE A

Attic
About 525–500 B.C.

Attributed to the Group of Courting Cups of the FP Class (Vickers).

Each side shows a horse and rider between naked youths, with a cloth hanging above the horse's rump. The horizontal palmettes flanking the handles give their name to the "Flower-Palmette", or FP Class, of which the Group of Courting Cups is a subgroup. The flower usually found beneath the handle is omitted.

White is used for the rider's short tunic and border of the palmette hearts. Red, which is unusually profuse, renders the horse's mane and tail; a spot on its flank; blotches on the chests of the youths; and the hair of the left-hand youth on either side.

On the interior, decoration is limited to a small reserved circle with, in the center, a hole edged in black which goes through to the foot of the cup. Two holes are drilled through the stem of the bowl. Michael Vickers saw that the purpose of these holes was to play a dirty trick on an unsuspecting fellow drinker: "The larger (hole) must have held a stopper, kept in position by means of a pin which

158b

passed through the smaller holes below. Imagine then a string attached to the pin, and a practical joker at the other end. . . ."

The cup has a high, lipless bowl; a stout stem with a slight thickening rather than a distinct fillet at the junction of the bowl and stem; and a heavy, flaring foot with a concave profile and reserved edge. The flat underside of the foot is reserved, the inside of the stem glazed up to 0.5 cm.

CONDITION: The cup was broken and repaired.

MEASUREMENTS: Height 11.5 cm. Diameter of bowl 22.7 cm. Width (across the handles) 28.8 cm.

PROVENANCE: Unknown.

BIBLIOGRAPHY: M. Vickers, "A Dirty Trick Vase," *AJA* 79, 1975, p. 282, pl. 50; and M. Vickers, "Another Dirty Trick Vase," *AJA* 84, 1980, p. 183.

COMMENT: For the FP Class see *Paralipomena* 80 and Boardman 107. On trick vases see Noble 1968, pp. 371–378.

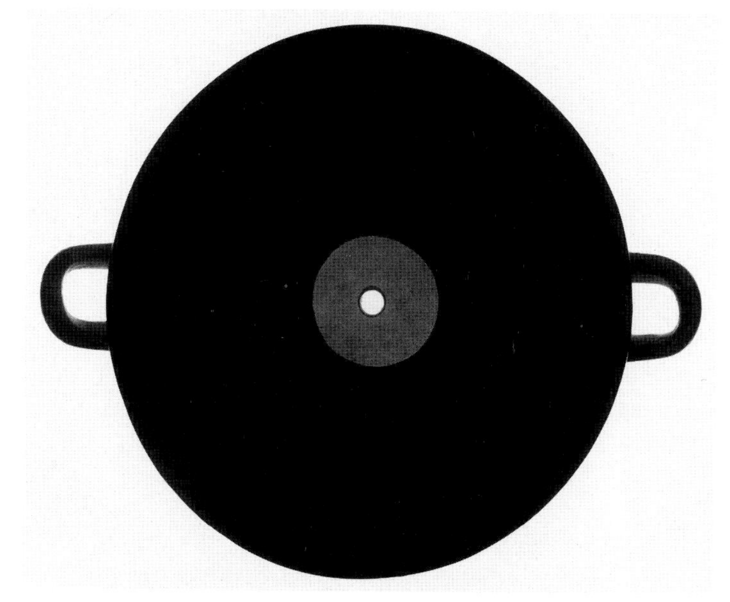

158c

159a

159

BLACK FIGURED EYE CUP OF SHAPE A

Attic
About 530 B.C.

Each side features a large pair of eyes with a small black nose. At the handles are the prows of ships, the sails raised. The eyes, apotropaic or evil averting, appear on cups and on vases of other shapes in the third quarter of the sixth century. Ships with prows in the form of a boar's head occur, for example, on the François vase in Florence (Museo archeologico 4209; *ABV* 76, 1). It is tempting to see an allusion to the language of the Homeric epics in the placing of "black ships" sailing on "wine dark seas," on cups and other vessels for drinking or serving wine.

Below the pictures are eight black bands. The inside is black, except for a small reserved circle with a black circle and dot. Added white has been used for the third circle of the eyes and for the sails of the ships; added red for the second circle of the eyes, the rails of the ships, and the fillet marking the join of bowl to stem.

CONDITION: The eye cup is intact but is chipped on the edge of the foot plate and on the inside, below the rim. Areas of abrasion exist on the handles and rim.

MEASUREMENTS: Height 11.3 cm. Diameter without handles 22.1 cm. Width across the handles 28.1 cm.

PROVENANCE: Formerly in the collections of the Earl Fitzwilliam and W. R. Hearst. Acquired in New York in 1951.

BIBLIOGRAPHY: Sale catalogue, London, *Christie's 15 July 1948*, no. 15,1;

159 b

sale catalogue, New York, *Parke-Bernet, 7 December 1951*, no. 3; *ABV* 223, under no. 65; C. Vermeule and D. von Bothmer "Notes on a New Edition of Michaelis: Ancient Marbles in Great Britain. Part Two," *AJA* 60, 1956, p. 346, pl. 113 fig. 38; C. Vermeule and D. von Bothmer, "Notes on a New Edition of Michaelis: Ancient Marbles in Great Britain. Part Three: 2," *AJA* 63, 1959, p. 346; D. von Bothmer 1961, no. 223, pl. 74; J. S. Morrison and R. T. Williams, *Greek Oared Ships*, Cambridge 1968, no. 59, p. 99, pl. 16 b; *Paralipomena* 104, 109.

COMMENT: On the eye cup as a mask see Boardman 1976, 288. The eight black bands circling below the pictures are unusual and link this kylix with one in Berlin attributed to Painter N and signed by Nikosthenes as potter, (Staatliche Museen 1805; *ABV* 223, 65). Black bands occur on the inside of a cup in Richmond (Virginia Museum of Fine Arts 62.1.11; *Paralipomena* 109), also a product of the Nicosthenic workshop. These cups and two others, all signed by Nikosthenes as potter (*ABV* 226, 66; 232, 15), share a similar foot type which is different from the foot of the Bastis cup. This would suggest a different potter, perhaps influenced by the large and successful Nicosthenic workshop. The way the ships are drawn also shows the influence of the Nicosthenic workshop (Morrison and Williams *op. cit.*, p. 97). For prows of ships around cup handles, D. von Bothmer refers to the following cups and cup fragments: Copenhagen (Ny Carlsberg Glyptotek I. N. 3385; *Paralipomena* 104); Oxford (Ashmolean Museum 1929.359, the foreparts conjoined); Sydney 47.03; (*ABV* 207, middle, the foreparts conjoined); Innsbruck (II 12, (12), the foreparts conjoined); Wolf Rudolph, fr. (the foreparts conjoined); New York (MMA 56.171.36; *ABV* 205, 14; *Paralipomena* 93); Centre Island, New York, private (fragments of three cups); Leipzig (T 472; *CVA* Leipzig 2, pls. 31,3–4 and 34,3); Tarquinia (571; *CVA* Tarquinia 2, pl. 21,3); and Malibu (81.AE.207.393 and 85.AE.334.A-E).

159 c

160 a

160

Attic
About 530 B.C.

The reserved handle zone on both sides shows a hen in the center, rendered in white, flanked by swans and deer.

CONDITION: The cup was broken and repaired; the join of bowl to stem is modern (the stem and foot are probably alien).

MEASUREMENTS: Height 13.9 cm. Diameter 20.8 cm. Width 28 cm.

PROVENANCE: Acquired in New York in 1948.

BIBLIOGRAPHY: Unpublished.

COMMENT: D. von Bothmer has observed that the figure work shows some resemblance to the Tleson Painter.

160 b

161

BLACK FIGURED CUP OF SHAPE SUB-A

Attic
500–490 B.C.

Attributed to the Caylus Painter (Leafless Group) (Beazley).

A satyr cavorts in the small reserved tondo on the inside of the cup. Both sides of the exterior show Dionysos, seated, holding a drinking horn, flanked by seated maenads holding wreaths, and dancing satyrs. A vine fills the scenes behind the figures and there is a dolphin under each handle. The figures are not centered on Side B.

CONDITION: The cup is intact, the surface abraded in places.

MEASUREMENTS: Height 8 cm. Diameter 19.3 cm. Width 25.9 cm.

PROVENANCE: Formerly in the collection of Samuel Untermyer. Acquired in New York in 1950.

BIBLIOGRAPHY: Sale catalogue, New York, *Parke-Bernet, 11 May 1940*, p. 72, no. 105; *ABV* 639, 90.

COMMENT: The Caylus Painter takes his name from two cups in the Caylus Collection in the Cabinet des Médailles, Paris. The summary execution is typical of artists of the Leafless Group and of many painters working in black figure after red figure had become the rule. Note the distinct discoloration on the inside, off center, caused by the foot of another kylix that was stacked on this one while both were fired in the kiln.

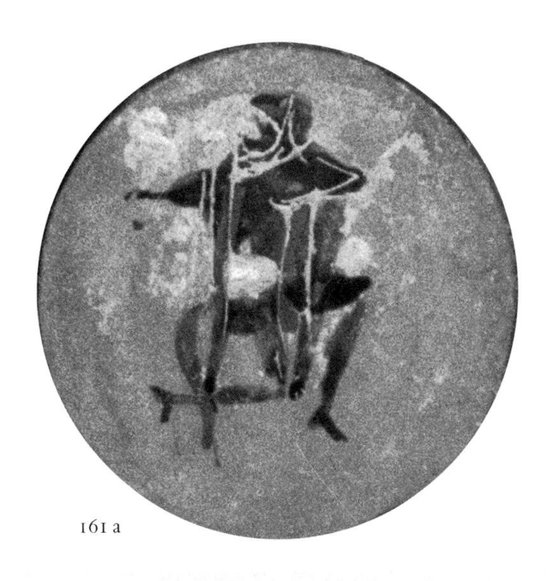

161 a

161 b

161 c

162 a

162

RED FIGURED STAMNOS

Attic
490–480 B.C.

Attributed to the Berlin Painter (Beazley).

Side A: Athena, wearing an Attic helmet and the aegis (but without gorgoneion), holding an *oinochoe* (jug) and spear, stands between Hera, seated on a stool, and Zeus, Athena's father, seated on a high-backed chair. Hera wears a crenellated polos on her head and holds a *phiale* (libation bowl) and scepter; Zeus holds a scepter and extends a phiale in his right hand to receive the libation from Athena's jug. Zeus' wreath and the goddesses' bracelets are red; dilute glaze is used to indicate that the jug is of bronze or gold and for the details of anatomy and dress.

Side B: A warrior in short chiton, cloak and helmet, carrying a shield (device: forepart of a lion) and spear, departs from home. At the left, a woman, perhaps his mother, holding an oinochoe and phiale, offers a libation for his safe return from war. At the right, an old man, probably his father, sits on a folding camp stool.

White is used for the hair on the father's balding scalp; red for his wreath and the mother's bracelets; dilute glaze for the warrior's blond hair, details of anatomy, and dress. There are no ornamental patterns. Graffito under the foot.

CONDITION: The stamnos was broken and repaired, missing pieces were restored on Side B; handle B/A restored. The vase has been cleaned since its publication in the *CVA* (see below).

MEASUREMENTS: Height 34.5 cm. Diameter 30.5 cm.; of foot 14.5 cm.; of lip 23 cm.

PROVENANCE: Formerly in the collection of the Marquess of Northampton, Castle Ashby. Acquired in 1981.

BIBLIOGRAPHY: J. D. Beazley, "Notes on the Vases at Castle Ashby," *Papers of the British School at Rome,* 11, 1929, pp. 20–21, no. 29, fig. 14, pls. 8:1–4; *ARV*[2] 207, 141; *CVA* Castle Ashby 1979, pp. 28–29 (for complete bibliography), pls. 46–47, no. 71; Sale catalogue, London, *Christie's, 2 July 1980*, pp. 56–59, no. 33; D. Kurtz, *The Berlin Painter,* Oxford 1983, pp. 95–96, pl. LVI.

COMMENT: The lack of ornament and the spare, three-figured compositions are typical of the Berlin Painter. The Bastis stamnos belongs in his early period (Beazley 1974, pp. 1, 5).

The graffito, a ligature of alpha and a tailed rho, may be the beginning of a name and is found on other vases by the Berlin Painter (Johnston 1979, p. 133, type 9E, nos. 88–90).

162 b

163

RED FIGURED HYDRIA (KALPIS)

Attic
About 480 B.C.

Attributed to the Syleus Painter (Beazley).

Poseidon combats the giant Polybotes. Poseidon heaves a huge rock, a piece of the island of Kos, at the giant Polybotes who has fallen and defends himself with spear and shield (device: horse or hindquarters of a horse) which has been pierced by Poseidon's trident or spear. According to legend, Poseidon's rock landed in the sea near Kos and became the island of Nisyros.

Red is used to render Poseidon's wreath and the giant's baldric; dilute glaze for details of anatomy and the chunk of Kos.

CONDITION: The hydria was broken and repaired; part of the foot is restored.

MEASUREMENT: Height 30.7 cm.

PROVENANCE: Formerly in the collection of William Rome. Acquired in New York in 1944.

BIBLIOGRAPHY: Sale catalogue, London, *Sotheby, 24 April 1902,* no. 136; sale catalogue, London, *Sotheby, 18 December 1907, no. 63,1;* D. von Bothmer 1961, p. 59, no. 231, pls. 82, 87; *ARV*² 252, 43; *Paralipomena* 350.

COMMENT: The scene is an excerpt from the epic battle of the gods and giants, a popular subject with vase painters and sculptors in the archaic period. This particular episode was a favorite, easily identified by the rock Nisyros that Poseidon hurls. The composition conforms to the type established in black figure during the sixth century B.C. (Heimburg 1968, pp. 44–48).

164 a

164 b

164

RED FIGURED OINOCHOE OF SHAPE IV

Attic
420–400 B.C.

A woman wrapped in a himation holds a round, shallow basket. Sashes are hung up to either side. On the lower edge of the neck is a band of tongues and dots. The drawing is summary, but the shape is elegant, with a distinct foot and a high handle which makes it a good ladler. The black glaze is lustrous and enhances the contour of the vase.

CONDITION: The oinochoe is intact.

MEASUREMENTS: Height 13.2 cm. With handle 15.8 cm.

PROVENANCE: Acquired in New York after 1948 with No. 146.

BIBLIOGRAPHY: Unpublished.

COMMENT: Oinochoai of shape IV are common in red figure during the second half of the fifth century, but the shape has a black figure precursor (Green 1972, p. 7; Robertson 1979, p. 129). The potting is close to that of oinochoai (shape IV) by the Bull Painter. For the simple groundline in lieu of the more usual egg-pattern, D. von Bothmer compares the similar oinochoe of shape IV in Woburn Abbey by the Bull Painter (*ARV*[2] 1349, 10).

165

Attic
About 490 B.C.

Attributed to the Eucharides Painter (Bothmer).

A youth, wearing a diaphanous himation, tempts a cat to climb a knotted pole to get the piece of meat he offers. Suspended behind him is his athletic equipment, sponge, strigil, and oil container. The groundline consists of framed ovules. The shoulder is black, with a ring of framed tongues around the neck. Red is used for the youth's wreath and the meat offered to the cat; dilute glaze for anatomical details. Traces of preliminary sketch lines are visible on the youth's legs.

CONDITION: The neck and rim of the lekythos were broken and repaired.

MEASUREMENTS: Height 33.1 cm. Diameter at shoulder 11.4 cm.; of rim 7.2 cm.; of base 7.2 cm.

PROVENANCE: Acquired in New York in 1982.

BIBLIOGRAPHY: Unpublished.

COMMENT: The proportions and pose of the cat resemble those of the Abyssinian short-hair, the type thought to be closest to the ancient Egyptian domestic cat. Representations of domestic cats are rare in Greek art, the spotted hunting leopard, probably imported from farther east, appearing much more frequently as the pet of aristocratic Athenian youths. In the series of Attic vases showing hunting leopards, a pelike in Philadelphia (University Museum MS 399) comes closest in subject and style to the Bastis lekythos: a spotted hunting leopard climbs up a knotted pole held by a youth (Ashmead 1978, p. 39, pl. 2). An unspotted domestic cat is represented on a relief on a marble base in Athens (National Museum 3476), dating to the end of the sixth century B.C., slightly earlier than the Bastis lekythos. Domestic cats were probably imported from Egypt where they enjoyed a comfortable position as honored members of the household. Herodotus says that when a cat died a natural death, dwellers in the house shaved their eyebrows in mourning (Book II, 66). The cat on this lekythos bears some resemblance to the creature on a neck-pelike fragment in Rome (Villa Giulia; *ARV*[2] 16, 12), identified as a weasel or marten (Caskey and Beazley 2, 1954, 1–2; 3, 1963, 29 and note 4; Berge 1979, no. 77). Llewellen Brown discussed the problem of distinguishing these beasts (W. Ll. Brown 1960, pp. 170–176).

166

Attic
About 490 B.C.

Attributed to the Berlin Painter (Bothmer).

Nike (Victory), wearing a finely pleated chiton and short himation, with a diadem and *sakkos* (hair net or snood) on her head, flies to the right, carrying a *thymiaterion* (incense burner). The scene is framed above and below by a border of maeander pairs, separated by saltire squares alternately upright and pendant. Around the neck are framed tongues with dots. Dilute glaze renders the thin folds of the chiton above the waists, the border of the himation and the small feathers on the upper part of the wings. Preliminary sketch lines indicate that the himation was originally intended to fall over the other shoulder.

CONDITION: The lekythos is intact, with minor surface pitting and abraded areas.

MEASUREMENTS: Height 33.2 cm. Diameter at shoulder 10.8 cm.; of rim 7.2 cm.; of base 7.3 cm.

PROVENANCE: Acquired in New York in 1984.

BIBLIOGRAPHY: Unpublished.

COMMENT: The ornament, which Beazley designated ULFA (Upper-Lower-Facing-Alternately), is typical of the Berlin Painter and his school (Beazley 1964, p. 7). For other vases showing Nike flying with a *thymiaterion*, see Isler-Kerenyi 1971, pp. 25–31, and Isler-Kerenyi 1969. On hair nets see Jenkins and Williams 1985, pp. 414–415, and note 28.

167

Attic
440–430 B.C.

Attributed to the Achilles Painter (Beazley).

Two women carry offerings to the tomb. The first carries a round, shallow basket, the second a *kothon* (perfume vase) and an alabastron. Suspended in front of the first woman is a mirror. The ornament consists of rightward key below the scene, maeander triplets with saltire squares, alternately upright and pendant, above the scene, and black palmettes and tendrils on the reserved shoulder.

The lekythos has a false bottom: a small inner receptacle is attached to the neck, so that the vase seems full while containing less than the outer appearance suggests. This economy measure is often employed in lekythoi intended as grave gifts and not made for use. A vent hole under the maeander below the picture allowed air to escape during firing.

CONDITION: The shoulder and handle were broken and repaired. There is a chip on the foot.

MEASUREMENTS: Height 35.5 cm. Diameter at shoulder 10.25 cm.; of rim 6 cm.; of base 6.6 cm.

PROVENANCE: Formerly in the Searles Collection, Rowland, Massachusetts, no. 1235. Acquired in New York in 1957.

BIBLIOGRAPHY: D. von Bothmer 1961, no. 237, pls. 85, 92; *ARV*² 994, 101; *Paralipomena* 438.

COMMENT: The funerary subject matter on this and the following vase, while regular on white ground lekythoi, is unusual on red figured ones. For the false bottom in lekythoi, see *ABL*, pp. 176–177, where credit is given to the Beldam Potter as the first to make false bottom tomb-lekythoi (Noble 1965, pp. 24–25; Kurtz 1975, pp. 86f.). Inner receptacles occur in several other shapes (Wallenstein 1972, pp. 458–474).

167a

167b

168

Attic
440–420 B.C.

Near the Klügmann Painter (Bothmer).

Women select offerings for the tomb. The woman on the left, standing before an open chest, fastens her cloak on her right shoulder. The woman on the right, probably the maid, holds out a basket, the chosen grave gift which might have contained jewelry, toiletries, or other small objects. Above and below the scene are bands of maeander triplets alternating with cross-squares, and on the reserved shoulder are black palmettes and tendrils.

CONDITION: The neck of the lekythos is broken and repaired.

MEASUREMENTS: Height 39.5 cm. Diameter at shoulder 10.9 cm.; of rim 6.7 cm.; of base 6.7 cm.

PROVENANCE: Formerly in the Searles Collection, Rowland, Massachusetts, no. 1164. Acquired in New York in 1957.

BIBLIOGRAPHY: *ARV*[2] 1200, 2; *Paralipomena* 462.

COMMENT: The reserved shoulder with three black palmettes may have been inspired by types used on vases by the Achilles Painter to whom the invention of this scheme has been attributed (Kurtz 1975, pp. 43–44).

168 a

168 b

169

Attic
480–470 B.C.

Attributed to the Bowdoin Painter (Beazley).

Artemis, rendered in outline, walks to the right, holding bow and arrows, her quiver suspended behind her. Ahead steps a fawn, painted in silhouette except for the tail drawn in outline. In front of Artemis is a meaningless inscription. ϟ . . ϟ T I .

The ornament consists of a row of rightward stopped maeanders above the scene, black palmettes on the shoulder, and narrow tongues on the neck. The shape and ornament are standard for the Bowdoin Painter and belong to his Class BL.

CONDITION: The lekythos is broken and repaired, the handle is reattached.

MEASUREMENTS: Height 30.7 cm. Diameter 9.9 cm.; of rim 6.2 cm.; of base 7 cm.

PROVENANCE: Acquired in New York in 1948.

BIBLIOGRAPHY: Hanfmann 1954, no. 294, pl. 83; D. von Bothmer 1961, no. 238, pls. 82, 87; *ARV*[2] 687, 215 and 1665; *Paralipomena* 406.

COMMENT: The outline drawing combined with black silhouette suggests an artist comfortable in both black and red figure techniques. Many scholars believe that the black figure painter known as the Athena Painter is the same as the red figure artist known as the Bowdoin Painter. The black and red figured vases share similar potter work, ornamental schemes, and style of drawing. For a summary of the pros and cons, see Kurtz 1975, p. 16.

170

Attic
Fourth Century B.C.

The body of the vase, shaped like an almond, is decorated with framed stripes, the lower tip with a dotted scale pattern. The mouth and outside of the handles are black, and there is a black band on the neck. This almond vase is a variant on the standard almond vase in which the body is reserved in the natural reddish color of the clay and the surface is pitted to look like the shell of an almond. Such vases were probably used to contain almond oil.

CONDITION: The vase is broken and repaired. Neck, mouth, and handles have been restored.

MEASUREMENTS: Height 12.7 cm. Width 5.5 cm.

PROVENANCE: Acquired in New York in 1945, with No. 173.

BIBLIOGRAPHY: Unpublished.

COMMENT: The Bastis almond vase goes with a group of almond vases in which the body is decorated. An example in Hamburg is covered with scales drawn very much like those on the Bastis piece, except for the mouth, neck, and handles which are black (Hamburg 1899.189; von Mercklin 1928, p. 331, fig. 50). Another in Athens has scales on the bottom, palmettes and an animal frieze on the main part of the almond, with the neck, mouth, and handles black (National Museum 2323; von Mercklin 1928, p. 331, fig. 52). For the pattern of stripes on the Bastis almond, compare another almond vase in Athens with impressed decoration (National Museum 2324; von Mercklin 1928, p. 333, fig. 53). For almond vases, see Beazley 1940–45, p. 14.

RED FIGURED LEBES GAMIKOS WITH LID

Early Lucanian
400–375 B.C.

Attributed to the Creusa Painter (Trendall).

Side A: A woman seated on a stool looks at herself in a mirror. A sash is suspended beside her.

Side B: Eros, with a wreath, stands in front of a *kalathos* (wool basket). Below, maeanders alternate with saltire squares; above are eggs and darts. On the rim is a tongue pattern. Under the handles are palmettes. The lid, with a pomegranate-shaped knob on a molded stem, has two concentric rings of ornament, tongue pattern and egg-and-dart.

CONDITION: The vase is intact.

MEASUREMENTS: Height with lid 16.2 cm.; without lid 10.5 cm.

PROVENANCE: Acquired in New York in 1973.

BIBLIOGRAPHY: A. D. Trendall, *Red-figured Vases of Lucania, Campania and Sicily, Second Supplement,* Institute of Classical Studies, *Bulletin Supplement* No. 31, London 1973, p. 166, no. 464 a.

COMMENT: The shape is rare in early Lucanian pottery. The drawing, while sketchy, provides good detail, especially the seat with turned legs and the mirror shown in three-quarter view.

171 a

171 b

172

Apulian
350–325 B.C.

The vase is modeled in the form of a bull's head. The ears, glazed black on the exterior, are red inside. The horns are white, tipped with yellow. Fur between the horns is rendered by incisions in the clay before firing, while one shock of hair was done in added white. The eyes, tinged with red, are bulging, with wrinkled skin above them, modeled realistically. The bowl, aligned with the head and flaring at the top, shows a woman with a tambourine and garland leaning against a pillar. A plant, a quatrefoil rosette, and sash fill the field. The scene is framed by palmettes on either side, with egg-and-dart ornament above. Liberal use of white highlights the pillar, plants, and jewelry.

CONDITION: The rhyton is intact except for a chip on the rim of the bowl.

MEASUREMENTS: Height 21.7 cm. Diameter of rim 11.4 cm.

PROVENANCE: Acquired in New York in 1973.

BIBLIOGRAPHY: A. D. Trendall and A. Cambitoglou, *The Red-figured Vases of Apulia,* Oxford 1982, p. 854, no. 552.

COMMENT: The subject, a woman leaning on a pillar, is not usually found in Apulian rhyta where Erotes, seated figures and female heads are the rule.

172 b

172 a

173

Sicilian
Fourth Century B.C.

Attributed to the Bastis Painter, his name piece (Trendall).

On the plate are a crampfish and two flounders, one shown with the flat side out. White is used for details of the fish, such as eyes, fins, and gills. A border of dots circles the plate and the edge is decorated with a laurel wreath. In the center is a circular depression, reserved in the red of the clay and decorated with a circle of waves. The depression was for the fish sauce to accumulate and prevent spilling.

CONDITION: The plate is broken and repaired. The attachment of foot to plate is modern.

MEASUREMENTS: Height 5.6 cm. Diameter 29.3 cm.

PROVENANCE: Acquired in New York in 1945.

BIBLIOGRAPHY: D. von Bothmer 1961, no. 256, pls. 92, 94; Trendall 1987, pp. 65–67, no. 1, B 14, pl. 15e.

COMMENT: In a letter Professor A. D. Trendall comments that "the Bastis Painter is a very important figure in the history of fish plates since he marks the transition from Sicilian to Campanian, his plates being found in Palermo, at various sites on the west coast of Calabria, and at Agropoli near Paestum, finishing up in Cumae. The Bastis plate goes very clearly into New York 06.1021.243 (same 'eyebrows', similar fins, same dotted border)."

174

Etruscan
Late Sixth Century B.C.

A panther on either side is elongated to fill the entire picture panel. On one side he is walking, on the other leaping. On the shoulder of the krater is a row of short vertical lines connected by a horizontal line. On the rim are two rows of dots separated by a line.

The lid, which may not belong, is brownish black, with a reserved band close to the outer edge.

The vase belongs to a group of Etruscan vases that imitate Corinthian black figure vase painting.

CONDITION: It is broken and repaired; the restored areas are visible on one side. The rim is chipped. It is doubtful if the lid belongs.

MEASUREMENTS: Height 23.3 cm. Diameter of rim 21.8 cm.; of lid 18.3 cm. Height of lid 6.9 cm.

PROVENANCE: Formerly in the collection of Alphonse Kann.

BIBLIOGRAPHY: Sale catalogue, New York, *American Art Association, 6–8 January 1927*, no. 9.

COMMENT: The whitish clay, red-brown glaze, and lively drawing suggest that the vase belongs to the Orvieto group (Beazley 1947a, pp. 19–20).

For Etrusco-Corinthian vases, see W. Ll. Brown 1960, pp. 52–59. The inspiration for the panthers on this example might have been coursing hounds, such as those on Proto-Corinthian kotylai (Payne 1931, pl. 5).

174 a

174 b

174 c

175

BLACK FIGURED NECK AMPHORA

Etruscan
6th century B.C.

Attributed to the Wolfshead Painter (J. Gy. Szilágyi). The painted decoration features three zones of animals: the principal zone around the belly shows two stags, a bull, a boar and a lion; the shoulder zone has on side A a boar and a lion, and on side B a marsh bird between sphinxes; the neck has on side A a sphinx, and on side B a griffin. The lions, with their wolf-like heads, give the Wolfshead Painter his name.

Space between the animals is filled with incised blob rosettes. Black bands of varying widths frame the animal zones; the black, splayed foot is ornamented with white dot rosettes. The combination of the dot rosettes of Proto-Corinthian vase decoration, and incised blob rosettes seen on mature Corinthian vases is typical of Etrusco-Corinthian vases.

Red is used for parts of the animals, and the bands around the vase, the foot, and inside the mouth.

CONDITION: Broken and repaired.

MEASUREMENTS: Height 35.7 cm. Diameter 23.4 cm.

PROVENANCE: Said to be from Italy, acquired before 1949.

BIBLIOGRAPHY: Unpublished.

COMMENT: The Wolfshead Painter was recognised by J. Gy. Szilágyi who discusses his stylistic peculiarities and his vases in Szilágyi 1968, pp. 10–13.

The neck-amphora was given to the Brooklyn Museum in 1969 (Acc. no. 69.111).

175 a

175 b

175 c

175 d

PART VII

Jewelry

by
Andrew Oliver, Jr.

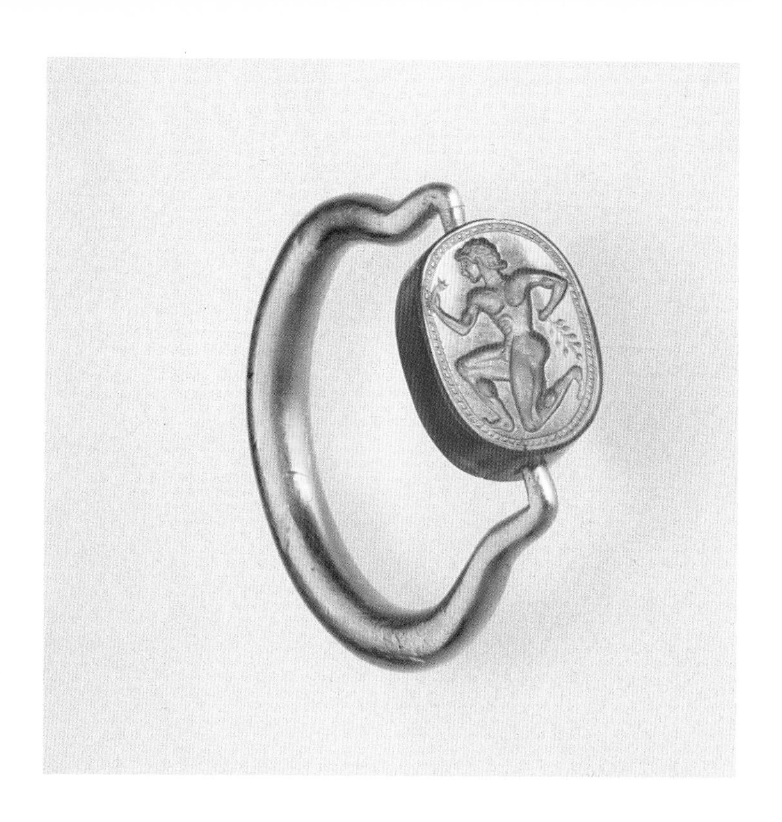

176

GOLD RING WITH A CARNELIAN SCARABOID

Greek
Late Sixth Century B.C.

The gold hoop is omega in shape, round in section, and holds a carnelian that swivels in its prongs. The bezel is engraved with a youth running to the left, holding a flower in one hand and a branch in the other. The border is hatched.

CONDITION: The ring is intact.

MEASUREMENTS: Diameter of hoop 3.2 cm. Length of stone 1.6 cm.

PROVENANCE: Unknown.

BIBLIOGRAPHY: Unpublished.

COMMENT: For the hoop, compare a swivel ring with a carnelian scaraboid from Cyprus in the Metropolitan Museum (Richter 1956, p. 11, pl. VII, no. 41). For the style of the carving of the youth, see the comparanda in Boardman 1968, chapter IX, especially no. 269.

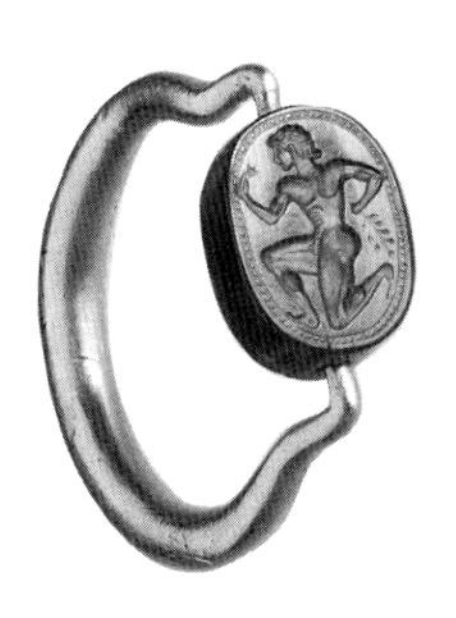

177a

177b

177

TWO SILVER ROUNDELS

Greek
Fifth Century B.C.

One roundel shows Perseus about to decapitate the gorgon, Medusa; the other shows Bellerophon, dismounted from his winged horse, Pegasus, about to slay an Amazon. The silver is worked in repoussé, negative images are visible on the back. Each roundel has a border of triple guilloche punched into the silver.

CONDITION: Both roundels exhibit breaks and repairs.

MEASUREMENTS: Diameter of Perseus roundel 4.35 cm.; of Bellerophon roundel 4.05 cm.

PROVENANCE: Acquired in New York in the 1970s.

BIBLIOGRAPHY: Unpublished.

178

SILVER AND BRONZE FIGURES OF SPHINXES

Greek
Fifth Century B.C.

Both sphinxes, one of silver, the other of bronze, are perched on Ionic capitals: the head of the silver one is turned to the left, the head of the bronze one to the right. Scales are indicated on the breast; feathers are done in two registers on the wings; hair radiates from a central point on the crown of the head. Breast, wings, and the head of the silver one are gilded.

CONDITION: The surfaces are worn.

MEASUREMENT: Height of both 3.0 cm.

PROVENANCE: Unknown.

BIBLIOGRAPHY: Unpublished.

COMMENT: Sphinxes were guardians. In stone, for instance, they flanked tomb entrances or sat upon grave stelai to prevent harm from coming to the deceased. Two tiny sphinxes recline on the rim of an East Greek silver ladle in New York (66.11.26; D. von Bothmer 1981, pp. 197–198, fig. 3). Perhaps they were thought of as keeping watch over the liquid poured from the ladle or as averting evil from the ceremony in which it was used. The Bastis sphinxes, perhaps coming from utensils, could have served similar purposes.

Bronze

Silver

179

GOLD EARRING WITH A SPHINX

Greek
Fourth or Third Century B.C.

The sphinx and her base, including the six loops, are modeled in one piece in repoussé and chasing. Drop-shaped pendants, three of them missing, are chained to the loops, which are reinforced with wire. The sphinx is backed by a flat, undecorated plate, cut to follow the contours exactly. A hook is attached to the back.

CONDITION: Except for the missing pendants, the earring is intact.

MEASUREMENTS: Length 6.9 cm.; without pendants 4.4 cm.

PROVENANCE: Unknown.

BIBLIOGRAPHY: Davidson and Oliver 1984, pp. 65–66, no. 63, ill.

COMMENT: A pair of earrings from a grave of the fourth or third century B.C., near Ordzhonikidze, South Russia, is similar in construction and style (Bacon 1972, p. 51, ill.). A related ornament in the form of a double-bodied sphinx, is in Providence (25.101, Museum of Art, Rhode Island School of Design, Hackens 1976, p. 60, no. 19, ill.).

180

GOLD FILLET WITH A HERAKLES KNOT

Greek
Late Fourth or Third Century B.C.

The central ornament of the fillet is a Herakles knot. Two palmettes with a rosette in the middle fill the center of the knot, while the four ends terminate in lion heads. The two lower lion heads hold rings in their mouths, from which tassel pendants hang. The tassels are gathered into open-ended beads. Between the pairs of lion heads on the knot are two exquisitely finished female heads. The chains of the fillet are connected to them. At the clasp end of the chains are lion-head terminals, each with a ring in its mouth.

MEASUREMENTS: Length 40.7 cm; length of knot 4.3 cm.

PROVENANCE: Unknown.

BIBLIOGRAPHY: P. F. Davidson, "The Bastis Gold," *Brooklyn Museum Annual* 8, 1966–67, pp. 90–95, figs. 1–6; H. Hoffmann, *Collecting Greek Antiquities,* New York 1971, p. 200, fig. 178; Davidson and Oliver 1984, pp. 37–38, no. 34, ill.

COMMENT: The fillet is said to have been found with the pair of Eros earrings (No. 181). It belongs to a class of fillets found in tombs in northern Greece, northwestern Asia Minor and South Russia on the Black Sea.

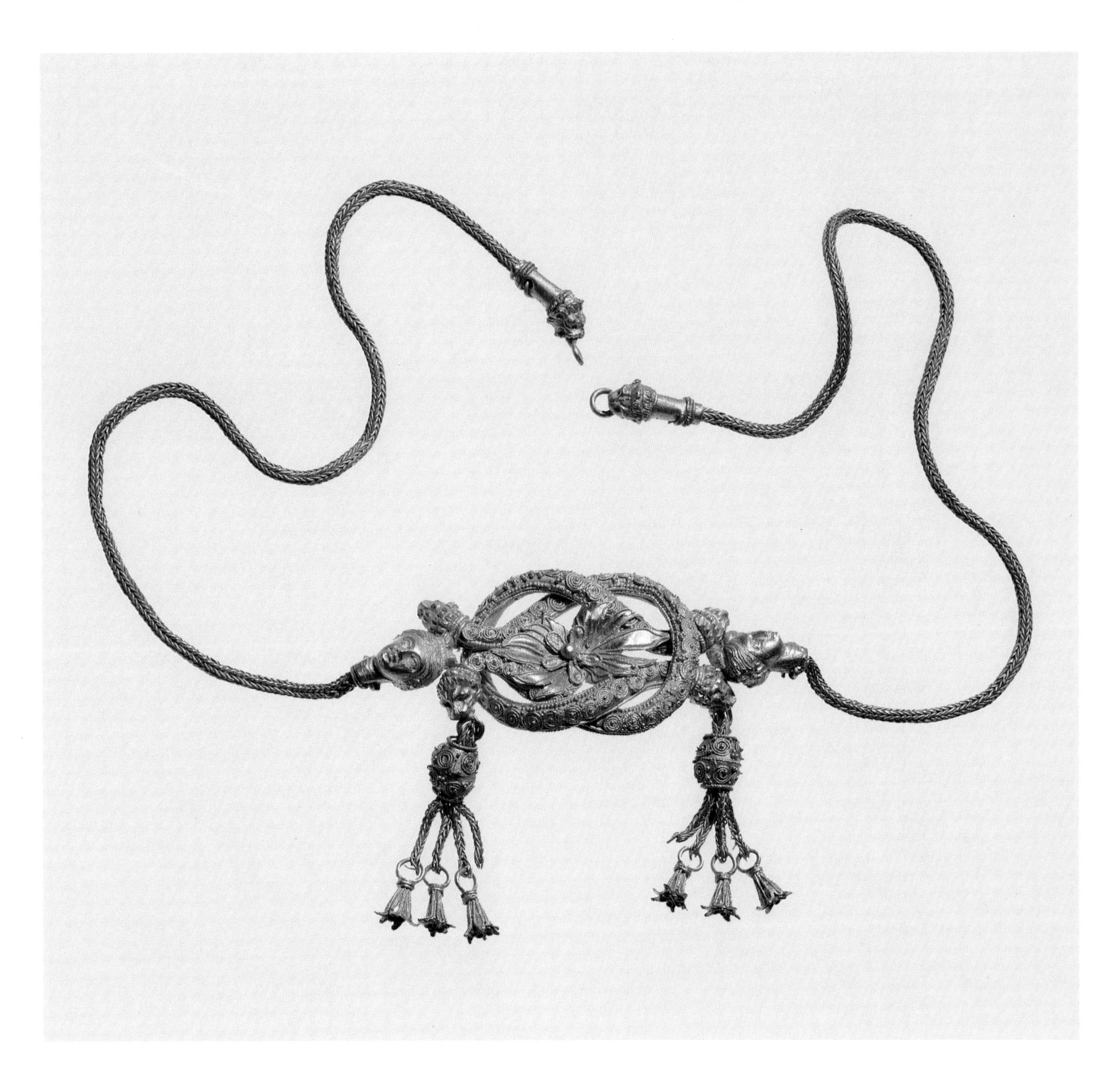

181

PAIR OF GOLD EARRINGS WITH EROTES

Greek
Late Fourth or Early Third Century B.C.

The earrings are made in two parts: a disk, on the back of which is a hock, and the pendant figure of an Eros carrying a torch. The central rosette on each disk is surrounded by four S-shaped coils of wire, the whole assemblage framed by a flange. The bodies of the Erotes are cast solid. The wings are made of sheet gold. Details, including face, fingers, and toes, are carefully indicated. The figures are made in mirror reverse to one another.

CONDITION: The earrings are intact.

MEASUREMENTS: Length 3.6 cm.; of figures 2.2 cm.

PROVENANCE: Unknown.

BIBLIOGRAPHY: P. F. Davidson, "The Bastis Gold," *Brooklyn Museum Annual* 8, 1966–67, pp. 95–97, fig. 7; Davidson and Oliver 1984, p. 68, no. 66, ill.

COMMENT: Earrings with pendant Erotes were common throughout the Hellenistic Period (Laffineur 1980, pp. 420–423). This pair comes early in the series and, like the fillet (No. 180) with which it is said to have been found, is exceptionally well crafted.

182

PAIR OF GOLD EARRINGS

Greek
Third Century B.C.?

Erotes ride birds, holding around their wrists the reins, which cross the birds' breasts in a "Knot of Herakles". The wings of the Erotes are attached by beaded wire halters around the necks and waists. The birds' wings, tail feathers, and the down on their heads, as well as the wings of the Erotes are accentuated with beaded wire arranged in circles and long loops. The birds' feet are done with three lengths of wire. The Erotes' hair is shown with fine granulation. The suspension wires of the earrings are hinged to sockets at the birds' tails, the free ends snapping into loops on the Erotes' heads. The birds seem to have been made in two halves, left and right.

CONDITION: The earrings are intact.

MEASUREMENT: Length 3.7 cm.

PROVENANCE: Unknown.

BIBLIOGRAPHY: Unpublished.

COMMENT: Erotes riding dolphins are relatively well known in Greek Art (Greifenhagen 1957, pp. 33, 70; Hackens 1975, p. 90). Less often they are shown riding birds. Compare a singleton in the Museo Archeologico, Taranto on which the Eros is playing a kithara; details of the bird are chased into the metal, and the bird's feet project from the body (De Juliis 1984, p. 177, no. 100).

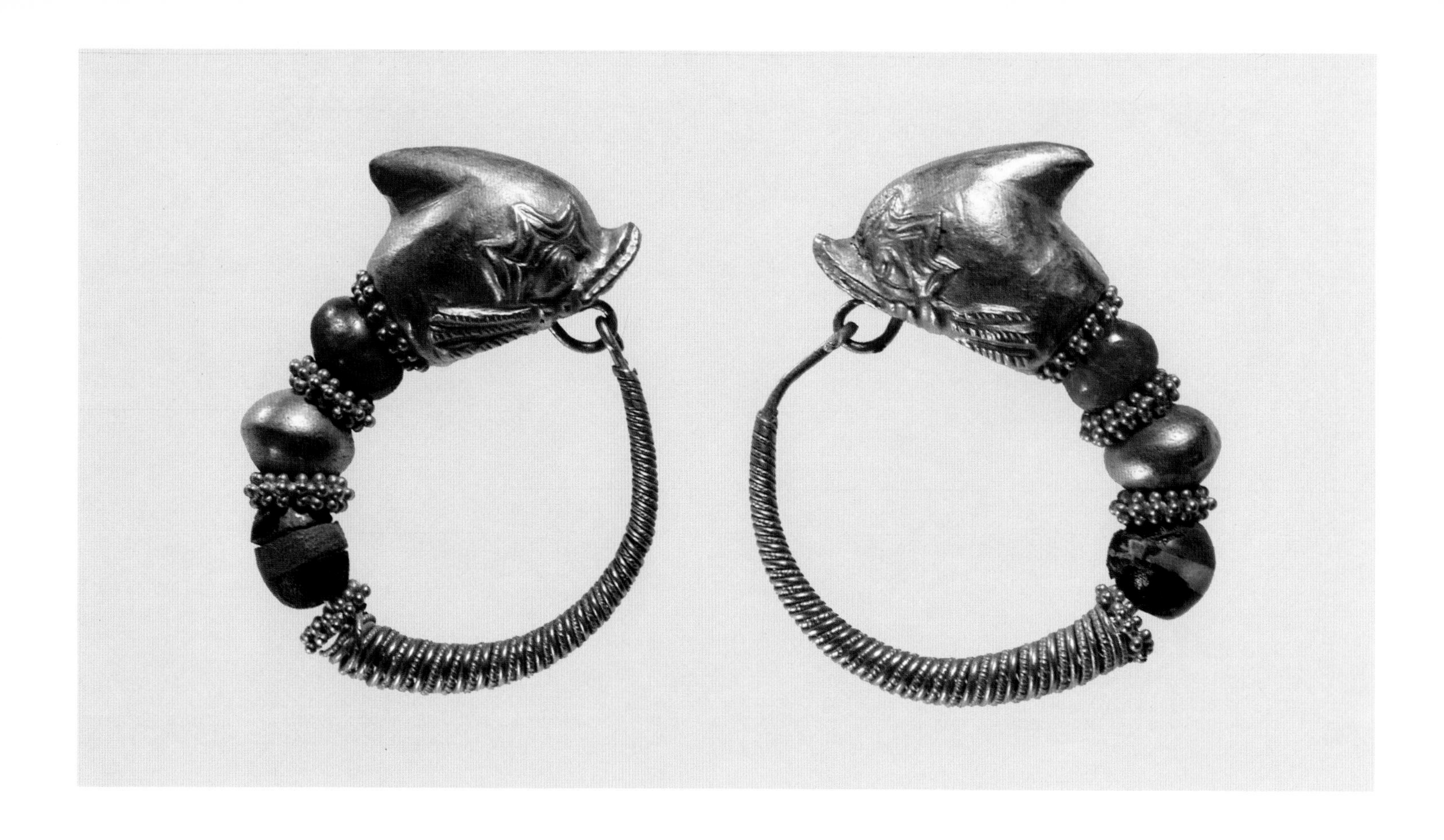

183

PAIR OF GOLD EARRINGS WITH DOLPHIN HEADS

Greek
Second or First Century B.C.

The careful modeling of the dolphin heads is done in repoussé and chasing. The hollow gold bodies are filled with a hard white core. The beads are of emerald, gold, and banded glass, collared by rings of gold granules. The hoops have a wire frame, on which the beads are also strung and around which four wires are spirally wound. The ends of the frames hook into loops below the dolphin jaws.

MEASUREMENTS: Diameter 4.0 cm. and 4.1 cm.

PROVENANCE: From Egypt.

BIBLIOGRAPHY: Davidson and Oliver 1984, pp. 63–64, no. 61, ill.

COMMENT: Animal heads, including those of dolphins, were standard features of hoop earrings in the late Hellenistic Period. Dolphin-head earrings have been found in Egypt and on Cyprus, Crete, and Delos, and were probably made at one or more workshops in the eastern Mediterranean (Davidson and Oliver 1984, p. 64).

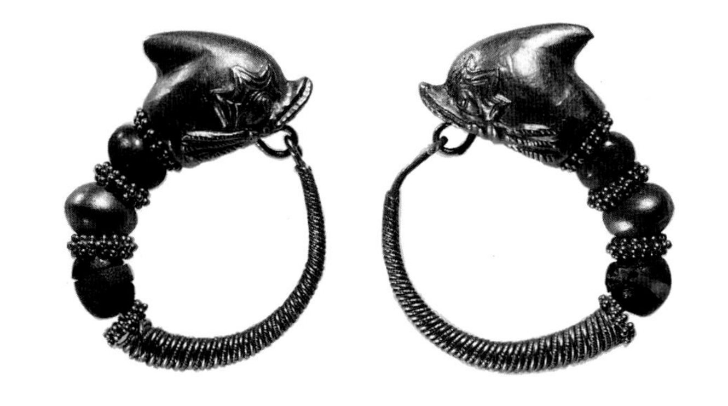

184

Greek
Third or Second Century B.C.

The upper element, embodying the hook, features an Egyptian Atef Crown. The sun-disk is done with a translucent stone, the twin feathers rendered with opaque black and white glass, all settings trimmed with beading. Satellite glass beads (red and white on one earring, red and green on the other) are wired below. A triangular sheet ornamented with granules partially conceals the hinge holding the pendant.

The heart-shaped pendant has a stone in the center, bordered by a band of black and white glass arranged in a saw-tooth design and set in gold cloisons edged with beading. Two glass beads are wired below, while a third, now missing, was secured between reel- and cone-shaped moldings at the bottom. Gold sheeting backs all the settings.

CONDITION: Except for the missing lower beads, the earrings are intact.

MEASUREMENT: Length 7.2 cm.

PROVENANCE: Unknown.

BIBLIOGRAPHY: Unpublished.

COMMENT: Earrings with representations of the sun-disk and feathers are not unusual (Davidson and Oliver 1984, p. 70).

185 GOLD RING WITH A CARNELIAN OR RED GLASS INTAGLIO

Roman
Second or Third Century A.D.

The shank is decorated with applied reliefs on each side, which show a draped female figure holding a lance against a griffin. Framed by a pair of branches, the intaglio features the draped bust of a woman in left profile, wearing a wreath and necklace.

CONDITION: The gold details are worn.

MEASUREMENTS: Diameter of ring 3.0 cm. Length of bezel 2.0 cm.

PROVENANCE: Unknown.

BIBLIOGRAPHY: Unpublished.

186

BRACELET WITH A CARNELIAN

Roman
Third Century A.D.

The hoop of the bracelet is made of four tubes spirally wound, terminating at each end in a corrugated sleeve. The setting for the stone is hinged to the capped ends of the sleeves. One hinge is permanently secured, while the other can be opened by removing a pin, allowing the bracelet to be sprung and slipped over the wrist. The carnelian is an ovoid cone, truncated at the top. The box setting has tapered sides. The stone is held in place by a serrated flange bordered by a twisted wire.

CONDITION: The tubes and sleeves are dented, the bracelet is otherwise intact.

MEASUREMENT: Diameter 6.5 cm.

PROVENANCE: From Egypt.

BIBLIOGRAPHY: Davidson and Oliver 1984, pp. 151–152, no. 207, ill.

COMMENT: Bracelets of this design are well known in Egypt, but the type has also been found in France.

187

SILVER STATUETTE OF APHRODITE

Roman
First or Second Century A.D.

The statuette was cast hollow, with the arms made separately and joined below the shoulders. The goddess is removing the himation which has fallen below her hips. She holds an apple, alluding to her beauty and the judgment of Paris, who voted for her over Hera and Athena.

CONDITION: The surface was damaged in places; repairs are visible on the upper arms and along the junction of torso and drapery in back.

MEASUREMENT: Height 17.2 cm.

PROVENANCE: Unknown.

BIBLIOGRAPHY: Unpublished.

COMMENT: Semidraped female figures of this type were first made in marble around 100 B.C., probably originating at an artistic center such as Rhodes (Bieber 1961 b, p. 133); in succeeding centuries they were copied and adapted in bronze, terracotta and silver.

187a

187b

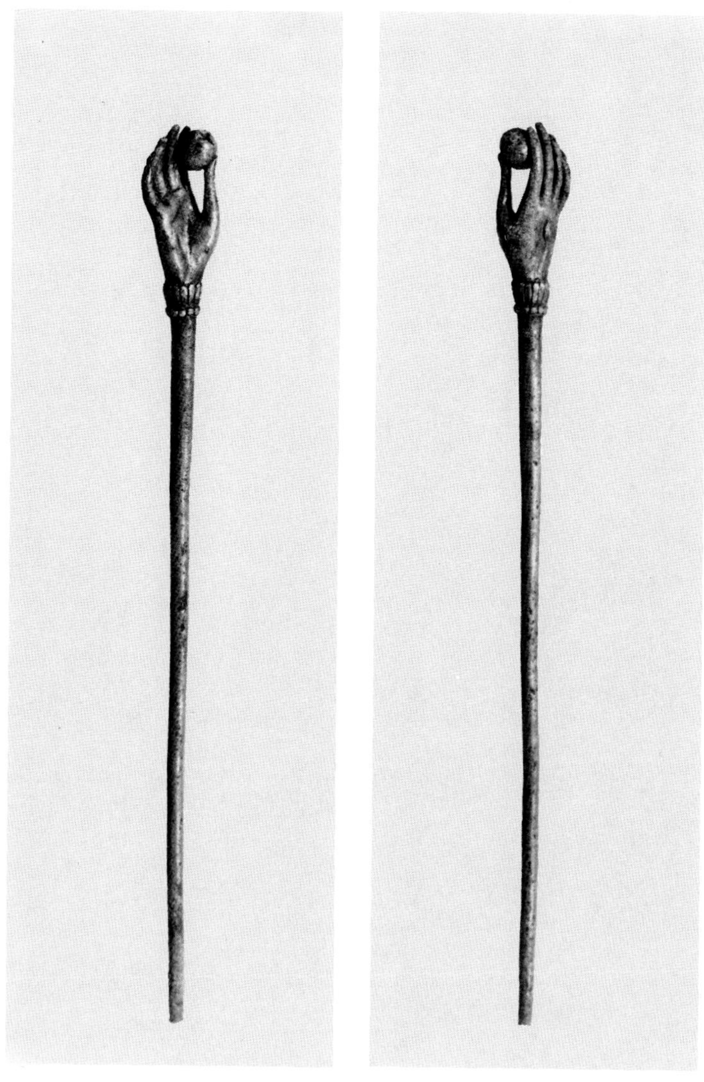

188 a 188 b

188

SILVER GILT PIN

Roman
First or Second Century A.D.

The pin ends in an extended right hand which holds between the thumb and the index and middle fingers a globular fruit with a cross-shaped incision on the top. The hand is well modeled, even to the point of showing the joints, fingernails, and lines of the palm. The wrist springs from a blossom of fifteen petals, set off from the stem of the pin by beading.

CONDITION: Hand and stem show areas of corrosion and pitting.

MEASUREMENTS: Length overall 13.8 cm; of hand 2.2 cm.

PROVENANCE: Unknown.

BIBLIOGRAPHY: Unpublished.

COMMENT: The object was probably used as a hair pin. Many similar ones are known such as the silver pin with outstretched right hand holding a pomegranate from Walbrook, London (British Museum 1964, p. 28, no. 12, fig. 14:12). Ivory pins featuring right hands, but without fruit, have been found at Pompeii, buried by Vesuvius in AD 79 (Ward-Perkins and Claridge II, 1978, p. 138, no. 60 c and e).

PART VIII

Antiquities Donated to The Metropolitan Museum of Art

by
Dietrich von Bothmer

A 1

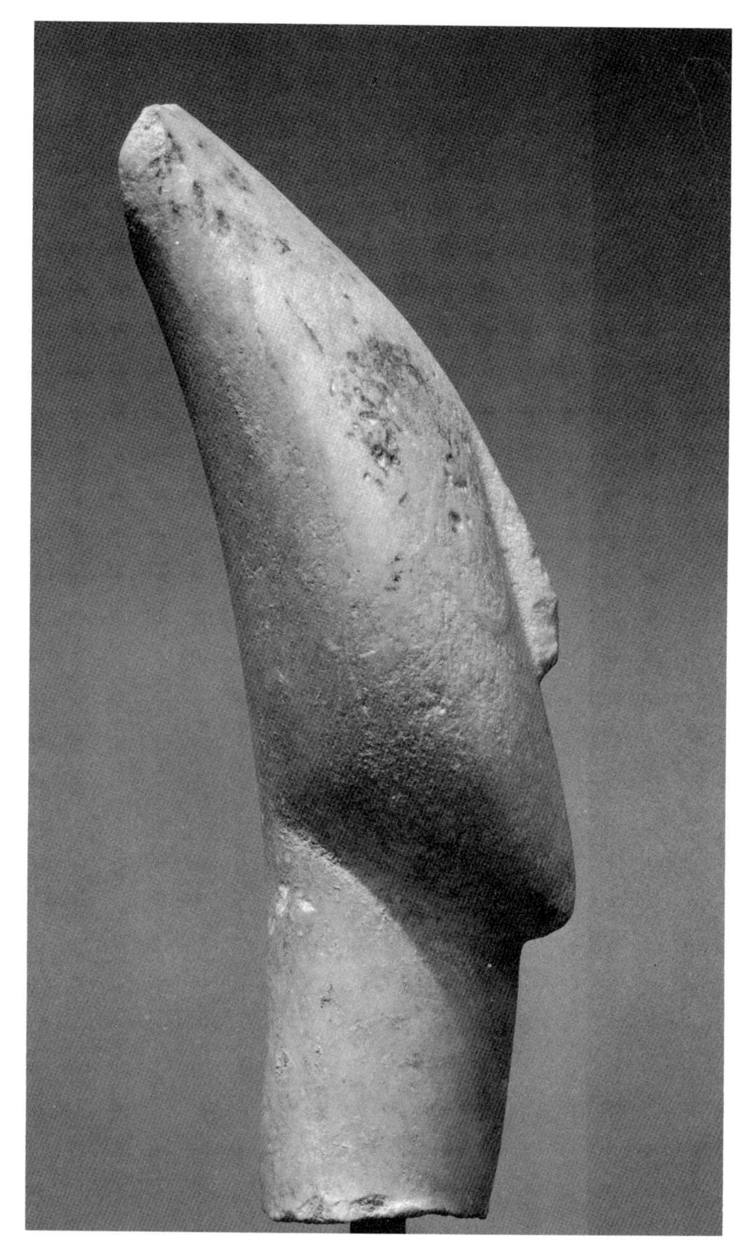
A 2

Cycladic

A. Marble head. Height 25.3 cm. About 2600–2500 B.C. Bibliography: J. Thimme, *Kunst der Kykladen* (Karlsruhe 1976), no. 202, ill.; *Greek Art of the Aegean Islands* (1979), no. 14, ill. MMA 64.246.

A 3

B. Marble statuette of a woman. Height 62.8 cm. About 2500–2400 B.C. Bibliography: *BMMA* 28 (1969–1970), p. 78; MMA, *Masterpieces of Fifty Centuries* (1970), pp. 102–103, no. 45; *Guide to MMA* (1972), p. 163, no. 2; D. von Bothmer, *Guide to the Collections, Greek and Roman Art*[3] (1975) p. 1, no. 1; MMA, *Notable Acquisitions 1965–1975*, p. 114; J. Thimme, *Kunst der Kykladen* (1976), no. 166 (ill.); *Greek Art of the Aegean Islands* (1979), no. 15; P. Getz-Preziosi, 1981, p. 27, figs. 60–61. MMA 68.148.

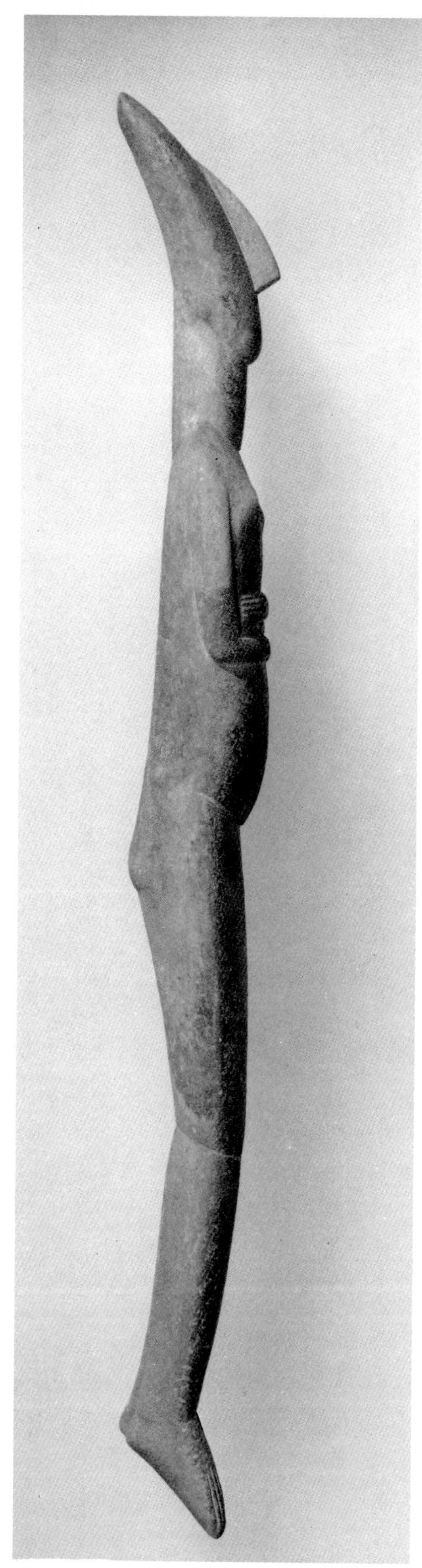

B 1

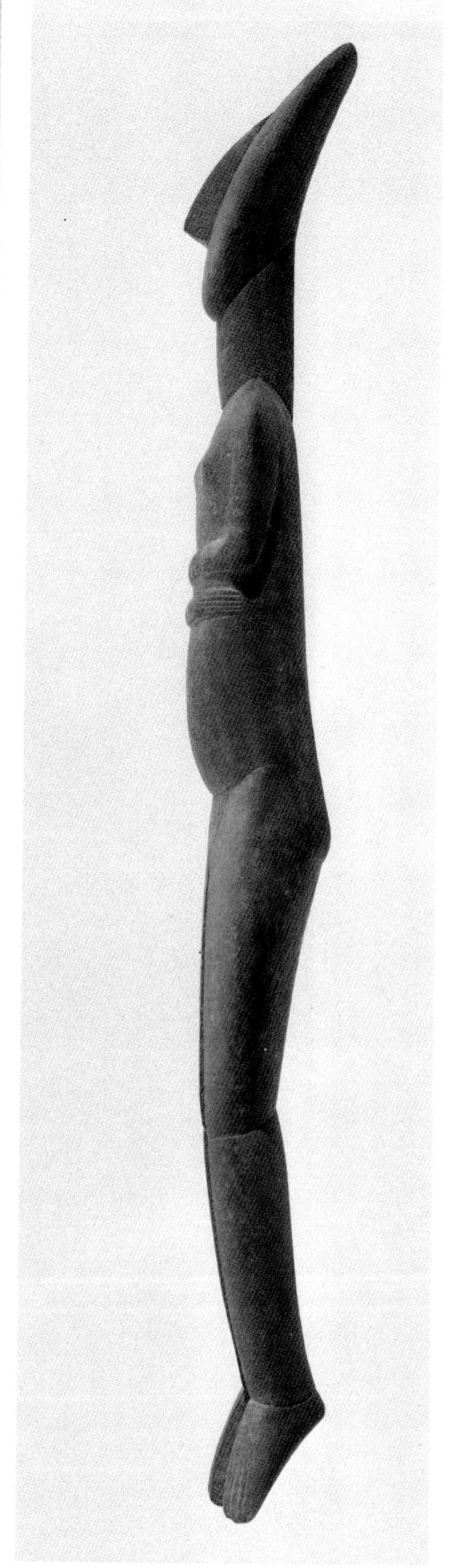

B 2

B 3

B 4

C 1

C 2

Greek Vases

C. Attic black-figured neck-amphora. Height now 30.8 cm.
A, Kaineus in Centauromachy. B, recovery of Helen. Attributed to the Antimenes Painter. About 520 B.C. Bibliography: *CVA* MMA fasc. 4 (1976) pp. 23–24 pl. 25 (with earlier bibliography); M. Castoldi, "Alcuni vasi attici a figure nere del Civico Museo Archeologico," *Rassegna di Studi del Museo Archeologico e del Civico Gabinetto Numismatico di Milano* 21–22 (1978), p. 11. MMA 69.233.1.

C 3

D 1

D 2

D. Attic black-figured neck-amphora. Height 41.7 cm. A, Apollo between Leto and Artemis. B, Iolaos, Herakles and the lion, Athena. Attributed to the Pasikles Painter. About 510 B.C.
Bibliography: *CVA* MMA fasc. 4 (1976), p. 35, pl. 34 (with earlier bibliography); L. Kahil, in *LIMC* 2 (1984) p. 707, no. 1106, pl. 533. MMA 67.44.1.

D 3

E 1

E 2

E. Attic black-figured neck-amphora. Height 40.6 cm. A, Dionysos between two maenads; B, woman with torch between man and woman. About 500 B.C. Bibliography: *CVA* MMA fasc. 4 (1976), pp. 45–46, pl. 39,5–8, A. W. Johnston, *Trademarks on Greek Vases* (1979), p. 128, type 8E, no. 19. MMA 69.233.2.

E

F. Attic black-figured kalpis. Height 35.0 cm.
Man courting woman; man addressing woman seated on porch. Attributed to the Eucharides Painter. About 500 B.C. Bibliography: D. von Bothmer, *Ancient Art from New York Private Collections* (1961), p. 54, no. 208, pls. 76, 78 (with earlier bibliography). *BMMA* 26 (1967–68), p. 73, ill.; MMA, *Notable Acquisitions, 1965–1975,* p. 126 ill.; R. Sutton, *The Interaction of Men and Women Portrayed on Attic Red-figure Pottery* (1981), p. 432, note 21. MMA 67.44.2.

G 1

G. Attic red-figured bell-krater. Height 40.6 cm.
A, Tydeus, Aktaion, Theseus, and Castor. B, three youths. Attributed to the Dinos Painter. About 520 B.C.
Bibliography: D. von Bothmer, *Ancient Art from New York Private Collections* (1961), pp. 58–59, pl. 86 (with earlier bibliography); J. D. Beazley, *ARV*[2] (1963), p. 1154, no. 36; idem, *Paralipomena*, p. 457; E. Simon, *Götter der Griechen* (1969), p. 197; MMA, *Notable Acquisitions 1965–1975*, p. 125 ill.; A. Kossatz-Deissmann, *Dramen des Aischylos auf westgriechischen Vasen* (1978), p. 146, n. 852; A. Greifenhagen, *Alte Zeichnungen nach unbekannten griechischen Vasen* (1976), p. 15, n. 34; A. Schnapp, "Pratiche e imagini di caccia nella Grecia antica," in *Dialoghi di Archeologia* 1 (1980), p. 58, n. 49; J.-M. Moret, *Oedipe, la sphinx et les Thébains* (1984), p. 82, n. 10. MMA 66.79.

BIBLIOGRAPHY AND ABBREVIATIONS PARTS II–VIII

ABL — C. H. E. Haspels, *Attic Black-figured Lekythoi* (Paris, 1936).

ABV — J. D. Beazley, *Attic Black-figure Vase-painters* (Oxford, 1956).

Adam 1984 — A.-M. Adam, *Bibliothèque Nationale, Bronzes étrusques et italiques* (Paris, 1984).

AJA — *American Journal of Archaeology.*

Amandry 1953 — P. Amandry, "Manches de patères et de miroirs grecs," *Monuments et Mémoires publiés par l'Académie des Inscriptions et Belles-Lettres,* Fondation Eugène Piot 47 (1953), pp. 45–70.

Amandry 1963 — –, *Collection Hélène Stathatos* III. *Objets antiques et byzantines* (Strasbourg, 1963).

Amyx 1958 — D. A. Amyx, "The Attic Stelai," *Hesperia* 27 (1958), pp. 163–254.

Ancient Art from Cyprus 1983 — The John and Mable Ringling Museum of Art, *Ancient Art from Cyprus: The Ringling Collection* (Sarasota, 1983).

Anderson 1982 — W. S. Anderson, "Euripides' *Auge* and Menander's *Epitrepontes*," *Greek, Roman, and Byzantine Studies* 23 (1982), pp. 165–177.

André Emmerich Gallery 1965 — André Emmerich Gallery, *Early Art in Greece: The Cycladic, Minoan, Mycenaean, and Geometric Periods* (New York, 1965).

André Emmerich Gallery 1977 — –, *Classical Art from a New York Collection* (New York, 1977).

Andrén 1939–41 — A. Andrén, *Architectural Terracottas from Etrusco-Italic Temples* (Lund, 1939–41).

Arnold 1969 — D. Arnold, "Die Polykletnachfolge," *Jahrbuch des Deutschen Archäologischen Instituts,* Ergänzungsheft 25 (1969).

ARV[2] — J. D. Beazley, *Attic Red-figure Vase-painters* 2nd ed. (Oxford, 1963).

Ashmead 1978 — A. Ashmead, "Greek Cats, Exotic Pets Kept by Rich Youths, in Fifth Century B.C. Athens, as Portrayed on Greek Vases," *Expedition* 20, 3 (Spring 1978), pp. 38–47.

Åstrom 1972 — P. Åstrom, *The Swedish Cyprus Expedition,* vol. IV, pt. 1B (Lund, 1972).

Babelon and Blanchet 1895 — E. Babelon and J. A. Blanchet, *Catalogue des bronzes antiques de la Bibliothèque Nationale* (Paris, 1895).

Bacon 1972 — E. Bacon, "The Gold of a Scythian Queen," *Illustrated London News* 260 (July, 1972), p. 51.

Banti 1973 — L. Banti, *The Etruscan Cities and their Culture* (Berkeley, 1973).

The Barakat Gallery 1985 — The Barakat Gallery, *A Catalogue of the Collection* I (Beverly Hills, 1985).

Barr-Sharrar 1982 — B. Barr-Sharrar, "Macedonian Metal Vases in Perspective ...," *Studies in the History of Art* 10, *Macedonia and Greece in Late Classical and Early Hellenistic Times* (Washington, 1982).

Barr-Sharrar 1987 — –, *The Hellenistic and Early Imperial Decorated Bust* (Mainz, 1987).

Beazley 1945 — J.D. Beazley, "Miniature Panathenaics," *Annual of the British School at Athens* 41 (1940–45), pp. 10–21.

Beazley 1947 a — –, *Etruscan Vase Painting* (Oxford, 1947).

Beazley 1947 b — –, "Some Attic Vases in the Cyprus Museum," *Proceedings of the British Academy* 33 (1947), pp. 195–242.

Beazley 1961 — –, "An Amphora by the Berlin Painter," *Antike Kunst* 4 (1961), pp. 49–67.

Beazley 1964 — –, *The Berlin Painter*, Melbourne University Press, Occasional Paper No. 6 (Melbourne, 1964).

Beazley 1974 — –, *The Berlin Painter* (Mainz, 1974).

Beazley Addenda 1982 — –, *Additional References to ABV, ARV², & Paralipomena* compiled by L. Burn and R. Glynn (Oxford, 1982).

Beazley and Ashmole 1932 — –, and B. Ashmole, *Greek Sculpture and Painting* (Cambridge/New York, 1932).

Bell 1981 — M. Bell, III, *Morgantina Studies* I. *The Terracottas* (Princeton, 1981).

Bellinger 1963 — A. R. Bellinger, *Essays on the Coinage of Alexander the Great* (New York, 1963).

Berger 1979 — E. Berger, "Auszug aus dem Jahresbericht 1978," *Antike Kunst* 22 (1979), pp. 44–48.

Berlin 1978 — Staatliche Museen Preussischer Kulturbesitz, *Römisches im Antikenmuseum* (Berlin, 1978).

Bernabò Brea 1981 — L. Bernabò Brea, *Menandro e il teatro greco nelle terracotte Liparesi* (Genoa, 1981).

Besques 1972 — S. Besques, *Catalogue raisonné des figurines et reliefs en terre-cuite grecs, étrusques et romains*, III: *Epoques hellénistique et romaine, Grèce et Asie Mineure* (Paris, 1972).

Bieber 1961 a — M. Bieber, *History of the Greek and Roman Theater* (Princeton, 1961).

Bieber 1961 b — –, *The Sculpture of the Hellenistic Age*, rev. ed. (New York, 1961).

Bieber 1977 — –, *Ancient Copies. Contributions to the History of Greek and Roman Art* (New York, 1977).

Biesantz 1965 — H. Biesantz, *Die thessalischen Grabreliefs. Studien zur nordgriechischen Kunst* (Mainz, 1965).

Birmingham Museum & Art Gallery 1968 — Birmingham Museum & Art Gallery, *Ancient Life in Miniature. An Exhibition of Classical Terracottas from Private Collections in England* (Birmingham, 1968).

Blinkenberg 1931 — C. Blinkenberg, *Lindos, Fouilles de l'Acropole 1902–1914* I. *Les petits objets* (Berlin, 1931).

Boardman 1968 — J. Boardman, *Archaic Greek Gems* (Evanston, 1968).

Boardman 1972 — –, "Herakles, Peisistratos and Sons," *Revue Archéologique* (1972), pp. 60–66.

Boardman 1973 — –, "Some Unusual Mycenaean Terracottas from the Citadel House Area, 1954–69," *Annual of the British School at Athens* 68 (1973), pp. 207–265.

Boardman 1974 — –, *Athenian Black Figure Vases: A Handbook* (London/New York, 1974).

Boardman 1976 — –, "A Curious Eye Cup," *Archäologischer Anzeiger* (1976), pp. 281–290.

Boardman 1979 — –, "The Kleophrades Painter's Cup in London," *The J. Paul Getty Museum Journal* I (1979), pp. 7–14.

Boardman and Schweizer — J. Boardman and F. Schweizer, "Clay Analysis of Archaic Greek Pottery,"

1973 — *Annual of the British School at Athens* 68 (1973), pp. 267–283.

Bonci 1977 — L. R. Bonci, "Resti di klinai in bronzo da Arno," *Studi in onore di Filippo Magi. Nuovi Quaderni dell' Istituto di Archeologia dell' Università di Perugia,* vol. 1 (Perugia, 1977), pp. 183–200.

von Bothmer 1957 — D. von Bothmer, *Amazons in Greek Art* (Oxford, 1957).

von Bothmer 1961 — –, *Ancient Art from New York Private Collections* (New York, 1961).

von Bothmer 1965 — –, Review of E. Diehl, *Die Hydria, Gnomon 37* (1965), pp. 599–608.

von Bothmer 1969–70 — –, "Greek and Roman Art" [Report of the Departments], *Bulletin, Metropolitan Museum of Art* 28 (1969–70), pp. 77–78.

von Bothmer 1975 — –, *Metropolitan Museum of Art, Guide to the Collections: Greek and Roman Art* (Third ed., New York, 1975).

von Bothmer 1981 — –, "Les trésors de l'orfévrerie de la Grèce orientale au Metropolitan Museum de New York," *Comptes rendus de L'Académie des Inscriptions et Belles-Lettres* (1981), pp. 194–207.

von Bothmer 1983 — –, "Observations on the Subject Matter of South Italian Vases," *Arts in Virginia* 23 (1983), pp. 28–43.

von Bothmer 1985 — –, *The Amasis Painter and his World* (Malibu/New York, 1985).

Boube-Piccot 1960 — C. Boube-Piccot, "Les lits de bronze de Mauretanie Tingitane," *Bulletin d'archéologie marocaine* 4 (1960), pp. 189–286.

Boucher 1970 — S. Boucher, *Bronzes grecs, hellénistiques et étrusques des musées de Lyon* (Lyon, 1970).

Boucher 1973 — –, "Trajets terrestres du commerce étrusque aux Ve et IVe siècles avant J.-C.," *Revue Archéologique* (1973) I, pp. 59–96.

Bouzek 1974 — J. Bouzek, *Graeco-Macedonian Bronzes* (Prague, 1974).

Braemer 1963 — F. Braemer, *L'art dans l'occident romain* (Paris, 1963).

Braun 1970 — K. Braun, "Der Dipylon-Brunnen B1. Die Funde," *Mitteilungen des Deutschen Archäologischen Instituts. Athenische Abteilung* 85 (1970), pp. 129–269.

British Museum 1964 — The British Museum, *Guide to the Antiquities of Roman Britain* 3rd. ed. (London, 1964).

A. C. Brown 1974 — A. C. Brown, "Etrusco-Italic Architectural Terra-Cottas in the Ashmolean Museum, Oxford," *Archaeological Reports for 1973–74* (1974), pp. 60–65.

W. Ll. Brown 1960 — W. Ll. Brown, *The Etruscan Lion* (Oxford, 1960).

Buchholz 1984 — H.-G. Buchholz, "Eine attisch-schwarzfigurige Kanne im Cyprus Museum, Nicosia," *Archäologischer Anzeiger* (1984), pp. 555–564.

Buchholz and Karageorghis 1973 — –, and V. Karageorghis, *Prehistoric Greece and Cyprus* (London/New York, 1973).

Burlington Fine Arts Club 1904 — Burlington Fine Arts Club, *Exhibition of Ancient Greek Art* (London, 1904).

Cahn 1950 — H. A. Cahn, "Die Löwen des Apollon," *Museum Helveticum* 7 (1950), pp. 185–199.

Cahn 1975 — –, *Kleine Schriften zur Münzkunde und Archäologie* (Basel, 1975).

Cain 1985 — H.-U. Cain, *Römische Marmorkandelaber* (Mainz, 1985).

Canessa 1919 — C. and E. Canessa, *Illustrated Catalogue of the Canessa Collection* (New York, 1919).

Carter 1975 — J. C. Carter, *The Sculpture of Taras,*

	Transactions of the American Philosophical Society, n. s. 65 part 7 (Philadelphia, 1975).
Caskey-Beazley	L. D. Caskey and J. D. Beazley, *Attic Vase Paintings in the Museum of Fine Arts, Boston* part 1 (Oxford, 1931), part 2 (Oxford, 1954), part 3 (Oxford, 1963).
Catling 1974	H. W. Catling, "Archaeology in Greece, 1973–74," *Archaeological Reports for 1973–74* (1974), pp. 3–41.
Charbonneaux 1973	J. Charbonneaux, R. Martin, F. Villard, *Hellenistic Art* (New York, 1973).
Coldstream 1968	J. N. Coldstream, *Greek Geometric Pottery* (London, 1968).
Comstock and Vermeule 1971	M. Comstock and C. Vermeule, *Greek Etruscan & Roman Bronzes in the Museum of Fine Arts Boston* (Boston, 1971).
Comstock and Vermeule 1976	–, *Sculpture in Stone. The Greek, Roman and Etruscan Collections of the Museum of Fine Arts Boston* (Boston, 1976).
Congdon 1981	L. O. K. Congdon, *Caryatid Mirrors of Ancient Greece* (Mainz, 1981).
Conze 1900	A. Conze, *Die attischen Grabreliefs II* (Berlin, 1900).
Cook 1976	B. F. Cook, *Greek and Roman Art in the British Museum* (London, 1976).
Crome 1938–39	J. F. Crome, "Kerykeia," *Mitteilungen des Deutschen Archäologischen Instituts. Athenische Abteilung* 63–64 (1938–39), pp. 117–126.
Crowfoot 1957	J. W. Crowfoot, G. M. Crowfoot, K. M. Kenyon, *Samaria-Sebaste* 3. *The Objects from Samaria* (London, 1957).
CVA	*Corpus Vasorum Antiquorum.*
CVA University of California	H. R. W. Smith, *CVA,* University of California, Berkeley (1936).
CVA British Museum 4	H. B. Walters, *CVA,* British Museum 4 (1929).
CVA Castle Ashby	J. Boardman and M. Robertson, *CVA,* Castle Ashby (1979).
CVA Leipzig 2	E. Paul, *CVA,* Leipzig 2 (1973).
CVA New York 4	M. B. Moore and D. von Bothmer, *CVA,* New York 4 (1976).
CVA Musée Rodin	N. Plaoutine, *CVA,* Musée National Rodin (1945).
CVA Tarquinia 2	G. Iacopi, *CVA,* Tarquinia 2 (1956).
Daux 1960	G. Daux, "Chronique des fouilles et découvertes archéologiques en Grèce en 1959," *Bulletin de Correspondence Hellénique* 84 (1960), pp. 617–869.
Davidson and Oliver 1984	P. F. Davidson and A. Oliver, Jr., *Ancient Greek and Roman Gold Jewelry in the Brooklyn Museum* (Brooklyn, 1984).
Dawkins ed. 1929	R. M. Dawkins, ed. *The Sanctuary of Artemis Orthia at Sparta, Journal of Hellenic Studies,* Supplementary Paper no. 5 (London, 1929).
De Juliis 1984	E. M. De Juliis, *Gli Ori di Taranto in Eta Ellenistica* (Milan, 1984).
Del Chiaro and Talocchini 1973	M. A. Del Chiaro and A. Talocchini, "A University of California, Santa Barbara, Excavation in Tuscany," *American Journal of Archaeology* 77 (1973), pp. 327–331.
Dentzer 1982	J.-M. Dentzer, *Le motif du banquet couché dans le proche-orient et le monde grec du VII*[e] *au IV*[e] *siècle avant J.-C.* (Rome, 1982).
De Ridder 1908	A. De Ridder, *Collection de Clercq* 5, *Les antiquités chypriotes* (Paris, 1908).
Devambez 1981	P. Devambez, "Amazones," *Lexicon Iconographicum Mythologiae Classicae* I (Zurich/Munich, 1981), pp. 586–597.

Diehl 1964 — E. Diehl, *Die Hydria* (Mainz, 1964).

Diepolder 1931 — H. Diepolder, *Die attischen Grabreliefs des 5. und 4. Jahrhunderts v. Chr.* (Berlin, 1931).

Dörig 1975 — J. Dörig, *Art Antique, Collections privées de Suisse Romande* (Mainz, 1975).

Dörpfeld 1927 — W. Dörpfeld, *Alt-Ithaka* (Munich, 1927).

Doumas 1986 — C. Doumas, *Cycladic Art: Ancient Sculpture and Pottery from the N. P. Goulandris Collection* (London, 1986 ed.).

Faider-Feytmans 1979 — G. Faider-Feytmans, *Les bronzes romains de Belgique* (Mainz, 1979).

Fischer-Graf 1980 — U. Fischer-Graf, *Spiegelwerkstätten in Vulci; Deutsches Archäologisches Institut, Archäologische Forschungen,* vol. 8 (Berlin, 1980).

Fogg Art Museum 1973 — Fogg Art Museum, *The Frederick M. Watkins Collection* (Cambridge, 1973).

Fol, Nikolov, Hoddinott 1986 — A. Fol, B. Nikolov, R. F. Hoddinott, *The New Thracian Treasure From Rogozen, Bulgaria* (London, 1986).

Foti 1972 — G. Foti, *Il Museo Nazionale di Reggio Calabria* (Naples, 1972).

Frankel 1983 — D. Frankel, *Early and Middle Cypriote Bronze Age Material in the Ashmolean Museum, Oxford. Corpus of Cypriote Antiquities, Studies in Mediterranean Archaeology* 20, 7 (Göteborg, 1983).

Franzoni 1980 — L. Franzoni, *Bronzetti etruschi e italici del Museo Archeologico di Verona* (Rome, 1980).

Frazer, ed. 1921 — J. G. Frazer, ed., Apollodorus, *The Library* (The Loeb Classical Library) (Cambridge, 1921).

Furtwängler 1895 — A. Furtwängler, *Masterpieces of Greek Sculpture,* edited by Eugenie Sellars (London/New York 1895/reprinted Chicago, 1970).

Furumark 1941 — A. Furumark, *The Mycenaean Pottery, Analysis and Classification* (Stockholm, 1941).

Gauer 1984 — W. Gauer, "Gerät- und Gefäßfüße mit Löwenpranken und figürlichem Schmuck aus Olympia," *Mitteilungen des Deutschen Archäologischen Instituts. Athenische Abteilung* 99 (1984), pp. 35–53.

Gaber-Saletan 1980 — P. Gaber-Saletan, "The Limestone Sculpture from Kition," *Medelhavsmuseet Bulletin* 15 (1980), pp. 41–49.

Gaber-Saletan 1986 — –, *Regional Styles in Cypriot Sculpture* (New York, 1986).

Getz-Preziosi and Weinberg 1970 — P. Getz-Preziosi and S. S. Weinberg, "Evidence for Painted Details in Early Cycladic Sculpture," *Antike Kunst* 13 (1970), pp. 4–12.

Getz-Preziosi 1978 — P. Getz-Preziosi, "Addenda to the Cycladic Exhibition in Karlsruhe," *Archäologischer Anzeiger* (1978) pp. 1–11.

Getz-Preziosi 1980 — –, "The Male Figure in Early Cycladic Sculpture," *Metropolitan Museum Journal* 15 (1980), pp. 5–33.

Getz-Preziosi 1981 — –, "Risk and Repair in Early Cycladic Sculpture," *Metropolitan Museum Journal* 16 (1981), pp. 5–32.

Getz-Preziosi 1984 — –, "Five Sculptors in the Goulandris Collection", *Cycladic Studies in Memory of N. P. Goulandris,* J. L. Fitton, ed. (London, 1984), pp. 48–71

Getz-Preziosi 1985 — –, *Early Cycladic Sculpture: An Introduction* (Malibu, 1985).

Getz-Preziosi 1987 — –, *Sculptors of the Cyclades: Individual and Tradition in the Third Millennium B. C.* (Ann Arbor, 1987).

Giglioli 1935 — G. Q. Giglioli, *L'arte Etrusca* (Milan, 1935).

Gimbutas 1974 — M. Gimbutas, *The Gods and Goddesses of*

Old Europe: 7000 to 3000 B.C. (Berkeley/Los Angeles, 1974).

Gjerstad 1948 — E. Gjerstad, *The Swedish Cyprus Expedition* vol. IV, pt. 2 *The Cypro-Geometric, Cypro-Archaic and Cypro-Classic Periods* (Stockholm, 1948).

Gjødesen 1944 — M. Gjødesen, "Bronze Paterae with Anthropomorphous Handles," *Acta Archaeologica* 15 (1944), pp. 101–187.

Green 1972 — J. R. Green, "Oinochoe," *Bulletin of the Institute of Classical Studies, University of London 19 (1972), pp. 1–16.*

Greifenhagen 1930 — A. Greifenhagen, "Bronzekline im Pariser Kunsthandel," *Mitteilungen des Deutschen Archäologischen Instituts. Römische Abteilung* 45 (1930), pp. 137–165.

Greifenhagen 1957 — –, *Griechische Eroten* (Berlin, 1957).

Gschwantler 1984 — K. Gschwantler, "Eine bronzene Eberstatuette aus Enns-Lauriacum," *Bronzes romains figurés et appliqués et leurs problèmes techniques,* Actes du VIIe Colloque internationale sur les bronzes antiques = *Alba Regia* 21 (Budapest, 1984), pp. 71–77.

Gusmani 1978 — R. Gusmani, "Zwei neue Gefäßinschriften in karischer Sprache," *Kadmos* 17 (1978), pp. 67–75.

Hackens 1976 — T. Hackens, *Catalogue of the Classical Collection. Museum of Art, Rhode Island School of Design. Classical Jewelry* (Providence, 1976).

Hanfmann 1954 — G. M. A. Hanfmann, *Ancient Art in American Private Collections* (Cambridge, 1954).

Harrison 1965 — E. Harrison, *Archaic and Archaistic Sculpture, The Athenian Agora* XI (Princeton, 1965).

Haynes 1966 — S. Haynes, "Neue etruskische Bronzen," *Antike Kunst* 9 (1966), pp. 101–105.

Haynes 1985 — –, *Etruscan Bronzes* (London/New York 1985)

Heilmeyer 1979 — W.-D. Heilmeyer, *Frühe olympische Bronzefiguren, die Tiermotive, Olympische Forschungen* XII (Berlin, 1979).

Heimburg 1968 — U. Heimburg, *Das Bild des Poseidon in der griechischen Vasenmalerei* (Freiburg, 1968).

von Heland 1970 — M. von Heland, "A Corinthian Alabastron in Uppsala and its Motive," *Studien zur griechischen Vasenmalerei, Siebtes Beiheft zur Halbjahresschrift Antike Kunst* (Bern, 1970), pp. 19–32.

Herfort-Koch 1986 — M. Herfort-Koch, *Archaische Bronzeplastik Lakoniens. Boreas,* Beiheft 4 (Münster, 1986).

Hencken 1958 — H. Hencken, "Syracuse, Etruria and the North," *American Journal of Archaeology* 62 (1958), pp. 259–272.

Hermary 1985 — A. Hermary, "Un nouveau chapiteau Hathorique trouvé à Amathonte," *Bulletin de Correspondence Hellénique* 109 (1985), pp. 657–699.

Herrmann 1964 — H.-V. Herrmann, "Werkstätten geometrischer Bronzeplastik," *Jahrbuch des Deutschen Archäologischen Instituts* 79 (1964), pp. 17–71.

Higgins 1986 — R. Higgins, *Tanagra and the Figurines* (Princeton, 1986).

Hill 1955 — D. K. Hill, "Six Early Greek Animals," *American Journal of Archaeology* 59 (1955), pp. 39–44.

Hill 1982 — –, "Note on the Piecing of Bronze Statuettes," *Hesperia* 51 (1982), pp. 277–283.

Hoffmann 1964 — H. Hoffmann, ed. *The Beauty of Ancient Art, the Norbert Schimmel Collection,* Fogg Art Museum (Mainz, 1964).

Hoffmann 1970 — –, *Ten Centuries that Shaped the West* (Houston, 1970).

Hornbostel 1973 — W. Hornbostel, *Sarapis* (Leiden, 1973).

Hornbostel 1979 — –, "Syrakosion Damosion. Zu einem bronzenen Heroldstab," *Jahrbuch der Hamburger Kunstsammlungen* 24 (1979), pp. 33–62.

Isaac Delgado Museum of Art 1966 — Isaac Delgado Museum of Art, *Odyssey of an Art Collector* (New Orleans, 1966).

Isler-Kerenyi 1969 — C. Isler-Kerenyi, *Nike: der Typus der laufenden Flügelfrau in archaischer Zeit* (Zurich, 1969).

Isler-Kerenyi 1971 — –, "Ein Spätwerk des Berliner Malers," *Antike Kunst* 14 (1971), pp. 25–31.

Jantzen 1953 — U. Jantzen, "Geometrische Kannenverschlüsse," *Archäologischer Anzeiger* (1953), cols. 56–57.

Jantzen 1958 — –, *Griechische Griff-Phialen, Berliner Winckelmannsprogramm* 114 (Berlin, 1958), pp. 5–29.

Jenkins and Williams 1985 — I. Jenkins and D. Williams, "Sprang Hair Nets: Their Manufacture and Use in Ancient Greece," *American Journal of Archaeology* 89 (1985), pp. 411–418.

Johnston 1979 — A. Johnston, *Trademarks on Greek Vases* (Warminster, 1979).

Jost 1975 — M. Jost, "Statuettes de bronze archaiques provenant de Lykosoura," *Bulletin de Correspondence Hellénique* 99 (1975), pp. 339–364.

Kanta 1979 — K. G. Kanta, *Eleusis: Myth, Mysteries, History, Museum* (Athens, 1979).

Karageorghis 1976 — V. Karageorghis, "Chronique des fouilles et découvertes archéologiques à Chypre en 1975," *Bulletin de Correspondence Hellénique* 100 (1976), pp. 839–906.

Karageorghis 1979 — –, "Material from a Sanctuary at Potamia," *Report of the Department of Antiquities Cyprus* (1979), pp. 289–315.

Karageorghis 1981 — –, "Chronique des fouilles et découvertes archéologiques à Chypre en 1980," *Bulletin de Correspondence Hellénique* 105 (1981), pp. 967–1024.

Kaufmann-Heinimann 1977 — A. Kaufmann-Heinimann, *Die römischen Bronzen der Schweiz* I, *Augst* (Mainz, 1977).

Kimbell Art Museum 1983 — Kimbell Art Museum, *Wealth of the Ancient World, The Nelson Bunker Hunt and William Herbert Hunt Collections* (Fort Worth, 1983).

Kiss 1975 — Z. Kiss, *L'iconographie des princes Julio-Claudiens au temps d'Auguste et de Tibère* (Warsaw, 1975).

Kleiner 1942 — G. Kleiner, *Tanagrafiguren, Untersuchungen zur hellenistischen Kunst und Geschichte. Jahrbuch des Deutschen Archäologischen Instituts* Ergänzungs-Heft 15 (Berlin, 1942, reprinted 1984).

Klumbach 1937 — H. Klumbach, *Tarentiner Grabkunst* (Reutlingen, 1937).

Kozloff 1982 — A. P. Kozloff, *Israel in Antiquity* (New York, 1982).

Kunze 1951 — E. Kunze, "Etruskische Bronzen in Griechenland," *Studies Presented to David Moore Robinson,* vol. I (St. Louis, 1951), pp. 736–746.

Künzl 1970 — E. Künzl, "Venus vor dem Bade," *Bonner Jahrbücher* 170 (1970), pp. 102–162.

Kurtz 1975 — D. C. Kurtz, *Athenian White Lekythoi* (Oxford, 1975).

Kyrieleis 1986 — H. Kyrieleis, "Chios and Samos in the Archaic Period," *Chios. A Conference at the Homereion in Chios, 1984,* edited by J. Boardman and C. E. Vaphopoulou-Richardson (Oxford, 1986), pp. 187–204.

Laffineur 1980 — R. Laffineur, "Collection Paul Canellopoulos (XV), Bijoux en or grecs et romains," *Bulletin de Correspondence Hellénique* 104 (1980), pp. 345–457.

Lamb 1929 — W. Lamb, *Ancient Greek and Roman Bronzes* (London, 1929).

Langlotz and Hirmer 1965 — E. Langlotz and M. Hirmer, *Ancient Greek Sculpture of South Italy and Sicily* (New York, 1965).

Lazarides 1959 — D. Lazarides, "Excavations and Researches in Amphipolis," *Praktika* (1959 [1965]), pp. 42–46.

Liepmann 1975 — U. Liepmann, *Griechische Terrakotten, Bronzen, Skulpturen.* Bildkataloge des Kestner-Museums, Hannover, XII (Hannover, 1975).

Maier 1967 — F. G. Maier, "Ausgrabungen in Alt-Paphos," *Archäologischer Anzeiger* (1967), pp. 303–330.

Maier and Karageorghis 1984 — –, and V. Karageorghis, *Paphos, History and Archaeology* (Nicosia, 1984)

Makaronas 1963 — C. Makaronas, "Antiquities and Monuments of Central Macedonia, Tombs near Derveni, Thessaloniki," *Archaiologikon Deltion* 18 (1963), *Chronika* pp. 193–196.

Mallwitz and Herrmann 1980 — A. Mallwitz and H.-V. Herrmann (eds.), *Deutsches Archäologisches Institut, Die Funde aus Olympia* (Athens, 1980).

Melis and Quilici Gigli 1972 — F. Melis and S. Quilici Gigli, "Proposta per l'ubicazione di pometia," *Archeologia Classica* 24 (1972), pp. 219–247.

von Mercklin 1928 — E. von Mercklin, "Antiken im Hamburgischen Museum für Kunst und Gewerbe," *Archäologischer Anzeiger* (1928), col. 273–497.

Mertens 1976 — J. Mertens, "A Hellenistic Find in New York," *Metropolitan Museum Journal* 11 (1976) pp. 71–84

Metropolitan Museum of Art 1979 — Metropolitan Museum of Art, *Greek Art of the Aegean Islands: An Exhibition* (New York, 1979).

Michaud 1974 — J.-P. Michaud, "Chronique des fouilles et découvertes archéologiques en Grèce en 1973," *Bulletin de Correspondence Hellénique* 98 (1974), pp. 579–722.

Mitten 1975 — D. G. Mitten, *Catalogue of the Classical Collection, Museum of Art, Rhode Island School of Design, Classical Bronzes* (Providence, 1975).

Mitten and Doeringer 1967 — –, and S. F. Doeringer, *Master Bronzes from the Classical World* (Mainz, 1967).

Moore 1971 — M. B. Moore, *Horses on Black-figure Vases of the Archaic Period* (New York University diss. 1971).

Muscarella, ed. 1974 — O. W. Muscarella, ed. *Ancient Art, the Norbert Schimmel Collection* (Mainz, 1974).

National Art-Collections Fund 1981 — National Art-Collections Fund, *Annual Report 1980* (London, 1981).

National Gallery of Art 1980 — National Gallery of Art, *The Search for Alexander, An Exhibition* (Boston, 1980).

Neugebauer 1923–24 — K. A. Neugebauer, "Reifarchaische Bronzevasen mit Zungenmuster," *Mitteilungen des Deutschen Archäologischen Instituts. Römische Abteilung* 38–39 (1923–24), pp. 341–440.

(Neugebauer) 1924 — (K. A. Neugebauer) Staatliche Museen. Antiquarium, *Führer durch das Antiquarium* I (Berlin, 1924).

Neugebauer 1943 — –, "Archaische vulcenter Bronzen," *Jahrbuch des Deutschen Archäologischen Instituts* 58 (1943), pp. 206-278.

Noble 1965 — J. V. Noble, *The Techniques of Painted Attic Pottery* (New York, 1965).

Noble 1968 — –, "Some Trick Greek Vases," *Proceedings of the American Philosophical Society* 112 (1968), pp. 371–378.

Nuber 1972 H. U. Nuber, "Kanne und Griffschale, ihr Gebrauch im täglichen Leben und die Beigabe in Gräbern der römischen Kaiserzeit," *Bericht der Römisch-Germanischen Kommission* 53 (Mainz, 1972).

Page 1941 D. L. Page, ed., *Select Papyri* III, *Literary Papyri, Poetry* (Loeb Classical Library) (Cambridge, 1941).

Papathanasopoulos 1961–62 G. Papathanasopoulos, "Kykladika Naxou," *Archaiologikon Deltion* 17 pt. A (1961–62), *Chronika* pp. 104–151.

Paralipomena J. D. Beazley, *Paralipomena: Additions to Attic Black-figure Vase-painters and to Attic Red-figure Vase-painters (2nd edition)* (Oxford, 1971).

Pasquier 1985 A. Pasquier, *La Vénus de Milo et les Aphrodites du Louvre* (Paris, 1985).

Payne 1931 H. Payne, *Necrocorinthia* (Oxford, 1931).

Payne 1940 H. Payne and others, *Perachora, The Sanctuaries of Hera Akraia and Limenia* (Oxford, 1940).

Petit Palais 1973 Petit Palais, *Pompei* (Paris, 1973).

Pfrommer 1983 M. Pfrommer, "Italien-Makedonien-Kleinasien. Interdependenzen spätklassischer und frühhellenistischer Toreutik," *Jahrbuch des Deutschen Archäologischen Instituts* 98 (1983), pp. 235–285.

Pfrommer 1985 –, "Zur Venus Colonna," *Istanbuler Mitteilungen* 35 (1985), pp. 173–180.

Popovic et al. 1969 L. B. Popovic, *et al., Anticka Bronza u Jugoslaviji* (Belgrade, 1969).

Poulsen 1927 F. Poulsen, *Das Helbig Museum der Ny Carlsberg Glyptotek, Beschreibung der etruskischen Sammlung* (Leipzig, 1927).

Pryce 1931 F. N. Pryce, *Catalogue of Sculpture in the Department of Greek and Roman Antiquities of the British Museum,* I, Part 2: *Cypriote and Etruscan* (London, 1931).

Renfrew 1972 C. Renfrew, *The Emergence of Civilisation: the Cyclades and the Aegean in the Third Millennium B. C.* (London, 1972).

Richardson 1964 E. H. Richardson, *The Etruscans* (Chicago, 1964).

Richardson 1971 –, "The Icon of the Heroic Warrior: A Study in Borrowing," *Studies Presented to George M. A. Hanfmann* (Cambridge, 1971).

Richardson 1983 –, *Etruscan Votive Bronzes, Geometric, Orientalizing, Archaic* (Mainz, 1983).

Richter 1940 G. M. A. Richter, *Handbook of the Etruscan Collection, The Metropolitan Museum of Art,* (New York, 1940).

Richter 1953 G. M. A. Richter, *Handbook of the Greek Collection, The Metropolitan Museum of Art* (Cambridge, 1953).

Richter 1956 –, *Catalogue of Engraved Gems, Greek, Etruscan, and Roman. The Metropolitan Museum of Art* (Rome, 1956).

Richter 1966 –, *The Furniture of the Greeks, Etruscans, and Romans* (London, 1966).

Roberts 1983 H. S. Roberts, "Later Etruscan Mirrors. Evidence for Dating from Recent Excavations," *Analecta Romana Instituti Danici* 12 (1983), pp. 31–54.

Robertson 1975 M. Robertson, *A History of Greek Art* (Cambridge, 1975).

Robertson 1979 –, "A Muffled Dancer and Others," *Studies in Honour of Arthur Dale Trendall,* ed. A. Cambitoglou (Sydney, 1979), pp. 129–134.

Robertson 1987 –, "The Attic Pottery", *Etudes Chypriotes* VIII, *La nécropole d'Amathonte, tombes 113–367* II. *Céramiques non chyp-*

riotes, eds. V. Karageorghis, O. Picard, Chr. Tytgat (Nicosia, 1987).

Robinson 1933 D.M. Robinson, *Excavations at Olynthus* part VII, *The Terracottas of Olynthus found in 1931* (Baltimore, 1933).

Rolley and Rougemont 1973 C. Rolley and G. Rougemont, "Catalogue des objets de metal, Travaux de l'Ecole Française en 1972: Delphes," *Bulletin de Correspondence Hellénique* 97 (1973), pp. 512–525.

Rolley 1980 C. Rolley, *Museum of Delphi. Bronzes* (Athens, n.d., ca. 1980).

Rolley 1983 –, *Les Bronzes grecs* (Paris, 1983).

Schefold 1960 K. Schefold, *Meisterwerke griechischer Kunst* (Basel, 1960).

Schmidt 1968 G. Schmidt, *Samos* VII, *Kyprische Bildwerke aus dem Heraion von Samos* (Bonn, 1968).

Seiterle and Mutz 1982 G. Seiterle and A. Mutz, "Ein hellenistisches Bronzebett im Baseler Antikenmuseum," *Antike Kunst* 25 (1982), pp. 62–70.

Seure 1925 G. Seure, "Chars Thraces," *Bulletin de Correspondence Hellénique* 49 (1925), pp. 347–437.

Shapiro 1984 H.A. Shapiro, "Herakles and Kyknos," *American Journal of Archaeology* 88 (1984), pp. 523–529.

Sieveking 1913 J. Sieveking, "Erwerbungen der Antikensammlungen München, II, K. Antiquarium 1912," *Archäologischer Anzeiger* (1913), col. 434–444.

Sieveking 1930 J. Sieveking, *Bronzen, Terrakotten, Vasen der Sammlung Loeb* (Munich, 1930).

Sogliano 1899 A. Sogliano, "Scafati – Avanzi di antica villa dell'agro pompeiano," *Notizie degli Scavi* (1899), pp. 392–398.

Sprenger and Bartoloni 1983 M. Sprenger and G. Bartoloni, *The Etruscans, their History, Art and Architecture* (New York, 1983).

Stenico 1963 A. Stenico, *Roman and Etruscan Painting* (New York, 1963).

Stewart 1980 A. Stewart, "A Fourth-century Bronze Mirror Case in Dunedin," *Antike Kunst* 23 (1980), pp. 24–34.

Svoronos 1908–1937 N.J. Svoronos, *Das Athener Nationalmuseum. Phototypische Wiedergabe seiner Schätze mit erleuternden Texten* (Athens, 1908–1937).

Swaddling 1978 J. Swaddling, "The British Museum Bronze Hoard from Paramythia, North Western Greece: Classical Trends Revived in the 2nd and 18th Centuries A.D.," *Bronzes hellenistiques et romains, Actes du Ve colloque international sur les bronzes antiques* (Lausanne, 1978), pp. 103–106.

Szilágyi 1968 J. Gy. Szilágyi, "Remarques sur les vases étrusco-corinthiens de l'exposition étrusque de Vienne," *Archeologia Classica* 20 (1968), pp. 10–13.

Thessalonike 1978 Thessalonike, *Treasures of Ancient Macedqnia* (Thessalonike, 1978).

Thimme 1977 J. Thimme, gen. ed., and P. Getz-Preziosi, trans. and Eng. ed., *Art and Culture of the Cyclades in the Third Millennium B.C.* (Chicago, 1977).

Thompson 1963 D.B. Thompson, *Troy*, Supplementary Monograph 3, *The Terracotta Figurines of the Hellenistic Period* (Princeton, 1963).

Thompson 1966 –, "The Origin of Tanagras," *American Journal of Archaeology* 70 (1966), pp. 51–63.

Touchais 1977 G. Touchais, "Chronique des fouilles et découvertes archéologiques en Grèce en 1976," *Bulletin de Correspondence Hellénique* 101 (1977), pp. 513–666.

Toynbee 1962 — J. M. C. Toynbee, *Art in Roman Britain* (London, 1962).

Trendall 1951 — A. D. Trendall, "The Vases in Australia and New Zealand," *Journal of Hellenic Studies* 71 (1951), pp. 178–193.

Trendall 1987 — –, I. McPhee and A. D. Trendall, *Greek Red-figured Fish Plates. Antike Kunst* Beiheft 14 (1987).

Tsountas 1899 — C. Tsountas, "Kykladika II," *Archaiologike Ephemeris* (1899), cols. 73–134.

Ure 1934 — P. N. Ure, *Aryballoi and Figurines from Rhitsona in Boeotia* (Cambridge, 1934).

Valenza Mele 1981 — N. Valenza Mele, *Catalogo delle Lucerne in Bronzo,* Museo Nazionale Archeologico di Napoli (Rome, 1981).

C. C. Vermeule 1974 — C. C. Vermeule, "Cypriot Sculpture: the Late Archaic and Early Classical Periods: Towards a More Precise Understanding," *American Journal of Archaeology* 76 (1974), pp. 287–290.

C. C. Vermeule 1981 — –, *Greek and Roman Sculpture in America* (Berkeley/Los Angeles, 1981).

E. Vermeule 1964 — E. Vermeule, *Greece in the Bronze Age* (Chicago, 1964).

Vocotopoulou 1975 — J. Vocotopoulou, "Le trésor de vases de bronze de Votonosi," *Bulletin de Correspondence Hellénique* 99 (1975), pp. 729–788.

Vian 1945 — F. Vian, "Le combat d'Hérakles et de Kyknos," *Revue des Études Anciennes* 47 (1945), pp. 5–32.

Vierneisel-Schlörb 1979 — B. Vierneisel-Schlörb, *Glyptothek München, Katalog der Skulpturen,* II, *Klassische Skulpturen des 5. und 4. Jahrhunderts v. Chr.* (Munich, 1979).

Wallenstein 1972 — K. Wallenstein, "Der Aryballos im Aryballos," *Archäologischer Anzeiger* 87 (1972), pp. 458–474.

Walter-Karydi 1981 — E. Walter-Karydi, "Bronzen aus Dodona – Eine epirotische Erzbildnerschule," *Jahrbuch der Berliner Museen* 23 (1981), pp. 11–48.

Ward-Perkins and Claridge 1978 — J. B. Ward-Perkins and A. Claridge, *Pompeii A. D. 79. Treasures from the National Archaeological Museum, Naples and the Pompeii Antiquarium* I–II (Boston, 1978).

Waterhouse 1952 — H. Waterhouse, "Excavations at Stavros, Ithaca, in 1937," *Annual of the British School at Athens* 47 (1952), pp. 227–242.

Webster 1969 — T. B. L. Webster, *Monuments Illustrating New Comedy* (second ed.) Institute of Classical Studies, *Bulletin* Supplement no. 24 (London, 1969).

Weinberg 1977 — S. S. Weinberg, "Anthropomorphic Stone Figurines from Neolithic Greece," in J. Thimme, gen. ed., and P. Getz-Preziosi, trans. and Eng. ed., *Art and Culture of the Cyclades in the Third Millennium B. C.* (Chicago, 1977).

Winter 1903 — F. Winter, *Die antiken Terrakotten* 3, *Typen der figürlichen Terrakotten* (Berlin/Stuttgart 1903).

Zandrino 1952 — R. Zandrino, "Il Thymiaterion della Boncia," *Studi Etruschi* 22 (1952), pp. 328–339.

Zanker 1965 — P. Zanker, *Wandel der Hermesgestalt in der attischen Vasenmalerei* (Bonn, 1965).

Zanotti-Bianco 1962 — U. Zanotti-Bianco, *La Grande Grèce* (Paris, 1962).

Zervos 1957 — C. Zervos, *L'art des Cyclades de début à la fin de l'âge de bronze, 2500–1100 avant notre ère* (Paris, 1957).

Zervos 1962 — –, *Naissance de la civilisation en Grèce* I (Paris, 1962).

Photo Credit

Collection C. G. Bastis, New York: p. 26, 27, 45, 90, 92

The Brooklyn Museum, New York: p. 12, 13, 20, 21, 22, 32, 34, 38, 40, 41, 44, 49, 50, 51, 57, 66, 67, 68, 75, 76, 86, 91, 92, 93, 94, 95, 113, 131, 145, 162, 170, 183, 184, 185, 186, 189, 217, 226, 227, 230, 233, 236, 263, 292, 293, 294, 295, 298, 301, 303, 304, 306, 307, 308, 309

Justin Kerr, New York: p. 8, 9, 202, 211

David A. Loggie, New York: p. II, 3, 4, 5, 6, 7, 23, 25, 28, 30, 33, 37, 39, 43, 48, 52, 54, 55, 60, 62, 63, 64, 65, 66, 72, 73, 74, 75, 78, 80, 81, 82, 84, 97, 115, 118, 119, 120, 124, 142, 155, 158, 159, 160, 163, 176, 177, 179, 187, 188, 197, 199, 201, 203, 208, 209, 210, 212, 215, 219, 221, 222, 225, 228, 231, 235, 242, 245, 246, 258, 259, 260, 261, 262, 264, 265, 270, 271, 282, 284, 285, 286, 289, 291, 300, 305, 318, 320, 322

Edward H. Merrin Gallery, Inc., New York: p. 89

Metropolitan Museum of Art, New York: p. 58, 109, 110, 119, 122, 123, 133, 136, 137, 138, 143, 144, 153, 155, 156, 157, 169, 174, 175, 190, 191, 192, 193, 194, 195, 205, 206, 207, 213, 248, 249, 250, 252, 253, 254, 256, 257, 269, 272, 273, 278, 279, 287, 314, 315, 316, 317, 318, 319, 321, 322, 323, 325, 326, 327

O. E. Nelson, New York: p. 267

The New York University, Institute of Fine Arts: p. 42, 70, 71, 85

Sarah Wells, New York: p. 1, 14, 17, 18, 22, 23, 35, 47, 53, 56, 59, 65, 75, 83, 87, 116, 127, 128, 129, 135, 139, 141, 146, 149, 151, 152, 167, 168, 169, 170, 171, 172, 173, 180, 181, 182, 189, 198, 203, 208, 214, 216, 218, 220, 223, 224, 229, 232, 237, 238, 239, 240, 243, 244, 247, 264, 273, 274, 275, 276, 277, 281, 282, 283, 288, 290, 299, 300, 311